# Contemporary Sexuality

## An Anthology

Third Edition

**Ivy Chen, MPH**
**John P. Elia, Ph.D.**
*San Francisco State University*

D1247401

**Kendall Hunt**
publishing company

Cover image courtesy of Shutterstock.

**Kendall Hunt**
publishing company

www.kendallhunt.com
*Send all inquiries to:*
4050 Westmark Drive
Dubuque, IA 52004-1840

Copyright © 2000, 2005, 2013 by Kendall/Hunt Publishing Company

ISBN: 978-1-4652-0871-2

Printed in the United States of America
10 9 8 7 6 5 4 3 2 1

# *Contents*

# *Preface and Acknowledgments*

The ideas for this edition of *Contemporary Sexuality: An Anthology* have been germinating for the past few years. We are gratified with this new edition. While we retained some of the chapters from the previous volume, there are a number of new contributions to this collection. Our intention is that this book be read as a supplement to a general survey textbook on human sexuality or as a stand-alone book filled with a collection of thought-provoking chapters on a variety of human sexuality topics. This book's strengths rest almost entirely on the fine work of the contributors. We are thankful a number of new contributors agreed to participate in this edition. They are:

Albert J. Angelo

Joel Baum

Michael Ferguson

Deb K. Levine

Kate McCombs

Malcolm Potts

Paul Rueckhaus

Ignacio Lozano Verduzco

Al Vernacchio

Donnovan Somera Yisrael

Besides our shared gratitude to the contributors, we have individual acknowledgments.

Ivy Chen—I am grateful to my friends and colleagues who have contributed to this anthology. Their generosity for sharing their expertise is very much appreciated. I am thankful for my mentor, dear friend and co-author Dr. John Elia. Lastly, I am lucky to have my family who supports me in doing what I love.

John Elia—I am comforted by the loving and dynamic family life I share with Gina, Brian, and Sparky. I am fortunate to have such a rich and fulfilling life with them. Also, I am lucky to have such a wonderful comrade and co-author, Ivy Chen, who is a caring, dedicated, and competent sexuality educator. She has touched thousands of lives as a sexuality educator of students from the elementary school level through university level. I dedicate this book to those human sexuality students who envision and work toward a world committed to sexual and social justice.

And, I could hardly omit the names of many wonderful doggies—both mine and those in the care of family and friends who have been wonderful companions of mine and others. They are: Ace, Biscuit, Copper, Dino, Sparky, Tyler, and Yogi. Their special and endearing qualities should not be underestimated.

We hope this anthology proves to be an interesting read and will provoke readers to think more deeply about a variety of sexual matters addressed in this volume.

*Ivy Chen, MPH and John P. Elia, PhD*
*San Francisco, CA*
*August, 2013*

# *Introduction*

# The Landscape of Contemporary Sexuality

*Ivy Chen, MPH and John P. Elia, Ph.D.*

This book has gone through a substantial evolution since the first edition was published over 13 years ago. The first (2000) and second (2005) editions were primarily comprised of articles that were previously published in both scholarly and popular press publications. Our main aim then was to include materials on topics that were only superficially covered—or simply not covered at all—in general survey human sexuality textbooks. Our aim with this edition of *Contemporary Sexuality: An Anthology* is along similar lines, but also we believe that this edition may also stand alone as a text that provides a broad brush approach to sexuality and gender issues. It is by no means a comprehensive text, but it does offer a number of interesting pieces on everything from art to sexuality and society. In fact this volume is broken into 6 sections. Section I encompasses *sexuality in history and culture*, and has two chapters. The first piece provides a treatment of the history and future of sex, and the second chapter takes a novel approach to intimacy, sex, and art. Section II comprises 4 articles on *gender* ranging in topics from the foundations of gender, masculinity and identity, whatever happened to June Cleaver, to the end of patriarchy. Section III deals exclusively with *adolescence and sexuality* and includes two fact sheets from the Guttmacher Institute on teens' sexual and reproductive health and on sources of information about sex. The penultimate chapter in this section deals with oral sex and adolescence, and finally the section closes with a piece on young men's reproductive health. Turning to some unconventional writings on sexual instruction, Section IV deals with *sexuality education*. This section begins with a chapter pointing to a number of merits of taking a general survey human sexuality course, and then the section turns to a chapter that addresses what makes sex good for individuals. What follows are chapters on what's missing from sexual health education, teaching about pleasure, strategies for communicating about sexuality with young people, and bisexuality and school culture. Section V provides chapters on a variety of issues dealing with *sexual behavior*. Such topics as conceptual models of sexual activity, reframing the categorization of "atypical" sexual behaviors, sexual addiction and compulsivity, and sex offenders are included. Finally, the last section of the book deals broadly with *sexuality and society* and it explores topical issues such as: sex and the internet, sex industry, sexuality and disability, and sexuality and spirituality.

We believe that all of the chapters in this volume not only reflect the diversity of human sexuality, but also include relevant topics to which most people can readily relate. Equally as important, most chapters were specifically solicited for this volume. Each author in her or his own way spurs readers to think more deeply about sexuality and gender. As the authors/editors of this book, we hope that the writings help readers develop a more thorough understanding of the complexities of sexuality and gender in the interest of fostering sexual literacy and in turn creating more rewarding and fulfilling sex lives.

To assist with a deeper understanding of the concepts introduced in each of the chapters, we have produced a *Study Guide*. Each chapter of the *Study Guide* begins with a chapter summary followed by a list key terms, true/false practice test items, multiple-choice practice test items, discussion questions, and study questions. Each chapter concludes with a list of the answers to the true/false and multiple-choice practice test items. We heartily recommend that you complete the *Study Guide* in order to get the most out of this volume.

If this book, in part, gets readers to think more deeply, thoughtfully, and critically about sexual and gender matters, spurs lively discussions or debates, fosters an appreciation for the complexity of human sexuality and gender, or helps individuals with their own sexual lives in one way or another, then this book has fulfilled our hopes. Additionally, we hope readers get as much out of reading this collection as we got from writing and editing it.

# *Section* I

# Sexuality in History and Culture

# Chapter 1

# *The History and Future of Sex*

*Marty Klien, Ph.D.*

Researching this paper, I realized how much I don't know about many things important to sexology. I realized how little I know about Prohibition, the Civil War, the Depression, segregation, and the history of technology, to name just a few. And I realized anew how important topics like those are for our field.

I also realized that the field of sexology knows a lot more about the phenomenology of sex than it does about social science. We know more about what individual people say they do and how they feel than about the role sexuality plays in the pageant of world events. While this is legitimate knowledge, it means that sexology has a limited perspective. History, economics, law, technology, religion, and other large-scale social forces dramatically shape people's sexual consciousness and behavior—which is what we sexologists purport to study. And so examining the past and looking toward the future are essential for sexological sophistication. Doing so demonstrates, as we are always saying, just how critical an interdisciplinary perspective is for our work. As we seek to understand sexuality, there is very little that is irrelevant.

Let's start with some examples of how technology in general drives history in unexpected ways:

1. In the 13th century, the flying buttress and the gothic vault were invented. These architectural structures took much of the weight off the external walls of churches. Within five years, a whole new kind of cathedral was being built, such as Westminster Abbey. The reduced weight on the walls made large windows possible, which allowed a brand new art form to develop: stained glass.

2. During the mid-19th century, train speeds increased every few years. Eventually, travellers who started in place A with their watches set correctly would arrive in place B with watches that were now incorrect, because they had traveled so far so quickly. To eliminate this problem, time zones were invented in 1883.

3. At the beginning of the 20th century, zippers were considered a novelty. Then World War I required American soldiers to go abroad for the first time. Because they were going to exotic foreign countries, they wanted to hide their money when they traveled. The holder of the zipper's patent sold money belts with zippers to the American government for its soldiers—and zippers became popular overnight.

4. Until the early 1960s, college administrations were expected to act "in loco parentis"—as substitute parents, making lifestyle decisions for students. For hundreds of years, students had to conform to college rules about dress, religion, sexual activity, and recreation. This arrangement ended in American colleges in the mid- and late-1960s because of the Vietnam War draft. Millions of young people reasoned that if they were old enough to get drafted and killed, they were old enough to run their own lives.

Throughout history, technological advances and social changes have had very different outcomes than were originally planned or predicted. This is the rule, not the exception. And it's true regarding sexuality.

Societal developments affect sexuality in two ways: directly and indirectly. Examples of direct influences include the invention of the birth control pill, the discovery of ovulation, and the invention of vasectomy.

But events can also affect sex indirectly. For example, during World War II, the few young men who were left in America's cities were suddenly a scarce commodity, and women started to compete for them. One way they did this was with sex—and quickly, initiating dates and being sexually aggressive became more culturally acceptable.

Interestingly, the indirect effects on sexuality are far more numerous and much more powerful than the direct sexual effects. Now, nobody is going to argue that the invention of the birth control pill or the discovery of ovulation are trivial. Nevertheless, as we look back over history, the indirect forces shaping sexual expression have been enormously important. Here is a small sample of historical events that shaped the course of human sexuality—indirectly:

- The story of Adam and Eve
- The story of 12 male apostles
- The invention of paper
- The destruction of the Roman Empire
- The development and spread of Islam
- The invention of the clock
- The founding of the Protestant church
- The Salem witchcraft trials
- Allowing women to act on stage
- The vulcanization of rubber
- The invention of photography
- The relocation of Mormans to Utah
- The transcontinental railroad
- The belief that conception required female orgasm
- The installation of gas lights for theaters
- No-fault divorce

Let's examine just one of these: the installation of gaslights in theaters. Up until then, theater productions did not take place at night, only in the daytime. Once theaters could install gas lighting, however, they could present shows at night. People could now go there on dates at night; they could go to the dark places in the theater, hold hands and cuddle—which totally changed courting forever.

In every era, new technologies are always adapted to sexual uses. Here are some examples:

pottery > pornography
car > drive-in
VCR > porn films
telephone > phone sex
printing > penny dreadfuls
photography > pornography
vulcanization > condoms
hormone research > contraception
Internet > cybersex

Let's look at a few examples.

Originally developed as a form of transportation, the car was quickly adapted for social uses, such as privacy. The "backseat of a car" even became a synonym for not-quite-legitimate privacy. Once the car became popular, motels outside of town were invented. Before then, there were hotels in town, for people who were travelling. Remember, travelling long distances in those days was a huge hassle. But once people had mobility and could use a car to get out of town for, say, half a day or just overnight, there was a reason for motels—outside of town.

The VCR was not invented for sexual purposes, but the VCR only took off as a consumer item when low-cost porn videotapes became available. The resulting demand for machines then lowered their price, making them affordable for everyone. In fact, the commercial battle over which tape format would become standard ended when Sony decided not to participate in pornography—which doomed Betamax to extinction. Over 500 million X-rated videotapes are now rented every year.

Soon after the telephone became a standard item in the American home, teenagers started using it. Domestic battling about phone use was one of the common themes of stand-up comedy in the mid-1950s and '60s. What the telephone actually made possible was that people could lay in their beds and talk to their sweetheart privately, could talk about sex, romance, and intimacy. Until that time, such conversations had been highly regulated by the physical separation of lovers required by the rules of courtship. Before the invention of the telephone, only married people had the opportunity to regularly lay in bed and cuddle with or whisper to their sweetheart.

Now let's look at some developments in the 20th century that had important—and unintended—sexual impacts.

### • Municipal electricity

At the start of the century, the widespread installation of municipal electricity allowed people to go out at night, and lighted places attracted people who wanted to see other people. Downtowns were transformed from places to go shopping during the day, to places where people congregated at night, places of evening entertainment—and suddenly there was nightlife all over the United States. Remember that when electricity became common in American cities, more than half of the country still lived in towns of less than 20,000 people. At that time, the idea of a downtown where people could congregate and go to a movie or have a soda together at night was quite risque.

### • Bicycles

Before the bicycle was invented, the average American woman had to wear an average of 37 pounds of clothes just to go out of the house. Once women started to ride bicycles, this wasn't practical anymore, and within two years, women were wearing less than half that amount to go out. Imagine the change that must have been in people's lives. The bicycle also led to the development of female athletics because it proved that women could exercise without physical harm.

### • High-density housing

Around the turn of the century, immigration and industrialization led people in cities to live in apartments. This meant that there was no more front porch, and courting could no longer take place within the bounds of the family's home. This led to unchaperoned dating for the first time.

### • Psychoanalysis

Psychoanalysis was the first intellectual movement in this country to suggest that sexual repression actually had an effect on people. It became quite a parlor game for people to sit around and speculate about criminals or others who were socially inappropriate—what sort of sexual repression was this or that person acting out? Psychoanalysis gave people a vocabulary with which to talk about sexual norms and libido, something they hadn't had before.

### • Prohibition

During Prohibition, drinking became sexy. It was an outlaw activity, something that sophisticated and wealthy people did. There were clubs where people gathered to drink—speakeasies—and a new genre of popular music. Like cigarette smoking in the 1960s, drinking became a symbol of eroticism during Prohibition. The glorification of alcohol, of course, heavily affected people's sexual decision-making and functioning.

### • The Depression

During the Depression there weren't enough jobs, so instead of going to work, teenagers went to high school. Suddenly, high school kids were surrounded not by adults but by other high school kids. Hanging out with so many of their peers, high school kids developed their own jargon, their own culture, and courtship patterns. "Dating" became an adolescent institution.

### • Gay Civil Rights

The last 25 years have seen a swell of rights for gay and bisexual people. This battle isn't finished yet, but one of the unexpected outcomes of the increased visibility of gay sexuality is that a certain amount of non-normative sexual activity has gone mainstream. I don't think it's a coincidence that the popular culture now talks so much more about S&M, anal sex, and non-monogamy.

During the 20th century there have been, of course, many developments specifically aimed at shaping sexuality. At the turn of the century there was a massive anti-masturbation campaign. The government, medical profession, Boy Scouts, army, and other institutions went out of their way to spread frightening lies about masturbation, whose legacy people are still dealing with.

Another thing that has shaped sexuality in this century is the invention and acceptance of sanitary pads and tampons, which are still not used in every country. In rural Russia, for example, a lot of women use pieces of cloth, and it's their mother-in-law's job to wash these out once a month. There is all this ritual and social meaning around it. You can imagine how the invention of menstrual supplies put individual women more in control of their periods, including the information about whether or not they were pregnant. Of course it also changed their relationship with the local grocer.

Other things in this century that have had a direct sexual impact include, the Kinsey Report, AIDS, pantyhose, birth control pills, Playboy magazine, the discovery of the clitoris and G-spot, penicillin, and the most important sex-related court case of the 20th century, Baird v. Eisenstadt. Named after the courageous Bill Baird, this decision gave people the right to use birth control even if they were single—less than fifty years ago. That established the constitutional right to privacy, cited several times a few years later in Roe v. Wade.

So now we are in the present, which only a few years ago was the past. And that past, and its past, could have helped us predict the future—which is now. Here are a few ways in which our current sexual challenges were predictable, if only we'd had a better grasp of history and the other social sciences:

Present:    Medicalization of sexuality & depression
Past:       Medicalization of "hysteria" and "self-abuse"

Present:    Mixed gender workplaces
Past:       Impact of the Industrial Revolution & factories

Present:    AIDS
Past:       Impact of the plague, TB, other epidemics

Present:    Anti-gay & anti-porn campaigns
Past:       The purity movements of 1910, 1930, & 1950

Present:    Internet & cybersex
Past:       Impact of the cinema, radio, & telephone

For example, the last 25 years has seen the increasing medicalization of sexuality and depression. This is no surprise when we look at history, because a hundred years ago we saw the medicalization of hysteria—a "woman's disease"—and of "self-abuse"—masturbation. A century ago, the medical profession became completely involved in these "problems'" diagnosis, treatment, and language. Most of what "modern" lay people knew about hysteria and self-abuse came from the medical profession. If sexology had studied that more we would be better able to understand the current medicalization of depression and sexuality.

The mixed-gender workplace is, according to the Institute for the Future's Wendy Everett, a turning point in human history. I think we could understand it better if we would examine the impact of the Industrial Revolution and factories on people's sexual and erotic relationships.

What happened to families in England, France, and Germany in the 1700s or 1800s when, for the first time, women actually left the house early in the morning and went to a factory and were surrounded by other women and other men? That must have been an enormous change. In fact, some historians say that a key trigger of the French Revolution was all the masses of people now walking to work every morning, with all that time to discuss how unhappy they were. This couldn't happen when people worked isolated among their families, but with industrialization they were walking ten abreast to the factories—complaining.

AIDS continues to have an enormous impact on sexuality. One of the ways we could better understand it is to look at the impact of other plagues, from the Bubonic in the thirteenth century to influenza, less than a hundred years ago. Pandemics are not just medical phenomena, they are social and cultural phenomena. Bioethicist Ina Roy says that one of the reasons society is having so much trouble dealing with AIDS today is because it's been conceptualized as a sexually transmitted disease rather than a communicable disease. She says if we talked about it more like tuberculosis than syphilis, we'd have more medical and social options. Looking at the impact other pandemics had on their respective cultures could give us clues about how to handle AIDS.

The dreadful anti-gay and anti-porn campaigns that we've been suffering through in the last 20 years are not unique in America. Back around 1910, again around 1930, and again around 1950, both of these campaigns of fear and hate were in vogue. Their structure looked similar to what we see now. It seems everyone is now talking about the Internet. This includes anti-pornography crusaders talking about how awful it is. Well, virtually every invention has been used for pornography when possible. People have always complained about other people—including "the children"—getting sexual information the newest form of telecommunications instead of from their families (or not at all).

When the cinema first became popular around 1915, self-appointed public guardians went crazy because they were afraid that the moving images would seep into people's brains, control their thinking and undermine their values. The same was said about radio, comic books, television, and now the Internet.

Another predictable thing is how the Right and certain elements of feminism are in bed together around issues of pornography and non-normative sexuality. This is not new; we have seen this coalition before, with the Women's Christian Temperance Union and other groups. In the 1900s and 1910s a group of right-wing religiously-oriented people wanted to "reform" Americans' behavior around issues such as sex, alcohol, tobacco, and language. A group of feminist women aligned with them, even though those people were against women working outside the home and women's suffrage. These regressive feminists aligned with these men because they recognized a joint goal—supporting the "purity of the home." So today's coalition is not new.

Now that we've looked at history, let's explore the future. I believe the future of sex will be determined along three dimensions—demographic, technologic, and cultural.

### • Demographic Trends

The fact that kids have so much private time after school is a huge change. When I came home from school as a kid, my mom was there with milk and cookies. This was true for most

American kids for the first two-thirds of the century—a mother or grandmother providing after-school supervision. We now have an enormous number of young people coming home from school with no supervision. Some of them are watching soap operas, some of them are talking on the phone, some of them are smoking dope, some of them are having sex with each other, and, I suppose, some of them are doing their homework.

Another demographic trend is the enormous push for abstinence education and anti-abuse programs. Some 20 years ago sex education was mandated in schools throughout the United States, a wonderful, progressive accomplish of SIECUS. The problem is that a lot of schools have twisted this mandate and now provide abstinence education instead of sex education. This is harming these children, and it will undermine their sexuality as adults.

Schools are also getting government money to provide anti-abuse programs, teaching seven-year-olds how to protect themselves from so-called bad touch. While we all want kids to be safe, I think it's a big mistake for kids to learn about all the ways they can be sexually exploited without learning about all the wonderful ways they can be involved in sexuality.

Unfortunately, this fits in with what a lot of younger parents: they're anxious that their kids are going to be kidnapped, terrified that their kids are going to be molested, they're overwhelmed by this social narrative of sexual danger, as if we were living in an erotic war zone—which, in reality, we're not. But there's a whole cohort of parents right now being trained by the media about how vulnerable their kids are. Even worse, this generation of kids now getting anti-abuse training is going to be parents one day, perpetuating this ugly mythology.

Another demographic change is that the population is aging. Many adults alive right now will live to be 100. Even more amazing, one out of three babies born in the year 2000 will live to be a hundred, so those of you who are looking for a marketing niche should consider eroto-gerontology. Issues that involve aging are going to be sexual issues as well, whether it's chronic pain, second, third, and fourth marriages, or how to be sexual when your medication steals your sexual desire. All of the lifestyle issues associated with aging are going to become sexual issues. Analgesics will soon be considered aphrodisiacs.

College cohorts are becoming much more heterogeneous. When I was in college all the students were the same age. Now in four-year colleges the ages of the students are much more mixed, even more so in two-year schools. So college students now spend several years in close proximity to people of widely varying ages. That means they're going to be exposed to various sexual cultures. It also means that the issue of student dating across generations will eventually be a cultural issue. As it is, colleges are already restricting the rights of students to have sex with the faculty. Not just faculty's rights to be sexual with students, but students' rights. People will soon be debating whether or not younger and older students should be allowed to have sex together, because the same power issues could be alleged.

There's also an increase in American society's cultural diversity. The amount of cross-ethnic and cross-racial cohabiting and marriage is skyrocketing, which obviously involves a mixing of sexual cultures. My therapy practice has lots of couples consisting of, say, an Indian engineer married to an American woman, or a Chinese engineer married to a Jewish man. Or it's two people from Thailand in an arranged marriage.

Western psychotherapy depends on concepts of individuation, decision-making, and personal responsibility. But what do we do when a guy comes in with erection problems and says he's in an arranged marriage? He's a responsible professional, an adult; but he says "this is who my mother told me to marry, so of course I did." We can't argue with that. But we are going to see more and more cultural diversity issues affecting people's sexual expression—and I frankly don't think we're prepared for it.

- **Technologic Trends**

We've already discussed that technology is always adapted to sexual uses, frequently in unanticipated ways. Take cell phones—invented for business situations in which telephones were unreliable, they are now in the hands of every junior high school kid. This completes the circle of privacy started by old-fashioned telephones, which established a person's private little world. Cell phones facilitate that private little world anyplace, anytime, and that's going to have an enormous sexual impact.

Everybody all over the country is getting access to the Web and getting hip to the Internet. For better or worse, the Net will be an increasing source of sexual information, as well as a means for people to meet. Virtual sex is an increasingly important part of many people's lives, and truly virtual sex is only a few years away. It will be interesting to see how this capability affects the use patterns of traditional pornography.

Pornography is everywhere now, more so than ever before. I don't think we have a clue as to what the impact of this is going to be.

All sexologists have their ideas about pornography, positive or negative. Regardless of our judgements, we're now looking at a whole new phenomenon. Porn started out restricted, and history has gradually democratized it via the printing press, nickelodeon, telephone, etc. With the Internet, everybody now can have as much of it as they want, whenever they want it, in as narrow a niche as they want. For example, there's actually a website called "Wet and Messy Shoes." You can see pictures of women who are fully clothed, wearing high heels—some of their shoes are caked with mud, some of them are dripping with milk, some of them are dangling in swimming pools. I don't think we have a clue about what the effect of all this pornography is going to be. We shouldn't be frightened, just very, very curious.

The medicalization of sexual dysfunction and its treatment is an increasing trend. Viagra is hot right now, but before Viagra there were Caverject, urethral suppositories, crude papaverine injections, and penile implants. So in the last 25 years we've watched the gradual medicalization of certain kinds of sexual difficulties—and we're going to see more and more of this.

A sublingual pill and even a topical cream to facilitate erection are in the works. Viagra is now being studied for its effects on women. Other scientists are investigating drugs that will help women have orgasms more easily.

While there's an exciting side to all this, I'm concerned about the relationships in which these pharmaceuticals are used. How often will these treatments imbalance or damage relationships in which people are accustomed to the erectile problem or the anorgasmia? Some women will think, "now that you can get it up, how do I know you won't be unfaithful?" And some men will think, "well, now that you come so easily, you're a slut."

We would like those people to get couples counseling along with their meds, but most are not interested in counseling. They just want to have decent sex. So we're going to see an increasing medicalization of sexual complaints. That means that insurance companies will be key players. You may remember that when Viagra first became available, people wondered how many pills their insurance company was going to cover—two a year? An unlimited supply? For many insurance companies, it's now five pills a month. It would be interesting to look at their company decision-makers. You can imagine six people sitting around a conference table and the first guy says, "Oh, three or four pills a month," and the second guy says, "Oh, three or four pills a month," and the third guy says, "Oh, I don't know, 20 a month . . ."

So we're going to see the pharmaceutical and insurance industries increasingly involved with sexuality. How much of our input are they getting? And how much of their process do we understand? We shouldn't be turning our backs on the drug companies. We should be pestering them and saying, "Hey, what about me? I know something that maybe you people haven't considered." We need to educate them, not reject or pooh-pooh them.

The disappearing line between contraception and abortion is an exciting development. I am really looking forward to the day when we're done with all of this fighting about abortion. I am against unwanted pregnancies. Sooner or later we're going to see the line between contraception and abortion completely wiped out. We already have the morning-after pill. There's a website where you can go and learn about the morning-after pill, even take the first steps toward ordering it. Sooner or later we're going to have RU486 (or its equivalent) legally and easily available in this country; it's a technologic and economic steamroller that just can't be stopped. The sense of desperation in the anti-choice people is not just that they want to stop abortion, it's that they realize that this is coming. Sooner or later a woman will be able to take a pill in the privacy of her own home that eliminates conception after the fact, and the fight over abortion will be over.

### • Cultural Trends

The first thing is ideas. Ideas have an enormous impact on sexuality. For example, in 19th century England people were quite certain that a woman had to have an orgasm in order to conceive. This was a medical fact, all the smart people knew this, and doctors taught their patients that if you're having trouble conceiving, it's because she's not climaxing, so do something about that. Ideas about what's normal, of course, have a big impact on sexuality.

The question of what is infidelity is now very interesting. Not whether infidelity is a good thing or bad thing, but the definition of it. Because with all of the technological ways that people now experience sex, it isn't so clear. For example, if somebody is having phone sex with a third party, is that infidelity? If somebody is masturbating while they're typing an e-mail, is that infidelity? I get people coming into my office and one of them wants to end the marriage because of the other's infidelity, and the partner says, "What are you so upset about? It was just a lap-dance, I don't even know the woman's name!" Or, "We typed some messages back and forth and I jacked off. What's wrong?" Conflicts like this will continue to escalate as technology creates more and more ways for people to be sexual together.

Most American religions are now facing internal power struggles. Who gets ordained—women? Gays? Divorced people? Will same-gender unions be blessed? Some clergy are saying they are obligated by their vows to God to perform same-gender marriages. And will traditional liturgies be rewritten—will it be God the Father or God the Incredible Cosmic Mother?

Since the 1970s, people have increasingly turned to the courts for guidance on their sexual rights. Do you have the right to be protected from unwanted sexual imagery at your job? Do you have the right to be protected from somebody making a pass at you? Do college students have the right to be sexual with professors? In Menlo Park, California, for example, one of the most liberal cities in the known world, a woman actually sued the city because there was a classic Greek nude statue in the lobby of the civic building where she worked. She said that this was sexual harassment and went to court.

One of the things we sexologists should be asking, is, which features of modern life are shaping the future of sexuality this very moment? What is it that we need to pay attention to in order to understand sexuality in the coming decade—or century? Examples might include:

- Amazon.com & e-commerce
- the mainstreaming of s/m
- the disappearance of downtowns
- life expectancy beyond age 100
- tampons
- artificial fertility technologies
- female clergy
- unsupervised free time for kids
- virtual sex
- low-fat diets
- public jack-off clubs
- talk radio
- John Gray's Mars/Venus paradigm
- Internet blocking software
- chlamydia
- the rise in cohabiting
- female athletics
- new pain medications
- young adults moving back home
- expanding definitions of date rape
- the normalization of female masturbation
- e-mail instead of written love letters
- the end of the Cold War
- the coming stock market crash
- bisexual chic
- people entering college in their 20s & 30s
- increasing interracial dating & marriage
- Internet penetration of daily life
- RU486
- the ubiquity of pornography
- the decreasing stigma of extramarital sex
- the increase in religiosity

- the disappearing availability of abortion
- female police & emergency personnel
- repetitive stress injuries
- cybersex
- increasing acceptance of psychotherapy
- pharmaceuticals that facilitate desire, arousal, & orgasm
- expanding definitions of "child molestation"
- tattoos and piercings
- whites becoming a minority
- managed health care & HMOs
- abstinence education
- bans on student-faculty dating
- steroids

How are these things shaping our sexual future? And what else is currently shaping our sexual future in ways we don't realize?

# Chapter 2

# Intimacy, Sex, and Art

*Michael Ferguson*

That what we are and can be as persons is bound up completely with the quality of our most important personal relationships should be so obvious as to need no proof (Guntrip, p. 194).

I am going to discuss three topics that are closely related. In fact, I see them as variants on a long spectrum of modes of communication of the inward heart. We'll begin with intimacy because it is the most profound form of human relating and basic to the other two types. Keep in mind that intimacy is essentially communication, and it is *communication of the inward heart.* By this I mean the *sharing* of our private inner world of thoughts, feelings, sensations, intentions, dreams, fantasies, or ideas that are in most circumstances kept private within ourselves. Such intimate communication at the same time reveals the structure and style of one's personality. It requires at least two people, but it could include more. There are many ways to share our inner experience: speech, touching, movements, gestures, actions, artworks, and sex are all modes of intimate communication. One can think of intimacy as emotional and psychological disrobing.

A *persona* is a mode of presenting ourselves publicly in order to promote smooth functioning in society. It is not necessarily false, although personas can often be very misleading. At best, it is only a very partial revelation of who we are. A persona is like a suit of clothes that we wear to meet expectations others have of us. It is only the top layer, which allows us to carry out daily activities without causing disturbance. There is much that goes on within us that is not revealed in how we present ourselves publicly even to close friends and family members. Intimacy is the process of revealing those deeper layers of our inner life. The audience for such revelations is typically small, although art is an intimate revelation that aims for a wide audience, or an undefined audience. We will discuss the peculiar qualities of artistic communication a little further on. But for now we will think of intimacy as communication of the inner self occurring within an interpersonal context.

Intimacy has degrees. In an interpersonal relationship intimacy is usually reciprocal to some extent, although that reciprocity will vary. Intimacy is rarely balanced and it is never perfect and it is never complete. A mother's intimacy with her infant or young child is weighted toward the child. The mother has greater awareness of the child's needs than the child has of the mother's. The intimacy of a doctor or a psychiatrist with a patient is weighted toward the patient. In every personal relationship the degree of transparency and opacity will vary

Reprinted by permission of Michael Ferguson.

considerably from one area to another. I like to think of relationships as having doors and windows that open and close. Some doors open and some remain closed. Some are closed after they have once been open. Some windows you can see through and some you can't. This is intimacy. It is highly variable depending on the person and on the relationship. We should avoid formulating an ideal of what intimacy should be like. Such ideals and expectations tend to be used to criticize and evaluate, and this tends to undermine intimacy. Intimacy depends on *acceptance*, which is a relaxation of our defenses, expectations, and preconceptions. Openness and receptivity are prerequisites to intimacy. One must suspend one's assumptions and expectations of another person in order to be intimate. Intimacy is always full of surprises, because you really know very little of what is inside another person, and a person's inner landscape is always in flux. To maintain an intimate connection with another person you have to pay attention. Rather than being something one strives for, intimacy depends on relaxation and allowing what is normally kept inward to emerge and flow freely into the mutual awareness between oneself and another. This can be very risky. There are good reasons why we keep many things private to ourselves. An outlook on life and on human beings heavily committed to moral strictures and or to an ideal of personal behavior is an impediment to intimacy. When a person fears judgment and censure, it is hard to be revealing. Creating an atmosphere where a person can feel comfortable sharing what is habitually kept inside and not outwardly expressed can take considerable time and skill. In some situations with a new person intimacy seems to appear suddenly and spontaneously. It may yield a feeling of elation or exhilaration. But such intimacy is only partial and often turns out to be temporary. Intimacy has a developmental line. It can broaden and deepen over time creating ever greater mutual awareness and interdependence, or it can shrink. It can ebb and flow like a tide that rises and falls. Relationships that have become dull or boring, that seem have lost their vitality, have probably lost their intimate connection. Small rejections and disappointments cause the doors and windows of intimacy to close. These small alterations in the avenues of inward communication accumulate over time. They are quite often so small and subtle that they often go unnoticed. But their cumulative effect is that the couple begins to lose interest in one another. One or the other might start to look elsewhere for the kind of connection they need.

Intimacy in an interpersonal context is habitual communication which creates a bond of the emotions and one's inner personhood. Repeated contact maintains and enhances this bond. Intimacy tends to establish patterns of relating, small unspoken understandings and agreements. An intimate connection that has fallen into neglect can be revived, but disuse can allow alterations in ones internal configuration to establish themselves that may make a revival of a previous intimacy difficult.

Intimacy should probably be distinguished from dependence, which is very common. Emotional dependence, the need for the reassuring presence of another, the need for constant attention, the desperate clinging to the attention and presence of another in response to a largely unconscious premonition of abandonment or loss, is a form of one-sided intimacy akin to that of a mother with her children. Communication and understanding flow mostly in one direction. This kind of connection is narcissistic in the negative sense, which I will explain a little further on. It is an unbalanced form of intimacy.

Despite the many obstacles to intimacy, it is something that occurs spontaneously and naturally among people. People want to be closely and emotionally connected to one another.

Even the most paranoid or schizoid person wants to be understood and accepted on his or her own terms. These great public conflagrations of rage and despair such as Adam Lanza's, Eric Harris and Dylan Klebold's, Seung-Hui Cho's, are meant to communicate with the entire society. The perpetrators of these spectacles don't want to just die, they want to be noticed. I doubt if there is any hope or expectation of understanding left in such people. Understanding is something they have had very little of in their lives and have long given up on. These actions are spectacular exhibitions of destruction and despair. Mass murder is intimate because it communicates and reveals the inward heart. The bond it creates with its victims and society is its continuing legacy of destruction.

# Empathy

Intimacy in its most mature form is related to empathy. Empathy is the ability to accurately grasp the inner life of another person, to understand how another person *feels* in a particular situation, to grasp the logic of their motives, to be able to anticipate their reactions or behavior. Empathy is not to be confused with *sympathy*, which is an attitude of benevolence or compassion toward another person. Empathy is strictly informative. It says nothing about how this accurate understanding another person's inner life will be applied. Salesmen need empathy, politicians need empathy, con men need empathy, torturers need empathy. And so do doctors, mothers, artists, and lovers. Empathy is only a tool. Like a hammer, it can be used to build a house, or to kill somebody.

Because empathy informs one of strengths, weaknesses, vulnerabilities in another, intimacy informed by empathy carries considerable risk. One becomes vulnerable in an intimate relationship. A person who knows you well can hurt you, and they know best how to do it. Exposure of one's inner self carries with it natural vulnerability. It takes courage and self-confidence to be intimate. Many people who lack such inner strength and confidence have difficulty becoming intimate with another person. Some people reach a certain level of intimacy and then panic at the realization of their own vulnerability. They may inexplicably withdraw at the very moment when the relationship seems to be close and deepening. Because of the high level of vulnerability entailed by intimacy, trust is an important ingredient in any intimate relationship. It is almost a prerequisite. People who are unable to trust others due to past injuries or painful relationships have difficulty forming intimate connections to others.

# Paranoid and Schizoid Defenses

Paranoia, which is essentially an abiding condition of fear that has been established through repeated attacks, is the great enemy of intimacy. Paranoia is a defensive system that operates on the assumption that all human relations are essentially antagonistic and exploitative. What it is defending against is an extreme sense of vulnerability, and rage against its many persecutors. Paranoid people simply don't believe in constructive, nurturing, benevolent relationships. Every good and positive outreach toward them is converted into something hostile or manipulative. If you succeed in penetrating the formidable defenses of a severely paranoid person, what you will find is a wounded, enraged person who sees herself or himself as the victim of attacks from all directions. You may find yourself playing a starring role in his or her persecutory delusions—not a position you want to be in.

Another common defensive system that seems to be increasingly popular in America is the schizoid. The schizoid person withdraws from human contact. They attempt to shrink the emotional life across the board keeping human interactions and emotional expression to an absolute minimum. Intimacy tends to be avoided at all costs, and when ventured into is an area of great difficulty. The schizoid challenge is disengagement. You can't reach the person on an intimate level. The paranoid is engaged, but it is a hostile, destructive engagement.

> They [the schizoids] are the people who have deep-seated doubts about the reality and viability of their very "self," who are ultimately found to be suffering from varying degrees of depersonalization, unreality, the dread feeling of "not belonging," of being fundamentally isolated and out of touch with their world.

> The schizoid problem is the problem of those "who feel cut off, apart, different, unable to become involved in any real relationships (Guntrip, p. 148).

These two defensive styles in a range of degrees and combinations are very widespread in American society and have influenced our laws and our culture to the extent that intimate relationships are difficult to achieve and maintain in contemporary America. Intimate relations are seen as hazardous—which they are—and are therefore not encouraged, or even actively discouraged, and sometimes persecuted—which tends to intensify the trend toward isolation.

The reasons for this increasing cultural trend are deep and complex and would make a good book, if someone out there wants to write it. But one important piece of evidence, I think, is the growth and success of science and technology, especially over the last couple of centuries. Science looks at the world in a totally impersonal way. Explanations of natural phenomena are sought in terms of mechanical causes and effects, not for personal reasons having to do with the human world. The success of this style of perceiving and relating to the natural world has encouraged its application to all areas of life. Schizoid personalities are very common among scientists and mathematicians. "Objectivity" means removing oneself from the matter at hand, perceiving and understanding a matter apart from one's personal interest in it. People are increasingly looking at one another in this depersonalized, utilitarian fashion.

The growth of corporations over the last century and a half, whose sole rationale and purpose for existence is to maximize profit, with all other values being subordinated to that overbearing imperative, have devalued the personal life of everyone in that economic system. Personal happiness, interpersonal satisfaction, sexual fulfillment, have no exchange value and therefore play no role in the economy. Increasingly one's personal life is forced to the sidelines as earning a living takes an ever greater proportion of time, energy, and attention. Modern life creates numerous obstacles to forming intimate relationships and places great challenges upon them, and this has created a society full of lonely, disconnected people hungry for connection yet finding it increasingly difficult to make the kind of fulfilling connections they seek.

What is the value of intimacy? Why strive for intimacy in our relations with others? Intimacy is the antidote to loneliness. Humans are by nature social. We are a species that has always survived in groups rather than as isolated individuals, like, say, orangutans. Humans need connection to others and that need is established in the earliest interactions between an infant and its mother. The lack of such a connection is experienced as painful distress. An abandoned infant will cry until it is exhausted. The need for reassuring connection to other human beings is deep in our nature and intimacy fulfills that need for connection. Our experience of ourselves is from the outset defined and established in relation to others, first and foremost, to our mothers. This earliest intimacy with our mothers establishes the development of our sense of self, the narcissistic structure of our personalities. This defines our need for intimacy and how that need is expressed and sought.

# Narcissism

Narcissism in the broadest sense refers to how one *experiences* oneself as a human being. It refers to one's feelings about oneself and one's abilities, one's personal appearance, one's physical capabilities and bodily integrity, and how one sees oneself in relation to others. It has to do with how one feels about life in general. Is it good? Is it bad? It is worthwhile or not? Should I continue living or not? These are narcissistic issues because they refer back to the self.

There are positive and negative aspects to narcissism. Narcissism in the positive sense is the regard one feels for oneself and one's own well being. The care one takes of one's own body, one's attention to grooming and appearance, the sensitivity one has to the impression one makes on others, the care and attention one gives to one's own health and well being, the satisfaction one feels in accomplishment or the realization of ambition, the sense of satisfaction one feels in helping others, teaching others, giving to others. Good parenting is narcissism in the positive sense, the satisfaction one takes in seeing one's children grow up healthy and constructively. Narcissism in the positive sense is feeling a sense of abundance in oneself, having the ability and the resources to share with others and enhance the lives of others. In a word, self-esteem. The satisfaction one takes in giving an appropriate gift is a narcissistic satisfaction. On the other hand, an inappropriate gift, a gift that is overly extravagant, or is otherwise not suited to the recipient shows a lack of empathy, a lack of understanding of the other person, a gift given to enhance the giver in his own eyes rather than from an appropriate understanding of the needs of the receiver is an example of narcissism in the negative sense, of deficient empathy and using others to enhance one's own self-esteem or sense of grandiosity. Pathological narcissism is obliviousness to the needs and feelings of others. It is not necessarily malicious, although it often comes off that way. It is actually a deficit in *emotional perception*. Pathological narcissism cannot see beyond its own needs and interests because of a great underlying sense of vulnerability. Pathological narcissism limits one's capacity for intimacy because one's need to enhance one's own self image is so great it overwhelms and excludes the ability to be receptive and open to the needs and feelings of another. Narcissism in the negative sense tends to exclude empathy or uses empathy selfishly and unsympathetically without consideration of the needs or feelings of others. The narcissistic structure of one's personality determines the degree of intimacy of which one is capable and the character of the intimate relations one is able to establish, whether constructive and enhancing, or destructive.

# Art

Art is also communication of the inward heart. An artist realizes his own inner self, or, let's say, an aspect of it, in a work or performance that can be viewed or shared by a public audience. This impulse to create and share one's internal self is a narcissistic need. Not everyone has this drive to create and share one's inner heart through external symbolic representations. It is a peculiarity of artists, the origins of which we will not explore here. Art is a form of intimacy in the sense that the artist shares his or her inward self and exposes it to an external audience. The size of the audience does not matter. What is important is that art reaches out for connection. Art is not masturbation. It is not something you do for your own private comfort or amusement. *Art connects you to other people.* There is a narcissistic satisfaction in creating something with great technical skill that others can recognize and admire. But what is essential to art is not this narcissistic satisfaction that the artist feels in his creative accomplishment, but rather the outreach to others from the core of the artist's inner self that a work of art represents. By creating something external to oneself, as opposed to simply daydreaming or fantasizing, one creates the possibility of a connection to others through their perception of one's artwork. When a person comes into contact with a work of art, they are coming into contact with a representation of the inner self of the artist who created it. One does not create randomly. This does not mean that a viewer can readily grasp the emotional and psychological meaning of a work of art upon encountering it. It takes considerable time and experience to understand an artistic language, and artists are often deliberately obscure and idiosyncratic in how they present themselves in their work. However, it is my view that artistic effectiveness is related to communicative effectiveness rather than to obscurity.

Architectural blueprints, anatomical diagrams, maps, graphs, are depictions of external reality. They are meticulous assemblages of facts, measurements, and objective characteristics that can be seen and verified by anyone. They are not usually thought of as art, because they do not reflect the *inner* self, the maker's subjective reaction or perspective on the subject presented. When Picasso did his painting of the Weeping Woman (1937) he was not trying to recreate this woman in a true to life rendering. Rather, this image reflects *how Picasso saw this woman* and how he chose to depict her out of all the many ways he could have chosen to do this painting. This painting is a subjective view of the woman, not an attempt to describe her body or her character with objective validity. Art is about illusions. It is about how the artist *needs to see* the world, not necessarily how the world *is*. And that is entirely based on his personal psychology. Even the Dutch masters who drew and painted meticulously accurate portraits of faces and people still had a personal style of their own. They had to choose how to portray their subjects, what manner of dress they should wear, how they should be posed, the circumstances in which they are set, the intensity and direction of the light, the mood or facial expression to be portrayed. These are all personal choices of the artist that go into the creation of a "realistic" portrait. So in this sense art is always a reflection of the subjectivity of the artist. Art is a partial intimacy because what the artist chooses to present of himself is carefully selected and meticulously prepared for public presentation to obtain a calculated effect. The intimacy of art tends to flow in one direction, from the artist to the viewer.

Reciprocity, that is, the viewer's experience or reaction to the artwork is not usually experienced directly by the artist, except for admiring applause or negative reviews. But that is not the most important impact of art upon its audience. The important and lasting impact of art is usually not expressed directly, and that is the expansion in the inner awareness of the viewer of an artwork, or an alteration in his or her perception and understanding of the external world, or of himself or herself.

I disagree with John Cage that art is non-intentional, that its purpose is to " sober and quiet the mind, thus making it susceptible to divine influences" (John Cage, johncage.org/autobiographical statement). This conception of artistic purpose rejects the communicative function of art and is the polar opposite from my own view. My understanding of art is narcissistic in the sense that it starts from the self of the artist and connects the artist to other selves through the communicative means of the artwork. Cage's conception of art stems from Zen Buddhist ideas that seek the annihilation of the self. Art becomes a means of "emptying" the self, reducing the self towards the ideal of nothingness. Nothing could be further from or more opposed to the point of view I am advancing here. My view is that life is a process of the growth of the self and the enhancement of the self through fulfilling connections to others, as stated in the epigraph at the outset. Art is a means toward that enhancement and fulfillment as is intimacy in personal relationships. Zen Buddhism essentially elevates the schizoid position of detachment and isolation to an ideal of human development, a view I am totally out of sympathy with.

What is the value of art? Art expands one's awareness of the internal life and enables one to perceive people, the external world, the social environment, and one's inner life in new ways. Art alters our way of looking at things and experiencing ourselves. In that sense art can be educational in that it offers modes of experiencing ourselves and the external world that might not otherwise be available through other channels. Art can change people in that it alters their perceptions and awakens them to aspects of inner and outer reality of which they may not be aware. In that sense art is volatile and can be subversive if it seeks to illuminate that which is officially suppressed. Art fosters intimacy by expanding awareness of the inner self and directing attention toward reflection on the inner life. Failure to educate in the arts, minimizing attention to the arts, devaluing the arts, indicate a lack of value placed on the development of the inner self.

# Sex

What does all of this have to do with sex? Sex is also communication of the inward heart and an expression of the narcissistic structure of the personality. It falls within the broader concept of intimacy, but it has peculiarities that set it apart from other forms of intimate communication. Sex is communication through the body that seeks the satisfaction of lust. Lust is a powerful connecting emotion. Lust impels one to seek contact with another person, and it is contact of a particular kind, namely contact leading to sexual arousal and genital contact. However, many other kinds of touch and many other aspects of intimacy occur within the context of sexual activity. Touch, physical affection, and bodily closeness are enormously reassuring and comforting. These needs for comfort, reassurance, and affection that occur alongside the satisfaction of lust are highly intimate and satisfy a deep longing for connection and bonding between people. This is perhaps the deepest form of intimacy because it is a sharing of the most intensely felt bodily and psychological longings. How one expresses and seeks to satisfy lust and the need for bodily closeness reflects the narcissistic structure of one's personality. Sex has a lot in common with art in that the mode in which one seeks to satisfy lust reflects one's narcissistic needs just as the art that one produces reflects the narcissistic structure of the artist's inner self. Sex says a lot about who you are. Sex is not only about the satisfaction of lust. Sex is a paradigmatic expression of narcissism. Because sex is communication, sex tells you where you are in a relationship with another person. When sex is going well and people find satisfaction and mutual pleasure in one another, it signifies a strong bond and a positive avenue of communication and understanding. Of course this is not the only aspect of a relationship that is important and it is not all there is to intimate communication. Some people use sex to cover up or avoid other issues that may be a source of discomfort. Sex can also be used to conceal and mislead. A dishonest heart can use sex to manipulate and destroy. The intimacy of sex is only partial. Sex is one aspect of intimacy, but a very important one because it embodies the energetic connection of lust and sexual arousal. But do not think that because you have sex with a person you know everything important about them.

# Kissing

There are numerous theories on the origin of kissing, and kissing can, of course, have many different meanings. Some cultures do not kiss at all, or very little. References to kissing in Western culture go back to ancient times, and the era of exploration and colonialism, as well as modern media have spread the practice of kissing around the world. Psychoanalytic theory sees the propensity to kiss stemming from the feelings of warmth, safety, nurturing, and well being in the infant's nursing at the mother's breast. Clamping the mouth on the nipple is a means of incorporation, of sustenance, dependence and survival. In adults the meanings and style of kissing can be many, but kissing always carries a message related to nurturing or incorporation. Gentle kisses of affection, pecks on the cheek and so forth, impart a message of affection, good feeling, warmth, reassurance, and nurturing. Kisses of passion and desire communicate a will to incorporate, to possess, consume, an emotional neediness, an inner longing and loneliness for which one is seeking solace in the other. Kissing—or not kissing—reveals how attracted a person is to your body, how much they need you, how much they like you, their willingness to depend on you, and the degree to which they can reciprocate your feelings and empathize with your needs. All of this can be communicated through kissing. Oral sex is a further extension of these feelings and needs of both giving and incorporating through the mouth, but applied to the genitals and the emotions of sexual arousal. The use of the mouth as a body connector is a very powerful and effective vehicle of intimate communication.

# Orgasm

Orgasm is understudied and not well understood. Most of what is known about orgasm has issued from studies of epilepsy and people who have had nerve damage, spinal and/or brain injuries. Physiologically, orgasm shares a lot of characteristics with epileptic seizures. There is no scientific consensus on the definition of orgasm or how it should be conceptualized. For this reason I am putting forward my own conceptualization of it here.

Sexual desire, lust, sexual arousal, and orgasm are hypnotic processes. They shift our awareness to special subjective states that mobilize emotional and physical response systems that are normally dormant during everyday experience. Sexual desire, or lust, is the *perception* of the sexuality of another person. It is looking at another person and *feeling* the possibility of sexual activity, creating a visualization of the other in a sexual context. It is a conscious awareness of desirable sexual interaction, which is a continuing state. It is different, from simply perceiving a person's existence, or the clothes they are wearing, or their ability to perform some task, or their physical characteristics. What makes it different is that it mobilizes our personal emotional response system and prepares us for sexual arousal in a way that other kinds of perception do not, and therefore it is an altered mode of awareness. Sexual arousal is the next level of intensification. The body becomes mobilized in anticipation of sexual activity. Internal physical sensations become more prominent in our awareness and other considerations that might inhibit sexual arousal tend to be excluded from consciousness. Arousal is intensified through physical stimulation of the genitals and other regions of the body as well as psychic stimuli such as sound, scenario, internal visualization (fantasy), and perhaps smell. At a certain threshold orgasm is triggered. Involuntary physical processes are set in motion accompanied by intense awareness of pleasurable sensation that excludes nearly everything else. Orgasm is a state where physical pleasure overwhelms consciousness and obliterates the ability to attend to other inputs to consciousness. Some people see a relationship between orgasm and the "loss of self" reported in some mystical experiences. My feeling is that orgasm differs from these mystical experiences in that in orgasm the self does not disintegrate. The self remains intact. But normal consciousness, which ordinarily processes input from numerous internal and external sources simultaneously, becomes overwhelmed during orgasm by internal physical sensations which become extraordinarily dominant. Other modes of perception and awareness are not extinguished. One can still see and hear during orgasm, but, orgasm is a state where interoception (awareness of the internal state of one's body) is magnified to a unique predominance. This makes it special. One must be able to relax one's external and internal perceptual apparatus in order to orgasm. Ordinarily we are bombarded by sensate experience from the external world as well as from our own internal thought processes. In order to orgasm one must be able to allow those perceptions to recede from consciousness so that the physical pleasure of the orgasm occupies one's awareness to the near exclusion of everything else. This is a hypnotic process. It is not entirely voluntary, but it is conditioned by experience. It is the capability of awareness to shift in a specific way under the conditions of intense sexual stimulation. One does not orgasm from driving a car or vacuuming the carpet. Orgasm is a special type of conscious experience that can only occur under very specialized conditions. In my view, this is the way orgasm should be understood.

Komisaruk, et al. (2006) argue that orgasm is not a *reflex*, but rather a *perception* (p. 137f.), and I concur with this valuable insight. That is, orgasm is not generated by muscular contractions caused by genital stimulation, which, in turn, lead to a reflexive action in the spinal column. Genital stimulation mobilizes neurons throughout the body sending greater and greater levels of excitation to the brain. The muscular contractions are indeed reflexive and can be elicited in the spinal column even when the spinal cord is severed. But *orgasm is not produced unless those muscular contractions are perceived by the brain as sensations.* This supports my view that orgasm should be understood as essentially a psychological phenomenon, not simply as a physical process. The physical concomitants of orgasm are, of course, noteworthy and important, but Komisaruk and his collaborators have shown that the physical processes themselves do not constitute orgasm. They can occur without the experience of orgasm, and orgasm can occur independently of physical arousal. Therefore orgasm must be understood as essentially a subjective experience, a particular state of altered awareness, that is usually (although not necessarily) accompanied by specific physiological processes under the conditions of intense sexual arousal. Orgasm is therefore primarily a narcissistic experience rather than a communicative one, although sharing orgasms is a powerful bonding experience, because sharing the special ecstatic state of orgasm is highly intimate.

## Sadism and Masochism

Sadism is the pleasure we take in the suffering of another. It is a spectrum that extends from gentle teasing to torturing someone to death. Sadism reflects ambivalence. It is essentially a hostile, destructive impulse that is mitigated by feelings of good will, love, guilt, and perhaps fear. We need the person toward whom we feel hostility, so we don't want to destroy them. But it feels good to see them suffer. It is the expression of the suppressed hostile impulse that is pleasurable. The spectrum is defined by the mix of hostile and positive feelings toward the victim. The greater the hostility, the greater the cruelty and the darker the expression. As the mitigating feelings tend toward zero, it becomes simply cruelty. Mild sadism is ordinary and commonplace. Jokes are often mildly sadistic and jokes that are overly hostile can lose their humor. Sadism is intimate because it expresses our conflicted feelings toward another person, and the pleasure we feel in the pain or discomfort of another is something usually kept private. Sadism is common in sexual activity to a greater or lesser degree, because sexual relationships are conflicted and often mixed with hostile aspects.

Masochism is using adversity to one's advantage and seeking it out for that purpose. I see it as a broader concept than sadism and it is related to depression and despair. Masochism is an adaptation of people who are habituated to suffering and adversity. The erotic aspect of it, feeling sexual arousal in response to pain, or pain as an intensifier of erotic feeling, comes from associating sexual arousal or love with painful experiences, neglect, disappointment, and abuse. One learns that to love, or to be aroused, hurts, and one comes to expect, or even to need, those feelings to occur together. In my eyes, masochism is harder to understand than sadism because in order to understand it one must grasp a lifetime of painful experiences that may not be easily accessible. In an erotic context it is not a neat complement to sadism, in general. It is much more complicated, whereas sadism, although conflicted, is relatively straightforward. For that reason I don't like the term 'sadomasochism'. It squashes together two things that I think are very different and don't necessarily complement one another.

## Love

Love is a word that is used in many different ways to mean many different things. I tend to avoid it because I always fear that I am giving the wrong impression. People attach very different meanings to 'love' and it raises all sorts of expectations that may not be realistic. However, it is enormously reassuring and people love to hear it, so we must deal with it. I will start with my definition of love in the best sense. Mature love is *good will* guided by *empathy* and tempered with a *respect for the separateness and individuality* of the other person. Empathy is very important. Empathy means you understand how the other person feels and what his or her real needs are. Most of what is called 'love' is not empathic and this leads to all sorts of turmoil. I disagree with defining love in terms of a willingness to sacrifice on behalf of the beloved. This is masochistic. It implies that you are giving up something you would rather not in order to benefit the beloved. You are inflicting some suffering upon yourself in order that your loved one may enjoy some benefit. Love is certainly characterized by a giving spirit and a desire to enhance and bestow advantage upon one's beloved. But rather than self denial, love represents a sharing of the *abundance* of one's physical and emotional resources. It does not necessarily expect anything in return, but it embodies a hope for attachment and good will and an intertwining with the life of the beloved. Love is an *expansion* of the self, an attempt to complete the self through emotional resonances and attachment to what is valued and idealized in the other. Whatever is done out of love does *not* occur beyond good and evil, as Nietzsche once suggested (*Beyond Good and Evil*, 153). Love can never be an excuse for reckless or destructive actions. Love lies squarely within the framework of our values and constructive human relationships. Mature love is closely related to respect for others and responsibility for oneself.

Our common notion of "romantic" love is characterized by strong emotion, passion, elation, anticipation, despair, jealousy, possessiveness, dependence and obsessive preoccupation with the beloved. This is what people usually mean by being "in love." This kind of love tends to be self-centered and unempathic, often lacking a realistic perception of the beloved as a complete person, sometimes ignoring serious character flaws in the other, and often a maintaining distorted understanding of the relationship itself. It is sometimes manifest as a furious, psychological dependence that devours and emotionally destroys the other through insatiable demands for attention and control. This is not mature love, in any way, shape, or form. However, these experiences can have great emotional and psychological significance. Relationships that start out this way can sometimes evolve into more mature forms of love without losing the passion and zest with which they began. This romantic kind of love brings people together, but it is not what keeps them together in a satisfying relationship over a long period of time. Empathy, good will, and respect are much more important for healthy, durable loving relationships than "love." Intimacy is an important element in a healthy loving relationship because intimacy informs and bonds. Intimacy enables one to be close to another person, to know the other person in depth, to be in touch with the other person's feelings, concerns, and needs. Intimacy gives a sense of connection, mutual dependence, and support. We do not face the world alone, we face it together as a couple giving strength and support to one another, informed by our intimate knowledge of one another and energized by lust and sexual pleasure. It's a good way to live, if you can achieve it.

# References

Guntrip, Harry (1973) *Psychoanalytic Theory, Therapy, and the Self.* New York: Basic Books.

Kirshenbaum, Sheril (2011) *The Science of Kissing: What Our Lips are Telling Us.* New York: Hachette Book Group.

Komisaruk, Barry. R.; Beyer-Flores, Carlos; & Whipple, Beverly. (2006) *The Science of Orgasm.* Baltimore: Johns Hopkins University Press.

Michael Ferguson received his PhD in philosophy of science from the University of Illinois at Chicago. He is an independent scholar who lives in San Francisco. Address correspondence to him at: mfsfusa@sbcglobal.net

# Section II

# Gender Issues

# Chapter 3

# Foundations of Gender

*Joel Baum, MS*

When a child is born, the first question most commonly asked of the new parent is "what did you have- a boy or a girl?" In fact, the focus on "what it is" often *precedes* the child's birth. But it is this seemingly simple question that is at the root of our understandings, or misunderstandings, about gender. This article will explore how complex this question actually is, as well as how a more nimble understanding of gender as a concept opens up space for all kids. Rather than limiting conventional beliefs, a fuller understanding of gender expands them. In taking a topic from a static, single aspect to a dynamic, multi-dimensional understanding, we more accurately reflect the richness and diversity that is human gender.

## What Is Gender?

For many people, the terms "gender" and "sex" are interchangeable. This incorrect notion has become so common, particularly in western societies, that it is rarely questioned. We are born, assigned a gender, and sent out into the world. For many people, this misunderstood idea is cause for little, if any dissonance. Yet biological sex and gender are different; gender is not inherently nor solely connected to one's physical anatomy.

*Biological sex* includes physical attributes such as external genitalia, sex chromosomes, gonads, sex hormones, and internal reproductive structures. At birth, it is used to **assign sex** as male or female. *Gender* on the other hand is far more complicated. Along with one's physical traits, it is the complex interrelationship between those traits and one's internal sense of self as male, female, both or neither as well as one's outward presentations and behaviors related to that perception.

## Dimensions of the Gender Spectrum

Western culture has come to view gender as a **binary** concept, with two rigidly fixed options: male or female. When a child is born, a quick glance between the legs determines the gender label that the child will carry for life. But even if gender is to be restricted to basic biology, a binary concept still fails to capture the rich variation observed. Rather than just two distinct boxes, biological gender occurs across a continuum of possibilities.

In fact, there are a variety of forms of **gender biology.** Individuals can be born with various forms of "intersex" conditions (current nomenclature is "Disorders of Sexual Development"

---

Reprinted by permission of Gender Spectrum.

or DSDs). A baby may appear to have typically female genitalia, while internally the child has "male" tissues or even fully formed organs. Some individuals will appear to be one gender, only to masculinize or feminize as they enter puberty. Still others can be born with ambiguous genitalia, or with genitalia not in evidence at all. Even in a small number of "typical" births, specialists are consulted to "confirm" the sex of the newborn. Add to this mix variation in chromosomal arrangements, protein processing differences and hormonal inconsistencies and a much more complicated picture of gender biology emerges.

This **spectrum** of anatomical variations by itself should be enough to disregard the simplistic notion of only two genders. Yet gender biology (i.e. sex) is only one dimension of a person's authentic gender.

## Gender Expression

Beyond anatomy, there are multiple domains defining gender. In turn, these domains can be independently characterized across a range of possibilities. This includes **gender expression,** which represents the second dimension of one's authentic gender. Gender expression refers to the ways in which people externally communicate their gender identity to others through behavior, clothing, hairstyle, voice, and other forms of presentation. Gender expression also works the other way around as people assign gender to or have expectations about others based on their appearance, mannerisms, and other gendered characteristics. Like gender biology, rather than a binary concept, gender expression too is a spectrum. There is a range of ways in which individuals present their gender. Gender expression is about *preferences*.

The norms for the expression of gender shift over time, and from one culture to the next. One need only look at the manner in which hairstyles have changed to see this changing landscape in action. Perhaps nothing illustrates the dynamic nature of gender expression more than the colors pink and blue. While today these colors are virtually unquestioned as a "girl color" and "boy color," respectively, it has not always been the case. Well into the twentieth century, the opposite prevailed. A *Ladies' Home Journal* article in June 1918 said, "The generally accepted rule is pink for the boys, and blue for the girls. The reason is that pink, being a more decided and stronger color, is more suitable for the boy, while blue, which is more delicate and dainty, is prettier for the girl."

Despite its shifting nature, it is on the basis of gender expression that many children face mistreatment from those around them. Especially in western culture, the "rules" of gender are rigidly enforced, by adult and kids alike. While there is noting inherently male or female about colors, toys, activities, mannerisms, or clothes, society frequently genders these and other forms of expression. When children step outside of these expectations, the reactions from those around them can often be cruel or even dangerous.

For educators, understanding and interrupting the assignment of gender to objects, activities, personal characteristics, etc. is critical in the creation of a gender inclusive school or classroom. Gender inclusion does not mean that there is something wrong about having preferences that are seen as typical for one's gender. There *are* patterns with regard to the expression of gender; for instance, girls more commonly wear dresses than do boys. However, **patterns of gender expression are not rules**. While girls may wear dresses more than boys, it does not mean they have to, nor does it mean that boys can't. The same goes for toys, colors, activities, and other forms of expression that have become gendered. Because gender expression is based on one's preferences, there is no right or wrong way. Rather than "girl toys" and "boy toys," there are instead just "kids toys."

## *Gender Identity*

The third dimension of gender is **gender identity**, which refers to one's innermost concept of self as male, female, neither, or somewhere along the spectrum. It is how individuals perceive themselves and what they call themselves. One's gender identity can be the same or different than the sex assigned at birth. Individuals become conscious of this between the ages 18 months and 3 years. Most people develop a gender identity that matches their biological sex. For some, however, their gender identity is different from their biological or assigned sex.

Gender identity represents an internal aspect of one's authentic gender. While biological sex can be assigned and expectations of gender expression imposed, gender identity comes solely from within. Individuals come to know for themselves who they are. Like the other dimension of gender, identity also offers a spectrum of possibilities rather than a simple binary. While many people will have a gender identity consistent with their assigned gender, this will not always be the case. Again, we have a pattern, but not a rule. Gender identity for some means a sense of self that is at once both male and female, or fluidly moving between them. Others will declare that they are neither, where one's own understanding of self fails to align with categories that do not resonate with the lived experience. Individuals who fall into this latter category can be likened to someone finding them in a train station where they do not speak the language. The people around you seem to know where they're going, yet you are not sure which way to turn.

Some individuals will have a gender identity that is "opposite" that of their assigned gender. That is, someone born with a penis knows *herself* to be female, or an individual born with a vulva firmly identifies *himself* as male. A term that is often used for individuals such as these is **transgender**. While there are a great many ways individuals use this term, for the purposes of this guide we will use it to refer to individuals whose sex assigned at birth does not match their gender identity (the prefix *trans-* literally means across, on the other side of).

Gender identity is not about preferences; rather, one holds a deeply felt sense of self. Frequently, this understanding of self emerges quite early, and will remain persistent and consistent throughout life. If aligned with the gender assigned at birth, the person experiences little if any dissonance. However, when identity and biology do not line up, the experience can be jarring—a collision within one's sense of self, as well as with the perceptions of others. In the former, gender dysphoria can emerge. This refers to an individual's experience of anxiety, uncertainty and persistently uncomfortable feelings when the gender that they were assigned at birth does not match one's sense of gender identity. In the latter, when the reaction of others to one's professed identity is negative, or disbelieving, the impact can be devastating. Dysphoria can increase significantly when an individual's professed identity is not accepted by those around them. This does not mean, however, that the internal sense of one's gender changes.

## *The Sum of it Parts…*

Alone, each dimension of gender challenges the binary model so common in our culture. But when considered as a whole, the full complexity of gender truly unfolds. Just as three dimensions of space provide a more detailed landscape for understanding physical objects, the three dimensions of gender provide a much richer model for exploring this misunderstood concept. When thinking about gender, it is the **interaction of the three dimensions** that really captures gender's complexity.

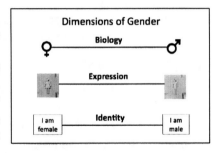

For many individuals, gender is "aligned." That is, the Gender Biology (assigned gender), Gender Expression (presentation of gender) and Gender Identity (internal sense of self) line

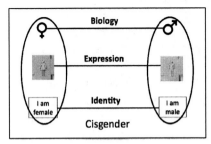

up. A term sometimes used to capture this idea is "cis-gendered." The prefix *cis-* comes from Latin and means "on the same side as" or "on this side of." While the most common pattern, even within this arrangement there is tremendous room for variation.

However, the above is not the only model available for capturing individual experiences of gender. Another possibility is for biology and identity to line-up, but for expression to be seen as inconsistent. Of course, the norms for expression that are seen as "male" or "female" we have already suggested are artificial; who decides? But there remain in many people's minds certain expectations, which can be described as follows:

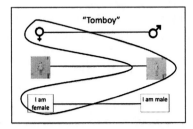
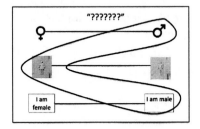

Consider the two figures above. On the left, a child assigned and identifying as female is seen by those around her to gravitate towards the masculine in terms of her expression of gender, while the child on the right, assigned and identifying as male is seen to favor more feminine expression. Despite being identical in profile, these two individuals may well face very different reactions from those around them. Particularly when young, while the girl on the left is celebrated as a "tomboy," the boy on the right may well become the target of others' disapproval. In fact, while the term "tomboy" is sometimes seen as favorable, we have no similar label for the child on the right. Sadly, instead this child often faces taunting with terms like "faggot," "sissy," "homo," or "gay," all being used in a decidedly mean way. Yet what is

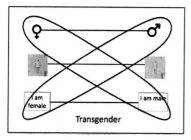

Transgender

the difference between these two young people, who simply have preferences that others have artificially gendered?

Finally, some individuals will be assigned one gender based on biology while identifying as the other. Where *cisgender* refers to someone whose identity is "on the same side as," their assigned gender, *transgender* refers to someone whose identity is "across from" their assigned gender. Expression for transgender individuals can be anywhere along the spectrum. There are transgender individuals who express gender in very stereotypical ways, and others who do not. In part, this may be about preferences, and in part this may be indicative of the context in which they find themselves. In other words, a transgender girl may wear jeans and tee shirts because they **like them,** or they may be forced to dress in such stereotypically male ways because the people around them will not allow a more typically feminine style.

In summary, the dimensions of gender provide a far more dynamic way to think about gender. Instead of the static, binary model produced through a solely physical understanding of gender, a far richer texture of biology, gender expression, and gender identity intersect in a multi-dimensional array of possibilities. Quite simply, the **gender spectrum** represents a more nuanced and accurate model of human gender.

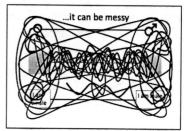

...it can be messy

# Falling Into Line

Gender is all around us. It is actually taught to us, from the moment we are born. Gender expectations and messages bombard us constantly. Upbringing, culture, peers, community, media, and religion, are some of the many influences that shape our understanding of this core aspect of identity. How you learned and interacted with gender as a young child directly influences how you view the world today. Gendered interaction between parent and child begin as soon as the sex of the baby is known. In short, gender is a socially constructed concept.

Like other social constructs, gender is closely monitored by society. Practically everything in society is assigned a gender—toys, colors, clothes, hairstyles and behaviors some of the more obvious examples. Through a combination of social conditioning and personal preference, by age three most children prefer activities and exhibit behaviors typically associated with their sex. Accepted social gender roles and expectations are so entrenched in our culture that most people cannot imagine any other way. As a result, individuals fitting neatly into these expectations rarely if ever question what *gender* really means. They have never had to, because the system has worked for them.

# About Gender Variance

**Gender variance** is when a person's preferences and self-expression fall outside commonly understood gender norms. Gender variance is a normal part of human expression, documented across cultures and recorded history. Non-binary gender diversity exists throughout the world, documented by countless historians and anthropologists. Examples of individuals living comfortably outside of typical male/female identities are found in every region of the globe. The *calabai*, and *calalai* of Indonesia, two-spirit Native Americans, and the *hijra* of India all represent more complex understandings of gender than the simplistic model seen in the west.

Further, what might be considered gender variant in one period of history may become gender normative in another. One need only examine trends related to men wearing earrings or women sporting tattoos to quickly see the malleability of social expectations about gender. As mentioned earlier, even the seemingly intractable "pink is for girls, blue is for boys" notions are relatively new.

## Gender and Privilege

When someone is "typically gendered," they benefit from gender privilege. For individuals whose biological sex, gender expression, and gender identity neatly align, there is a level of congruence as they encounter the world. Like many forms of social privilege, this is frequently an unexamined aspect of their lives. Forms they fill out, the clothing stores in which they shop, identification papers they carry, bring few if any second thoughts.

Yet for a transgender or gender nonconforming person, each of these, and many more examples, are constant reminders that they move about in a culture that really does not account for their own experience. Social privilege comes from an assumption that one's own perspective is universal; whether related to race, or language, or gender, privilege comes from being part of the "norm." For children who express gender in a way others consider inconsistent, this plays out as the taunts on the schoolyard, enforced isolation by peers, or hurtful words and lack of understanding from the adults surrounding them.

To understand this more intuitively, think about the last time you were in a public setting and needed to use a restroom. For gender-typical individuals, this rarely presents a problem or question (issues of cleanliness notwithstanding!). Yet for an individual who does not fit into narrowly defined expectations of gender presentation or identity, restroom use can present a whole host of challenges, sometimes even becoming a matter of life and death. The daily need to make judgments about what one does, or wears, or says based on other people's perceptions of their gender is a burden that many people never encounter. These everyday reminders of being different are also constant reinforcement of being "other."

## Conclusion

Perhaps the most fundamental aspect of a person's identity, gender deeply influences every part of one's life. In a society where this crucial aspect of self has been so narrowly defined and rigidly enforced, individuals who exists outside its norms face innumerable challenges. Yet this does not have to be the case. Through a thoughtful consideration of the uniqueness and validity of every person's experiences of self, we can develop greater acceptance for all.

# About the Author

Joel Baum, MS, is the Director of Education and Training with Gender Spectrum (www .genderspectrum.org), which provides education, resources and support to help create a gender sensitive and inclusive environment for all children and teens. Responsible for all aspects of the organization's educational programs, he's an award-winning middle school science teacher and school administrator, has served as a district administrator in Oakland, CA and as a school reform coach with the National Equity Project. Joel has also been a Professor of Educational Leadership at CSU East Bay.

# Chapter 4

# Masculinity and Identity: Restrictive Ways of Being?

*Ignacio Lozano Verduzco*

Because it is a theme of epistemological importance, the concept of identity is well discussed throughout the social science literature in different disciplines. Some views on identity prioritize a lens that focuses on understanding identity as an individual construct, a-historical and a-cultural (Erikson, 1985/2000; Freud, 1903/1972; Sullivan, 1953), while others, which this author finds much more useful, understand identity as a concept that requires a socio-historical space in order for it to be defined (Careaga, 2004; List, 2005; Suyemoto, 2002). I understand identity as the story an embodied subject tells itself, or in other words, that which a determined body knows or can achieve to know.

In this chapter, how gender norms regarding masculinity affect the construction of one's self, specifically men, using examples from the author's experience in research and community interventions in Mexico, will be explored. Even though the data presented is located in a particular country, this does not mean that masculinity and gender systems are not present in other cultures. Because of the theoretical literature reviewed, it is suspected that masculinity, in all its hegemony, is a global phenomenon with some variations in each culture.

## Gender and Identity

Identity tries to ask and answer the question "who am I?" putting an emphasis on the self and on a dialectic characteristic in the process of the construction of subjects. This dialectic implies a permanent dialogue between the person and all its contexts. In social sciences, particularly psychology, this concept of identity is studied by social constructionism and symbolic interactionism, because both recognize the relationships each person has and how this allows for the interpretation and meaning-giving processes that each subject is capable of incorporating into their sense of self. Given this background, it is important to understand identity under a situated knowledge feminist perspective, as a product of particular cultural spaces (Blazquez, 2010; Harding, 2010). It is not possible to understand identity without understanding the social, cultural, political and familiar contexts of each person. This means that identity is a symbolic game, where signs and symbols are learned and each one holds a particular meaning for each person.

It is with this in mind, that context and social systems become fundamentally important, since it is with them that each person holds dialogue with, and through which each person constructs a sense of self. Feminist theory and movement have made it evident that the gender system is a structure and a system that guides life in all its environments. Some authors hold that gender is a system that orders social reality and that is a priori to the individual (Butler, 2001; de Lauretis, 2008). For them, gender is a social system that orders relationships (Rubin, 1986), and identities (West & Zimmerman, 1987), as well as ideas, believes, attitudes and constructs that exist in a particular cultural space around the idea of men and women (Lamas, 2000), based on what Connel (1995) calls the "reproductive arena," on the bodies and their ability to reproduce. It is important to keep in mind that these differences are marked by power, where men, as a collective, use patriarchal pacts to locate themselves in a place of hegemony over women (Amorós, 1992; Connel, 1995; Kaufman, 1989; Millet, 1995). This supra-ordination is not only over women, but over what each collective means. When men don't fulfill with the social expectations, this results in an opportunity to marginalize them (Kaufman, 1989).

Literature on the topic of gender has coined the term "masculinities" to understand and study gender aspects of men (Connel, 1995). Other authors have underlined the importance of hegemonic masculinity (Connel, 1995; Kaufmna, 1989, 1999; Kimmel, 2008), a concept that refers to an ideal model of being male, to the characteristics that every man "should" possess. Hegemonic masculinity is translated into efforts and performances in the daily lives of men; performances that try to comply with masculine norms. According to Connel (1995), hegemonic masculinity is "*the configuration of gender practices that encompass the currently admitted response to the problem of legitimacy of patriarchy, that guarantees the position of men and the subordination of women*" (p. 77).

Current research helps understand masculinity in power relations (Kimmel, 2000; Toro-Alfonso, 2009). Men are the ones who, because of their bodies, inherit power, as well as actively build, produce and reproduce it in everyday life. Masculinity is a constant exercise, not always voluntary, that goes beyond the notion of individuality and contributes to the production of normative systems that constrain and oblige men to behave in certain ways (Amorós, 1992; Butler, 2001; Castañeda, 2007; Foucault, 1978; Millet, 1995; Rubin, 1986).

However, hegemonic models of masculinity become an ideal, impossible to fulfill 100%. Not complying with this model pushes men into marginalization and rejection; while those who do comply exercise this rejection and violence. This patriarchic system has different expressions in different cultures, but is always invested in and reproducing power. What seems clear, however, is that being born in a male body does not make someone a "real man," but that body must perform masculinity in order to be labeled as "manly."

Post-structural visions of feminism understand gender culture as a system that orders reality before the existence of the subject. In other words, it is this gender system that allows the subject to exist, all the while this subject enact gender performance. A fundamental aspect of gender is that it stipulates a series of rules and mandates that must be fulfilled. For example, possessing erotic desires for people of the other sex, through a monogamous, long-lasting relationship (Butler, 2004; Rubin, 1986; Schwartz, 2007). The concept of *gender performance* is one coined by Butler (1992), and it refers established and normative ways of behaving and presenting one's body. It is through these performances that gender and the subject are reproduced.

# Hegemonic Masculinity and Resistance

From an identitary level, masculine expressions are formed and produced from a cultural and discursive space. This means that cultural dynamics "explain" to people how to behave depending on the body they were born in. Michael Kimmel (2008) understands three cultural dynamics that produce these expressions. Through this proposal, the author makes it evident how all members of society contribute to the formation of hegemonic models that not only affect women, but also men.

> Culture of right: it is the "prize" for ascribing to masculine norms, it is the right to power and the exercise of power, just for being male.
>
> Culture of silence: the silence that men and women keep, even if they don't agree with the "right to power" of men. People keep silence because of fear of being punished for not ascribing to normativity, for fear of being expelled, punished or violated, because silence is part of becoming masculine.
>
> Culture of protection: silence becomes a way of protecting those men who exercise masculine violence. This violence teaches "new" men that there is no problem in enacting these performances, even if they affect others. Protection is necessary in order to continue patriarchy.

These cultural dynamics show the premises on which hegemonic masculinity is constructed, as well as the constant way in which violence is carried out, not just against other people, but against the men themselves. Anther attractive reference in regards to masculinity is the one proposed by Kaufman (1989), who affirms that the central axis of hegemonic masculinity is violence, understood as an exercise of power and authority. The author describes men's contradictory experiences with power: on the one side, due to men's gender condition, it is expected that they exercise power over others, be the ones that lead, to make decisions, are the ones who are allowed to occupy public space, among other things. This power, when it is assumed by men's identities, becomes a constant exercise that is not only lobbied against other people, but against themselves, as well. Kaufman speaks of three different types of men's' violence:

1. Violence against women: it is the most frequent and is expressed in different forms: physical, psychological, sexual, etc.
2. Violence against other men: a constant in men's relationships, it is expressed in rivalry and competition.
3. Violence against oneself: it is the price paid for exercising power against other people, through the suppression of emotions, needs and possibilities.

As was pointed out before, Kaufman's proposal is important because it is the first to point out the risks involved for men in the construction and development of masculinity and it's norms. Under these norms, socializations and social learning from early stages for men, restricts the expression of certain emotions. Boys learn how not to express, and later how not to feel fear, sadness, solitude, tenderness, joy and shame (Castañeda, 2007). These aspects of masculinity can be understood as violence, because it means to use power over aspects of oneself.

Thanks to these authors' work, it is evident how power occupies such an important part of men's lives, and how important it is to understand masculinity studies; it seems that men construct their identity in a permanent relationship with power. These constructions result in marginalization, subordination and violence. No man is exempt, even though some groups are more subordinated or excluded than others. According to these authors, hegemonic masculinity is an ideal model that men strive to achieve everyday. An ideal that demands the demonstration of constant power, and whose non-compliance results in social punishment. Because gender is a big system, it is kept thanks to the interactions between men and women. It seems that no man escapes power, be it as an oppressor or as with the oppressed. This is what Kaufman calls "contradictory experiences with power," since on occasions men hold power, and on other occasions are victims to it. According to a few authors, the non-compliance with the ideal masculinity, is proximal to feminity, something that is not forgiven (Butler, 2001; Castañeda, 2007; Connel, 1995; Kaufman, 1989; Kimmel, 2008; Núñez, 2000; Schwartz, 2007). One of the most punished characteristics, from hegemonic masculinity, is homo-eroticism*; in groups of men, openly homo-erotic men, or homosexual/gay men are the most marginalized.

This means that there is an intricate weave between gender order and heterosexuality, a complicity that allows power to be sustained, not only for the masculine, but for the heterosexual as well. Not only by being expected to feel attraction towards people of the other sex, but also for being socialized in institutions that advocate for reproduction and production, such as marriage and family. Schwartz (2007), identifies some rules in the heterosexual script (as in sexual scripts), which points to a discursive pre-written reality that is shared socially and goes beyond the notion of individuality; it is what is shared in the culture (see Kimmel, 2007). The premises that this author identifies are:

- Heterosexuality confabulates with gender: particular roles and traits are assigned to women and for men.
- Heterosexual performances must be seen and applauded by others: heterosexual requirements on the body (how to present it), allows it to be seen as hetero-erotic and avoid homo-erotic attributions.
- People must have a certain type of body that reveals heterosexuality: a body that does not show a clear assignation to one of two genders causes anxiety.
- In order to be heterosexual, one must feel attracted only to people of the other sex: any signs of flexibility in sexual attraction is observed going against heterosexuality and as a psychic instability.
- Heterosexual arousal must be strong and unambiguous; any act such as not holding an erection or achieving vaginal lubrication is seen as a bad sexual performance or a possible deviation.
- Persons of the other sex must feel attraction toward oneself; sexual identity is so liquid, that it can change due to the attention that others pay onself.

---

*The term "homo-eroticism" refers to those people, in this case men, whose desire and sexual attraction are towards people of their same sex. This is different from homosexual or gay men in the sense that the latter speak of an identity, while homo-eroticism speaks only of desire (Núñez, 2005).

- Once heterosexuality is performed, it must be stable and unconflicted. However, social research shows that sexuality fluctuates and depends mostly on the relationships each person has.
- Penile-vaginal penetration is the common trade in heterosexuality . . . everything else is just games.

It is in this way, that masculinity has an important basis on the "reproductive arena," on the possibility of bodies to reproduce. However, this ability to reproduce becomes a norm that socializes bodies, a rule that is part of hegemonic masculinity, and that thus, must be achieved by men.

As was stated earlier, hegemonic masculinity is a model, because not all men are capable of fulfilling its requirements. A model built in opposition to femininity. Gender system is thus a binary and dichotomous model that allows for the existence of two realities, and only two. For Butler (1992), who uses Foucault to understand the way in which a person is subjectivized, reality and gender systems are a form of subjectifying to the norm. For Butler, the way in which a body makes sense of itself is through performative iteration (repetition) of norms. The social weave, that includes identities, is a restricted reality, a system that does not allow for the exploration of more than the binary. However, Butler's work, as well as that of other queer theorists, questions the supposed naturalness of men's superiority and power.

# Gender Culture's Effects on Men's Identities

Even though masculinity locates men in a participation that guarantees power, that stipulates a series of attributes, meanings, behaviors, expectations, norms and roles to fulfill, such as being autonomous, hypersexual, intelligent, hard workers, rational, superior, active, dominating and aggressive, these attributes-falsely sustained—allow that they assume a certain superiority over women, of the masculine over the feminine, that in turn sustains and justifies violence and discrimination against women and groups considered feminine—such as gay men, indigenous groups, boys and senior citizens. All these groups are not considered "masculine" because in some way, they break the masculine norm, which is then translated into loss of power. However, from a gender perspective, the group named "men" is not that homogeneous or coherent, but the other way around. There is a large diversity of "being a man" in what behaviors, practices, desires, roles and traits regard. Despite the evident difficulty in cohesion, hegemonic masculinity works as a "guide model," because it is a direct reference to masculine identity (Bonino, 2001; Connel, 1995; Olavarría, 2005).

Even though hegemonic masculinity does affect men and their experiences, this does not mean that men are exempt from the power that it gives them, which locates men at a higher level than women. However, the author's perspective is to question the whole gender system, and not just masculinity, because it is a system that puts bodies in restricted and unequal spaces. Gender systems restrict the expression of desire, sexuality and identity itself; and they produce inequality because they give advantages and preferences to certain men rather than others, or women.

As many authors have made evident, the role of the body and its health is not a priority in the construction of masculine identities, due to the fact that risk taking and the perception of being invulnerable are a constant in men's lives (Burin, 2000; Connel, 1995; de Keijzer, 2001; Kimmel, 2008). Mexican national statistics show that men get sick and die form different illnesses and reasons than women. For example, data from the National Survey of Psychiatric Epidemiology show that in general, more women (11.2%) than men (6.7%) live with any type of affective disorder throughout their life. The case of anxiety disorders is similar, where more women (18.5%) than men (9.5%) present any of these disorders throughout their life. When it comes to substance abuse disorders, the numbers are inverted; it is more common for men (17.6%) to present a substance abuse disorder in comparison to women (1.7%) (Medina-Mora, Borges, Lara, Benjet, Blanco, Fleiz, Villatoro, Rojas, Zambrano, Casanova y Aguilar Gaxiola, 2003). In the case of suicidal ideation, attempt or planning, the National Psychiatric Comorbidity Survey shows that women present these types of symptoms more than men. 10.4% of women and 6.1% men present suicidal ideation at some point in their lives; 3.9% of women and 2.4% of men plan their death; and 3.5% of women and 2.0% of men actually make an attempt to take their life. Benjet, Borges, Medina-Mora, Méndez, Fleiz, Rojas y Cruz (2009) found important differences by sex in the prevalence of mental disorders in Mexican teenagers whereby teenage women presented higher frequencies of affective, anxiety and impulsive disorders than did men, and men showed higher frequencies of substance abuse disorders than women.

Regarding the use of tobacco, the National Institute of Statistics and Geography (INEGI) and the National Institute of Women (INMUJERES) (2010) reported that women are now smoking more than men– 76% of women and 51% of men reported being active smokers. This is radically different data than the data-set presented by the same institutions in previous years. In 2009, it was reported that 39% of men and 13% of women were active smokers, even though women reported smoking cigarettes more than men. These changes indicate two things. First, that the use of tobacco increased enormously from one measurement to the other, and second, that there is a "masculinization" in the use of tobacco. Or seen another way, a feminization of the use of tobacco. Regarding the use of alcohol, 61% of men reported being a "drinker", while 34% of women reported being one. The data also reveal that more men drink between 1 and 5 drinks per occasion, while more women drink 6 or more drinks per occasion (INEGI, 2009), even though it is more frequent for men to have problems due to alcohol use (such as problems wit the police or relatives) and more frequent for women to seek help to reduce or stop their drinking (INEGI, 2010). Regarding the use of illegal substances, such as cocaine, heroin and marihuana, more men than women rely on these substances, while more women consume pills (INEGI, 2009). Looking at the main causes of death, it is evident that more men die from traffic accidents and aggressive acts. Actually, no women die from these causes. Men also die more frequently than women from heart disease and liver illnesses that are correlated with the use of tobacco and alcohol.

These data make it very clear, men die and are sick for different reasons than women. Women usually present psychiatric symptoms because femininity norms allow for emotional expression. Masculinity and its norms punish the expression of a wide range of emotions for men; men must always act strong and whole at all times. Things such as talking about emotions, expressing them, and sometimes even identifying them, are indicators of femininity (Bonino, 2000; Burin, 2000; Connel, 1995; de Keijzer, 2001; Kaufman, 1989; Kimmel, 2005, 2008). Psychiatric disorders, in particular affective and anxiety disorders, are conditions where emotions such as sadness, pain and general discomfort are put forth (DSM-IV-R, 2002). Men hardly ever communicate this type of discomfort, keeping them from seeking specialized attention or health care, they also divulge their feelings less than women, leading them to higher levels of stress. This stress has effects on the cardiovascular system, resulting in cardiovascular health issues (INEGI, 2009; Sabo, 2000). In conclusion, hegemonic masculinity is significantly related to poorer states of health (Díaz-Loving, Rocha & Rivera, 2007; Sabo, 2000).

Kaufman (1999) argues that the experience of emotional restriction is one of the effects that patriarchy has on men. He names these effects as contradictory experiences with power, because the status of manhood has costs for men. It not only gives men power and hierarchy, but it leads men to painful experiences.

Substance abuse can be seen as a form of men's violence towards oneself, identified by Kaufman (1989). In other words, the prolonged use of substance, particularly cocaine, heroin, tobacco and alcohol, is a way of violating the body. Alcohol use is related to one of the leading death causes in men: traffic accidents, because these usually occur when men are under the influence. That men drive in a state of inebriation and at high speed, are also demonstrations of how tough they are, because there is no notion of vulnerability in masculinity (de Keijzer, 2001).

Men express ideal masculinity through violence towards other people. Death buy homicide is common in men, as well as committing crimes with violence (INEGI, 2009; Sabo, 2000). These are examples of men's violence towards others, against men and women. For example, Mexican national statistics show that in more than 90% of the cases, women are victims of sex crimes; while in more than 70% of cases, men are victims of aggressive crimes (INEGI, 2009). Clearly, women are observed as a body that can give sexual pleasure, even if she doesn't want to. The male body is not seen this way, but it is a body that a man must compete with and can openly violate. This shows specific violences towards men, and others toward women.

Another example of contradictory experiences with power is one regarding "subordinated" men (Connel, 1995), i.e. gay men. From the gender order, gay men are "less" than men because it is considered that they renounce to one of their patriarchal privilages; when demonstrating non-heterosexual desire, they break a patriarchal pact. This is made evident in the levels of homophobia directed towards gay men (CONAPRED, 2010; Lozano & Díaz-Loving, 2010; Britto, Jiménez, Sívori, Lacerda, Glockner y de la Garza, 2012). This same homophobia also affects gay men in their daily lives. Frost (2011) explains how stigma affects sexual minorities, making it clear that discomfort lived by gay men is not a result of the sexual orientation, but because there is a social construction in gender that locates them in a space of stigma.

Homophobia, more than referring to rejection of non-heterosexual identities and behaviors, is more related with the punishment of gender non-conformity or transgressing gender stereotypes. Because gay men are perceived as more feminine, this is what causes more rejection. Blashil and Vander (2010) found that those gay men that are more concerned with expressing their emotions in public and being perceived as more feminine have a higher tendency to feel depressed. These results, as so many others do (Castañeda, 1999, 2006; Lozano y Díaz-Loving, 2011; Sandfort, Melendez y Diaz, 2007), point out that homophobia is not so much the rejection of homo-erotic behaviors and identities, but more the rejection to the transgression of the gender order.

These data show that there is a particular stigma that discriminates gay men, and that is linked to the gender order. Because gay men don't fit into the social normativity established for them, they are not included in the category of "men" or "masculine". Thus, these men are the target of social punishment, discrimination and rejection also known as homophobia. This homophobia plays a determining role in how they live their daily life and build identity, which is filled with pain and discomfort. However, men's experiences in general, straight and gay, show the different ways in which life can take meaning from one single type of body. In other words, male-bodies can have a wide range of experiences, but are restricted because of a social order linked to gender.

## Conclusions

Throughout this text, the author has tried to show how gender systems function as a type of controlling mechanism that orders bodies under certain cultural dynamics and normativities. Even though his data is in a particular cultural context, it must be understood that some elements of this masculine culture are due to globalization. In other words, technologies such as the Internet, television, cinema and publicity are spaces where masculinity is not only reproduced, but also shared through international borders and frontiers. This means that gender culture is produced and reproduced in similar ways in different countries, having similar effects on subjectivity.

From gender and feminist studies, the existence of a "guide model" can be proven, it acts as social imaginaries that allow people to make sense of what should and shouldn't be done. However, men's experiences also show the heterogeneity that exists in women and men; this model is in fact a guide, it does not exist in everyday life. But they also show the fragility of masculine norms, because they are so hard to comply with. For queer theory, the way in which one is subjectified (or becomes a subject) is not in discoverimg what one is, but in the way that social norms are reproduced; the subject emerges from within gender norms, a person is subjectified by gender. This means that the possibility of being is in a restricted identity, restricted by this normativity. For post-feminist theory, the concept of intersectionality is fundamental, for it speaks of the complexity of identity; gender is not the only system women and men are constructed upon, but it interacts constantly with other social constructions such as race, ethnicity, class and sexual orientation, which allows for a heterogeneous range of identities to exist. The intersectionality is the space where these categories mesh and mix up together to create and generate a particular identitary space. In other words, that story each person tells himself or herself in order to answer the question "who am I?" is connected to what is interiorized and symbolized from social interactions framed in particular gender and other social systems.

However, an opportunity to break this restriction in hegemonic masculinity does emerge. For example, the gay movement has questioned stereotypes, such as whether gay men become less of a man because of their desire, and particular identities have emerged, such as *bears* and *leather* men, that utilize typically masculine images, incorporating them into their sense of identity in order to question this patriarchal order. What this means is that the rupture with normativity lies within the norms themselves. Butler's (2004) concept or reiteration can be useful. She argues that the way to subvert patriarchal norms is in repeating and repeating these norms. According to this author, the repetition of the norm is never like the original norm, it is changed and transformed. Gay men are a clear example of male bodies that perform masculinity in many areas except in their desires.

What this means is the possibility of breaking this restriction is in people's daily lives. Everyone must only ask themselves "why do I do what I do?" and "how can I do it differently?" These questions may be the beginning of a bigger identitary transformation, not only at an individual level, but a social one as well because humans are in a permanent dialogue with their contexts. This allows society to subvert the norms that affect men and women so much. Identity is then a game of possibilities and limits, of exploring the self in particular contexts, and how, through reiteration, contexts can be ruptured and transformed. Even though humans are never outside normativity, it is inside normativity where we can find ways to change it.

# References

American Psyichiatric Association (2002). *Diagnostic and Statistical Manual of Mental Disorders.* 4th and Revised edition.

Amorós Puente, C. (1992). Notas para una teoría nominalista del patriarcado. *Asparkia, Investigación Feminista.* 1. 41–58.

Benjet, C., Borges, G., Medina-Mora, M., Méndez, E., Fleiz, C., Rojas, E., y Cruz, C. (2009). Diferencias de sexo en la presencia y severidad de trastornos psiquiátricos en adolescentes de la Ciudad de México. *Salud Mental,* 32 (2) 155–163.

Blashill, A.J., Vander Wal, J.S. (2010). Gender Role Conflict as a Mediador Between Social Sensitivity and Depression in a Sample of Gay Men. *International Journal of Men´s Health.* 9 (1). 26–39.

Blazquez Graf, N. (2010). Epistemología feminista: temas centrales. En Blazquez Graf, N., Flores Palacios, F., Ríos Everardo, M. (coords.). *Investigación Feminista: Epistemología y Representaciones Sociales.* (pags. 21–38). México. UNAM-CEIICH-CRIM-Facultad de Psicología.

Bonino, L. (2001). *Salud, varones y masculinidad.* Escrito presentado para las Jornadas sobre Mainstreaming de Género en Salud y organizadas por OMS-Europa, en septiembre de 2001 y publicado en Seminario sobre Mainstreaming de género en las políticas de salud en Europa Madrid: MAS. Instituto de la Mujer.

Brito, A., Jiménez de Sandi, A., Sívori, H., Lacerda, P., Glockner, N., de la Garza, L.A. (2012). *Política, derechos, violencia y sexualidad. Encuesta Marcha del Orgullo y la Diversidad Sexual Ciudad de México-2008.* Centro Latinoamericano en Sexualidad y Derechos Humanos-Instituto de Medicina Social-Universidad del Estado de Río de Janeiro.

Burin, M. (2000). Atendiendo el malestar de los varones. En, Burin, M., Mele, I. (comps.). *Varones, género y subjetividad masculina.* Buenos Aires. Paidós Ibérica.

Butler, J. (1992). *El Género en disputa.* México. Paidós

Butler, J. (2001). *Cuerpos que importan.* México. Paidós

Butler, J. (2004). *Deshacer el género.* México. Paidós.

Careaga Pérez, G. (2004). Orientaciones Sexuales. Alternativas e Identidad. En Careaga, G. y Cruz, S. *Sexualidades Diversas. Aproximaciones para su análisis* (págs. 171–188). México: Miguel Ángles Porrúa-PUEG.

Castañeda Gutman, M. (1999). *La Experiencia Homosexual. Para comprender la homosexualidad desde dentro y desde fuera.* México: Paidós.

Castañeda Gutman, M. (2006). *La nueva homosexualidad.* México. Paidós.

Castañeda Gutman, M. (2007). *El machismo invisible regresa.*México: Trillas.

CONAPRED (2010). *Encuesta Nacional sobre Discriminación.* Consejo Nacional para Prevenir la Discriminación.

Connel, R. (1995). *Masculinities.* California: University of California Press.

de Keijzer, B. (2001). Hasta donde el cuerpo aguante: Género, Cuerpo y Salud Masculina. En: Cáceres, C., Cueto, M., Ramos, M., Vallenas, S. (coords.). *La salud como derechos ciudadano: perspectivas y propuestas desde América Latina.* Lima: Universidad Peruana Cayetano Heredia. Disponible en linea www.umng.edu.co/www/resources/**Genero,Cuerpoy**Sal**Masculina**.pdf *consultado del 21 de julio de 2011.*

de Lauretis, T. (2008). *Gender identities and bad habits.* Conferencia Magistral del 4o Congreso Estatal Isonomía sobre Identidad de Género vs. Identidad Sexual. Universitat Jaume I.

Díaz-Loving, R., Rocha, T.E., Rivera, S. (2007). *La instrumentalidad y expresividad desde una perspectiva psico-socio-cultural.* México. Miguel Ángel Porrúa y UNAM

Erikson, E. (1985/2000). *El ciclo vital completado.* Buenos Aires. Paidós.

Freud, S. (1903/1972). Tres ensayos de una teoría sexual. En, Freud, S. *Obras Completas* Tomo VII. (pp. 111–211). Buenos Aires. Amorrortu Editores.

Frost, D.M. (2011). Social Stigma and its Consequences for the Socially Stigmatized. *Social and Personality Psychology.* 5 (11). 824–839

Harding, S. (2010). ¿Una filosofía de la ciencia socialmente relevante? ARgumentos en torno a la controversia sobre le punto de vista feminista. En Blazquez Graf, N., Flores Palacios, F., Ríos Everardo, M. (coords.). *Investigación Feminista, epistemología, metodología y representaciones sociales.* (pags. 39–68). México. CEIICH-CRIM-Facultad de Psicología.

INEGI (2009). *Mujeres y hombres en México, 2009.* México. Instituto Nacional de Estadística y Geografía, Instituto Nacional de las Mujeres.

INEGI (2010). *Mujeres y hombres en México, 2010.* México. Instituto Nacional de Estadística y Geografía, Instituto Nacional de las Mujeres.

Kaufman, M. (1989). *Hombres. Placer, poder y cambio.* Santo Domingo: CIPAF.

Kaufman, M. (1999). Men, feminism and Men's Contradictory Experiences with Power. In Kuypers, J.A.(ed.) *Men and Power.* Fernwood Books: Halifax. pp. 19–83.

Kimmel, M. (ed.)(2007). *The sexual self. The construction of sexual scripts.* Nashville. Vanderbuilt Press.

Kimmel, (2008). *Guyland, the perilous land where boys become men.* New York. Harper.

Lamas, M. (2000). Diferencias de sexo, género y diferencia sexual. *Cuicuilco.* Vol. 7(18).

List, M. (2005). *Jóvenes corazones gay de la Ciudad de México.* Puebla, BUAP.

Lozano, I., Díaz-Loving, R. (2010). Correlatos de la homophobia en México. *Archivos Hispanoamericanos de Sexología.*

Lozano, I., Díaz-Loving, R. (2011). Medición de la homofobia en México: Desarrollo y Validación. *Revista Iberoamericana de Diagnóstico y Evaluación Psicológica.* 30 (2). 105–124.

Medina-Mora, M., Borges, G., Lara Muñoz, C., Benjet, C., Blanco Jaimes, J., Feliz Bautista, C., Villatoro, J., Rojas, E., Zambrano, J., Casanova, L., Aguilar-Gaxiola, S. (2003). Prevalencia de trastornos mentales y uso de servicios: resultados de la Encuesta Nacional de Epidemiología Psiquiátrica en México. *Salud Mental* , 26 (4). 1–16.

Millet, K. (1969/1995). *Política sexual.* Madrid. Cátedra

Núñez Noriega, G. (2005). *Diversidad sexual y afectiva, un nuevo concepto para una nueva democracia.* México. MIMEO.

Núñez Noriega, G. (2000). *Sexo entre varones: poder y resistencia en el campo sexual.* México: Porrúa y PUEG.

Olavarría, J. (2005). La masculinidad y los jóvenes adolescentes. *Reflexiones Pedagógicas. Docencia, 27,* 46–55.

Pujal i Llombart, M. (2004). La identidad (el self). En Ibáñez, T. (coord.). *Introducción a la Psicología Social.* 93–137. Barcelona. Editorial UOC.

Rubin, G. (1986). El tráfico de mujeres: nota sobre la "economía política" del sexo. *Revista Nueva Antropología.* 30 (VIII). 95–145.

Sabo, D. (2000). *Comprender la salud de los hombres: un enfoque relacional y sensible al género.* Organización Panamericana de la Salud, Harvard Center for Population and Development Studies.

Sandfort, T.G.M., Melendez, R.M., & Díaz, R.M. (2007). Gender nonconformity, homophobia and mental distress in Latino gay and bisexual men. *Journal of Sex Research, 44(2):181-9.*

Schwartz, P. (2007). The social construction of heterosexuality. En Kimmel, M. (ed.). *The sexual self, the construction of sexual scripts.* Nashville. Vanderbuilt University Press.

Sullivan, H.W. (1953). *La teoría interpersonal de la psiquiatría.* Buenos Aires. Editorial Psique.

Suyemoto, K.L. (2002). Constucting Identities: A feminist, culturally contextualized alternative to "personality". En Ballou, M. y Brown, L.S. (eds.) *Rethinking Mental Health and Disorder.* New York. The Guildford Press.

Toro-Alfonso, J. (2009). *Masculinidades subordinadas: investigaciones hacia la transformación del género.* Puerto Rico. Publicaciones Puertorriqueñas.

West, C., Zimmerman, D.H. (1987). Doing Gender. *Gender & Society.*1(2). 125–151.

# Chapter 5

# *Whatever Happened to June Cleaver?*
# *The Fifties Mom Turns Eighty*

*Laura Katz Olson*

## Abstract

June Broson Cleaver represents the quintessential American woman of the 1950s. Because of social pressures, women were encouraged to stay at home and make marriage and motherhood their primary career. These were reinforced by institutional barriers, legal restrictions and business practices that limited women's employment options considerably. Thus women were expected to be dependent on their husbands financially. Those who did work were relegated to low-paid jobs that offered few—or no—benefits. At the same time, the vast majority of African American females had to work to support themselves and their family; they were among the lowest paid employees, barely earning a subsistence wage. This article shows how women of the 1950s, who followed the "prescribed rules", fared during their retirement years. Because of their labor force situation as well as the structure of the Social Security System, based on female dependency and male workforce and retirement patterns, a significant percentage of single older women—especially minorities—end up living in poverty or near-poverty conditions.

## Keywords

nineteen fifties, domesticity, marriage and motherhood, female employment, African American women, Social Security, older women.

June Broson Cleaver, the quintessential American mother and wife of the 1950s television series "Leave It To Beaver," is probably approaching 80 years old today. As depicted by her television persona, her fulfillment as a woman accrued from cooking, shopping, attending church meetings, crocheting, making curtains, and, most importantly, tending to the needs of her two children, Wally and Beaver, and husband Ward. Similarly to other wives on family sitcoms at the time, such as Margaret Anderson ("Father Knows Best"), Donna Stone ("The Donna Reed Show"), and Harriet Nelson ("Ozzie and Harriet"), the kitchen was the center of June's life. In contrast to her husband, we know little of her past life except that she attended a state university and did volunteer work at the USO during World War II. Thus, the college educated June Broson's real life begins, as so many women of the times were told it should, with marriage and motherhood.

In fact, the 1950s were a unique time for women and their families, one that rested on a sharp demarcation of gender roles. For one, after World War II, the United States experienced a period of great fear along with rising expectations. The nation became hysterical about the menaces of communism, both internally and externally, and its presumed threat to the American way of life. The nuclear family came to symbolize the ideal social unit in a free-enterprise system, and even democracy itself: "Marriage and family, it was insisted, were the bedrock of our society, the foundation of capitalism" (Ford, 1999). And full-time mothers were needed to inculcate democratic values and appropriate morals in their children (Kaledin, 1984).

The cold war in a nuclear age, with its risk of annihilation, was a constant source of anxiety and stress, as well. The domestic realm would offer "a secure private nest removed from the dangers of the outside world" (May, 1988). In order to secure fully their safety and protection, middle-class young women were advised to choose solid, reliable husbands as breadwinners (Harvey, 1993).

At the same time, it was an era of unprecedented economic prosperity, consumerism, and materialism. The United States was in a privileged financial position world wide, in terms both of its manufacturing potential and the ascendancy of the dollar. Pent-up desires along with enhanced purchasing power among the population fueled the production of consumer goods; during the military conflict, Americans had accumulated more savings than in any equivalent period of time (May, 1988). Young married couples bought cars, televisions, washing machines, dishwashers, vacuum cleaners, and other assorted modern appliances and household furnishings. From 1945 to 1960, the GNP increased by approximately 250 percent, and per capita income rose by 35 percent, further stimulating the economy (Coontz, 1992).

Second, the middle-class nuclear family, ensconced in a suburban ranch house, became the mark of success, the achievement of the American dream. Aided by government-supported low-interest mortgages and federal subsidies for highways, by 1960 sixty-two percent of American families owned their own homes, up from forty-three percent in 1940; eighty-five percent of the new construction was in the suburbs (Coontz, 1992). The primary beneficiaries were white middle- and working-class families.

Third, married women, including those with young children, had been encouraged—indeed actively recruited—to enter the labor force during the war. A significant number had obtained well-paid jobs in heavy industry, such as in automobile and steel plants, previously reserved for men. By 1945, nearly 25 percent of all married females were working (May, 1988). Although most of these women indicated an interest in retaining their positions, they were either summarily fired or pressured into leaving, through a variety of forces, to make room for returning veterans.

Domesticity was promoted relentlessly by political leaders, educators, psychologists, the popular media, and other social commentators, and women's choices narrowed appreciably during the period (Ford, 1999). Brett Harvey (1993) observes:

> . . . in the fifties as in no other decade, the current of the mainstream was so strong that you only had to step off the bank and float downstream into marriage and motherhood.

Women's and girl's magazines, including *The Ladies Home Journal, Saturday Review, Fortune, McCall's, Redbook, Life,* and *Seventeen,* which exalted housework and glorified motherhood, urged women to return to the home. Working women were castigated for neglecting their children.

Television emerged as the major form of entertainment, and by 1960 nearly 90 percent of all Americans owned at least one set. Dramas and sit-coms depicted the model female as achieving her primary identity and ultimate fulfillment through motherhood and the domestic life. Harvey (1993) notes that the 1950s was actually a "decade-long celebration of maternity," as womanhood became equated with motherhood.

Advertisers, which financed the shows, unabashedly fostered images of wife and mother that would promote the newly booming market in household and children's products. And, as Eugenia Kaledin (1984) suggests, television "catered to advertisers' dreams of what the ideal woman consumer should be." These images were brought straight in the living rooms of Americans across the nation.

A wide variety of other commercial interests joined in. Even a wedding industry emerged, complete with etiquette guides, bridal registries, showers, and special magazines, encouraging consumerism and glamorizing marriage (Ford, 1999).

In fact, many psychologists and popular writers of the era insisted that personal happiness could not be achieved without marriage and children. They claimed that since a woman's nature and genetic makeup render her best suited for home management and child rearing, these roles should be her primary occupation. Not only must husband and children come first in her life, but she also must subordinate her own needs to theirs.

Moreover, in the late 1940s, Alfred Kinsey had documented a high incidence of premarital sex among young adults. In an effort to control this practice, psychologists, social workers, public officials, and others promulgated the message that health and satisfying sexual expression could only take place between husband and wife; they urged early marriages (May, 1988). Importantly, abortion was illegal in every state, and therapeutic abortions were increasingly restricted during the 1950s. Since single-parenthood was not socially acceptable, marriage and motherhood constituted the only viable option for white, middle-class single women who did engage in sex and become pregnant.

Educators, including those at the college level, began launching programs and curricula aimed at making women better wives and mothers. Courses in home economics, child development, interior decorating, gardening, and other domestic programs proliferated, especially at women's colleges (Chafe, 1972). Marriage also often meant the end of higher education for middle class females. Though larger numbers of women began college in the 1950s than in previous decades, only 37 percent actually graduated (Kaledin, 1984; Harvey, 1993).

Those who did not succumb to an exclusively domestic role through social pressures faced institutional barriers, legal restrictions, and business practices that limited their options considerably. Kaledin (1984) tells us that the work world "openly discriminated against women."

As suggested earlier, many economic opportunities were closed off to women after the war. For one, Congress had passed the Selective Service Act, which, in practice, granted veterans the right to displace women workers who had been hired during the war. In some jobs throughout the 1950s, including that of airline stewardess, the employee had to quit when she married; at age 35 she was forced to retire. William Chafe (1972) found that some large firms, such as Detroit Edison, Thompson Aircraft, and IBM, imposed regulations against hiring married women. In the vast majority of occupations, pregnant women were expected to quit; those who did not do so voluntarily were fired when their condition became noticeable. Lack of publicly-supported child care also kept many women out of the labor force. In fact, by early 1946 Congress had closed the limited number of nurseries that had been set up for working women during the war (May, 1988).

For the most part, except for nursing, teaching or social work, women's professional choices were severely limited. Institutional policies, including ceilings on the percentage of women admitted into professional schools, restricted their opportunities. For example, medical schools enforced a five percent quota on female admissions, most hospitals denied women residencies, and many medical associations refused them membership (Chafe, 1972; Kaledin, 1984). Professional women, who were disparaged as unfeminine and neurotic, often were forced to choose between family and career. Consequently, a decreasing percentage of women even aspired to professional occupations or pursued graduate study (Mintz & Kellogg, 1988). Barbara Deckard (1983) shows that the percentage of female college professors, scientists, mathematicians, and the like actually declined during the fifties.

The mix of social pressures, public policies, and institutional barriers produced impressive results:

> For the first time in more than 100 years, the age for motherhood and marriage fell, fertility increased, divorce rates declined and women's degree of educational parity with men dropped sharply (Coontz, 1992).

According to Steven Mintz and Susan Kellogg (1988), these patterns differed substantially from those both historically and in the years that followed. By 1959, nearly half of all brides had married before reaching nineteen years of age, and only 21 percent of women were single, compared to 31 percent in 1940 (Harvey, 1993). For every 1000 women between ages 15 and 24, there were 123 births (Kaledin, 1984). The birth rate for a third child doubled and for a fourth one tripled between 1940 and 1960 (Chafe, 1972). Moreover, children were born sooner after marriage and were closer in age than in prior years (May, 1988).

Harvey (1993) concludes, "women were expected to seek—and find—everything in marriage and family: love, identity, excitement, challenge, and fulfillment." Those who did not adhere to these social norms were labeled "unnatural," maladjusted, immature, deviant, and/or emotionally disturbed (Coontz, 1992). Like June Cleaver and other television moms of her ilk, wives were expected to be submissive and dependent on their husbands both emotionally and financially. Women could not borrow money in their own name, purchase a home, secure insurance or even sign a contract on their own. Self-supporting women were viewed suspiciously (May, 1988).

Yet, despite these constraints, female employment climbed through the 1950s, and there was a growing split between the image of the ideal middle-class household and the reality of women's lives (Mintz & Kellogg, 1988). By the end of the decade, women comprised approximately 35 percent of the labor force; forty percent of all women over sixteen had jobs

(Chafe, 1972; Rowbotham, 1997). Significantly, a third of all wives were working, up from only 15 percent in 1940 (Kaledin, 1984).

Many women who had been fired or forced out of their war jobs either remained in or soon returned to the labor force, shifting into lower paid positions. As Harvey (1993) puts it: "Rosie the Riveter didn't necessarily leave the work force; she just moved—or was moved—over into clerical and sales jobs . . ." Most of these workers were married women over age 35 who had already fulfilled their role as mother—a significant minority was middle-class (Chafe, 1972). The number of females in the labor market over age 35 increased from 8.5 million to over 13 million from 1947 to 1956 (Kaledin, 1984).

Most single, middle-class women also worked, but it was viewed as a holding pattern until "Mr. Right" came along, presumably someone like Ward Cleaver. A large number of wives helped put their husbands through college and/or graduate or professional school. Many young married women stayed in the labor force until they became pregnant with their first child.

However, the traditional middle-class household of the 1950s was short-lived as these couples entered middle- and later, old age. In her study of 1950s suburban housewives, Harvey (1993)found that nearly all of the women experienced substantial changes in their lives during the two decades after the 1950s: some finished college; others went to work. As their children entered school, growing numbers of suburban moms began to move back into the paid labor force (Ford, 1999). Since most women had completed their families in their late twenties, they were not needed for full-time child care by the time they reached their mid-thirties (May, 1988). At the end of the 1950s, 39 percent of women with children aged 6 to 17 held jobs (May, 1988; Kaledin, 1984).

As Sheila Rowbotham (1997) explains:

> . . . the gap between assumption and actuality was being experienced by more and more white middle-class women . . . They were compelled to adapt to a cultural schizophrenia in which economic pressures pulled one way and prevailing attitudes the other. An uneasy compromise was struck: women's work was seen as helping out, a secondary income rather than a career.

Instead of challenging the cultural imperatives of the times, these women contended that they sought employment to improve their family's standard of living, pay off mortgages, send children to college, save for a vacation, or afford luxuries (Mintz & Kellogg, 1988). They did so while maintaining prevailing domestic power relationships, their main identity as homemakers and mothers, and their husband's role as primary breadwinner (Coontz, 1992; Rowbotham, 1997).

The labor market became strikingly gendered, as well (Deckard, 1983). The postwar boom had generated an ongoing demand for clerical and sales jobs, secretaries, and bank tellers, pink-collar work that was advertised in sex-segregated newspaper advertisements. Whether working for "extras" or out of economic need, women were relegated to these poorly paid positions, most of which offered few benefits or opportunities for advancement (Harvey, 1993). Within large firms, the percentage of women allowed to participate in company-run training programs, one of the primary routes for upward mobility, was often severely restricted (Kaledin, 1984).

Consequently, the Women's Bureau found that the median wage of working women in 1959 was 61 percent that of men (Deckard, 1983). And, according to "Womenpower in Today's World," a study by the National Manpower Council, women performing identical work as men earned one-third less (Kaledin, 1984).

Not all middle-class women, of course, joined the labor force full-time. May (1988) writes:

> As they moved into the expanding suburbs and settled in with their growing families, they put their best efforts into living out the post-war version of the American Dream.

By the end of the 1950s, about 70 percent of white American households looked similar to the Cleavers: a breadwinner, housewife, and two or more children (Mintz & Kellogg, 1988). Many suburban mothers worked intermittently and/or obtained part-time positions. Others pursued volunteer work in their community while their children were at school. A substantial percentage of women viewed being a housewife as their life work, and found immense satisfaction in rearing their children, serving as their husband's help mate, and participating in a wide variety of community and charity activities (Mintz & Kellogg, 1988; May, 1988). Coontz (1992) found evidence that the actual amount of time spent on child care and house work actually increased during the 1950s. The husband's income was viewed as the family wage; there was never any serious thought given to paying wives directly for their domestic work.

## Race and the 1950s Experience

There was, of course, an underside to the 1950s culture, "The Other America," as described by Michael Harrington (1962) and others. Suburbia was not part of the African American experiences—few residents in these areas were single adults, elderly or members of any minority group (May, 1988; Mintz & Kellogg, 1988). While June Cleaver lived in an indistinct suburban neighborhood, her African American counterpart resided in an equally indistinct urban ghetto, a commuter ride away.

Beginning in the 1940s and accelerating in the 1950s, millions of African Americans had migrated from the south into urban areas, where they faced multiple problems such as overcrowding, crime, drugs, and oppressive discrimination. Legally sanctioned segregation in the south, as well as redlining, restrictive covenants and other forms of institutional racism in the north, prevented minorities from moving into the suburbs (Coontz, 1992). By 1960, a majority of African Americans resided in cities, mostly ghettos, as compared to three-quarters who lived in southern agricultural districts before the war.

Moreover, though the expansion of the economy in the 1950s generated growing real wages, by 1959, fifty-five percent of African American families lived in poverty compared to seventeen percent of whites (U.S. Census Bureau, 1998a). At the same time, there was a massive immigration of Puerto Ricans, most of whom found themselves in a similar plight.

Cultural expectations differed markedly: whether single or married, African American women, like their mothers and grandmothers, expected to work in order to support themselves and their family. Since employed African American men averaged about half the wages of white men in 1960, husbands rarely earned a family wage. In 1970, the labor force rate for married African American women was 70 percent compared to 49 percent for white wives

(Daily, 1998). As Coontz (1992) reports: "The June Cleaver . . . homemaker role was not available to the more than 40 percent of black women with small children who worked outside the home." Nearly 25 percent of African American women headed their own households.

For the most part, however, African American women were the lowest paid employees in the country, barely earning subsistence wages; despite the fact that some were finding pink- and white-collar jobs for the first time, the vast majority worked as domestic servants or other subordinate sectors of the labor market (Rowbotham, 1997). In 1950, their income remained less than half that of white women (Kaledin, 1984). Both African American men and women also suffered steadily rising unemployment and periodic layoffs, contributing substantially to their dire economic situation.

On the other hand, according to May (1988), the popular imperative for motherhood was so pervasive during the 1950s that minorities and various ethnic groups had trends in fertility similar to those of middle-class whites living in suburbia. In addition, choices for poor, pregnant, unmarried African American women were even more limited than those for whites since they had less access to safe abortions (Harvey, 1993). Overall, African American women experienced greater poverty, single parenthood and divorce, and a lower rate of re-marriage than their white counterparts (Coontz, 1993).

# June Cleaver Reaches Eighty: Social Security and Older Women

The Social Security system, while initially structured in 1935, was shaped by the same middle-class, white values and household composition prominent in the 1950s: "traditional" families consisting of a primary male breadwinner and an unpaid female housewife/caregiver who is economically dependent on her husband; any income earned by the wive is not considered essential to the family unit. The design of the program measures work and productivity by male standards and stages throughout the life cycle. As Nancy Dailey (1998) suggests, retirement has been viewed, through the ideological lens of white men, as a single event. Yet women's pattern of employment differs—they tend to move in and out of the labor force, raising children and caring for their elders.

The system actually penalizes those who do unpaid caring work. Benefit levels are based both on wage levels and on continuous thirty-five year participation in the labor force; unwaged domestic responsibilities are calculated as zero earnings, thereby lowering any pensions earned by women in their own right. Consequently, only 20 percent of women, compared to sixty percent of men, have the minimum 35 years of covered earnings (GAO, 1997).

Because they experience lower average earnings as well as interrupted work histories, many women forego Social Security benefits based on their own record. In 1998, although two-thirds of female beneficiaries earned benefits as workers, half of them—who were dually entitled—received the higher spousal amounts (SSCA, 1999a,b).

As a result most married women, regardless of whether they participated in the labor force, collect auxiliary pensions based on their husbands' wage records. When they become widowed or divorced, the vast majority depend on these pensions for nearly all of their financial support. And there is no minimum benefit that meets their basic needs. Consequently, older women are more likely than older men to live in absolute as well as relative poverty. Nearly twenty-five percent of all single elderly females have incomes below the official poverty level—$7,800 in 1998 (U.S. Census Bureau, 1998b); they comprise 73 percent of the aged poverty population.

So whatever happened to June Cleaver? Her life might have taken one of several paths as she aged, relegating her to a number of divergent economic circumstances. As did many of her white middle-class contemporaries, June could have remained a housewife throughout the decades, retiring with her husband, when he reached age 65, to a warm climate.

Today, they would be economically comfortable, presumably with some savings and an annuity from his private pension. In fact, forty-one percent of older white couples receive revenue from a private pension, and 78 percent from their assets (SSA, 1999a). Their income from Social Security alone, consisting of Ward's primary benefit and June's fifty percent dependent's allowance, would be about $15,712 in 1998, the median for white couples (SSA, 1999b); this amount would be actuarially reduced if Ward retired at age 62, the average age for men (Dailey, 1998). Given their potential access to such diverse sources of support, only 5 percent of all older married white women are poor (SSCA, 1999b).

Even if June had entered the labor force, either full or part-time, after her children went to school, as suggested earlier it most likely would have been in low-wage clerical, sales or service work. It is doubtful she would qualify for a private pension, and she would receive very little even if she did. Moreover, though she would have contributed thousands of dollars into the Social Security System, her benefit would be exactly the same amount as if she had not worked at all. As one observer reports, Social Security imposes some of the heaviest marginal tax rates on working women (SSCA, 1999a).

Most probably, however, at age 80 June is widowed, living alone, and struggling to support herself on Social Security. Women, whose average longevity is greater than men, tend to outlive their husbands. At birth, the life expectancy for white men and women is 74 and 80, respectively. For whites reaching age 65, men can expect to live another 16 years compared to 20 years for women (GAO, 1996).

Significantly, forty percent of single women depend on Social Security for 90 percent of their total income; for twenty-five percent, the program is their only source of support (SSCA, 1996; GAO, 1997). If Ward had died after retirement, the odds are that June's benefit would be reduced to approximately $8,824, the median income for nonmarried white beneficiaries (SSA, 1999b). His death at a much earlier age would result in measurably lower amounts.

It is questionable whether she is relying on Ward's private pension for significant support, even if he had one; if the annuity was not terminated upon hies death, it would be providing her, as a surviving spouse, only about half of the original amount, averaging around $3,468 (SSCA, 1999a; SSA, 1999c). And these pensions are vulnerable to inflation since they generally are not indexed to the rising cost of living. Moreover, as with many widows, she may have been forced to slowly spend down any assets she and Ward had accumulated (SSCA, 1999a).

Currently there are 1.4 million aged widows, approximately 18 percent of the total, who live below the poverty level (SSCA, 1999b). As Colette Browne (1998) points out, more than half of the widows living in poverty were not poor before the death of their husband.

Suppose, however, that after thirty or more years together, June and Ward had dissolved their marriage. Underneath "the image of domestic tranquility celebrated in the popular media" were many unhappy couples (Mintz & Kellogg, 1988). Fearing social ostracism and/or maladjusted children, few individuals viewed splitting up as a viable option during the early years of their marriage. However, according to several analysts, from twenty-five to thirty-three percent of marriages forged in the 1950s eventually did end in divorce (Coontz, 1992; Mintz & Kellogg, 1988).

In her fifties, having spent her years promoting Ward's career, caring for the family, volunteering for charities, and/or working at low-paid jobs, June would have had limited earning ability. At age 60, she would become eligible for half of her ex-husband's Social Security benefit when he decided to retire, and his widow's pension if he died. On average, divorced women received about $4,365 from the program in 1998 (SSA, 1999d). She might secure a portion of whatever assets the couple had accumulated together, and perhaps a piece of his private pension if she is successful in court. About 22 percent of divorced aged women experience an impoverished old age SSCA, 1999b).

As Mintz and Kellogg (1988) indicate:

> The fifties ideal of a marital partnership was based on the assumption of a wife's role as hostess and consort. This was essential for the smooth running of the household and for the promotion of her husband's career.

Many men were able to rise in the business and professional worlds partly because of their wives' social functions (Kessler-Harris, 1981). Ward would be well-situated by his fifties for a decent retirement income.

Regardless of her current status, the odds are that June had some responsibilities for elder care during her middle-age years or later, further disadvantaging her position in the labor force and any future Social Security benefits in her own right. More than one in four families, primarily women, are involved in caring for an older relative (Gould, 1999); many now spend more years tending aging parents than they do raising children (Abel, 1991; Gannon, 1999).

In a few years, she will need help herself; approximately half of the elderly over age eighty-five require assistance with at least some activities of daily living (Baines, Evans, & Neysmith, 1995). Frail older men generally receive hands-on aid from their wives. Despite a lifetime of providing care to others, women are more at risk than men of lacking any assistance for themselves (Hooyman, 1999). At the more advanced ages, elderly women tend to live alone, and consequently when they become chronically ill and dependent have difficulty remaining in their own homes. If June's income is typical of widowed or divorced older women, she will not have the resources for purchasing sufficient help privately, and if she does, will deplete her assets in a few years.

Nor will she be entitled to publicly supported home and community care. Medicaid, the major financial source for government long-term care, pays primarily for nursing homes, and only after residents exhaust any of their accumulated assets. Unless single women can rely on their adult children—for the most part daughters—to attend to their needs, they often end up in institutions. June must depend on the assistance of her two sons, or more likely that of her daughters-in-law, if she is to avoid institutionalization. Nearly one-quarter of people age eighty-five and over, mostly unmarried females, reside in a nursing home (Birenbaum, 1995).

And June Cleaver's African American female counterpart? It is questionable whether she reached age eighty: her life expectancy at birth was 74 years. However, if she attained age 65, she could have expected to live, on average, another 18 years. (African American men have a life expectancy of 64 and average only 14 more years at age 65, GAO, 1996).

Most likely, prior to retirement she was a single head of household who had worked for forth years or more at low wages. Because of the regressive nature of the Social Security payroll tax, she had paid more in payroll taxes during this period than in income taxes. At age 80, there is a good chance that she is unmarried—fifty-four percent of all older African Americans are single females—and dependent on her own worker's Social Security benefit, an amount that is probably less than that of a widow of a high earner, such as June Cleaver. In 1998, single African American women averaged $6,813 annually from Social Security while married African American couples obtained $12,700 (SSA, 1999b). Nearly 7.8 million older women, mostly immigrants of color, receive no Social Security benefits at all due to their work as domestics (Browne, 1998).

Only a small number of widowed, divorced or never married female African Americans have income from assets or private pensions 19 percent and 13 percent, respectively (SSA, 1999a). Overall, they experience a poverty rate of over 30 percent (SSCA 1999a).

## Conclusion

Political leaders in the twenty-first century are focusing on strengthening the financial integrity of the Social Security program. Most recommendations maintain its current design but tinker with the benefit formula. However, by solving the economic problems faced by the system, certain changes potentially could worsen the financial situation of vulnerable groups.

Raising the normal and/or early retirement age, for example, translates into a benefit cut for those in poor health, limited job prospects, and an already inadequate retirement income, particularly older minorities (GAO, 1996). Increasing the period of time for calculating benefits means more zero years, and therefore lower benefits for women who take time out for child care, and increasingly to assist their elderly parents. Lowering cost-of-living adjustments, or other across-the-board reductions, burdens women, minorities and other low-income elderly the most, especially those who are hovering at the poverty level. Any cuts in dependent benefits, of course, would disadvantage females.

Raising payroll taxes is another strategy that seeks to restore the long-term solvency of the system while maintaining its traditional structure. This solution would increase the regressive aspect of our federal taxes even further, burdening those with the lowest wages.

Other public officials and analysts concentrate on restructuring the system, urging some form of privatization. Individual accounts, for instance, would move the program away from its current emphasis on defined benefits toward a defined contribution system, advantaging high-income earners (GAO, 1999). Such an approach stresses individual equity over income adequacy; while there is greater potential for higher rates of return (and risk), it would be difficult to maintain the progressive benefit formula that helps working women, especially women of color. Individual accounts also do not protect against inflation, again harming women disproportionately since they tend to live longer than men (SSCA, 1999a). Adequate support for dependents and survivors could be in jeopardy as well, especially if the breadwinner has had more than one wife (SSCA, 1999b).

Despite public debate on the subject, there appears to be only limited concern over the adverse impact of various reform proposals on single older women and minorities. There is even less interest in improving their economic situation; none o the recent Social Security reform packages strives to better meet the financial needs of disadvantaged sectors of our population. Such proposals could include a wage-indexed, adequate minimum benefit to keep older women out of poverty (SSCA, 1999a), an increase in the allowable years for caregiving, earnings sharing between couples, and exempting a portion of wages from Social Security taxes. Moreover, some solutions that could measurably improve the solvency of the program without affecting low-income wage earners are rarely considered (i.e., expanding the tax base to include assets and other sources of individual wealth). If we ensure the system's stability without enhancing features to protect single women, African Americans and other economically deprived groups, June Cleaver's granddaughter could find herself and her African American friends in similarly adverse financial circumstances.

# Bibliography

Abel, E. K. (1991). *Who cares for the elderly?: Public policy and the experiences of adult daughters.* Philadelphia: Temple University Press.

Baines, C., Evans, P., & Neysmith, S. (1998). Women's caring: Work expanding, state contracting. In C. Baines, P. Evans, & S. Neysmith (Eds.), *Women's caring: feminist perspectives on social welfare,*pp. 3–22. New York: Oxford University Press.

Birenbaum, A. (1995). *Putting health care on the national agenda.* Westport, CT: Praeger.

Brody, E. (1995). Prospects for family caregiving: Response to change, continuity and diversity. In R. Kane & J. Penrod (Eds.), *Family caregiving in an aging society.* Thousand Oaks, CA: Sage.

Browne, C. V. (1998). *Women, feminism and aging.* New York: Springer.

Chafe, W. (1972). *The American woman: Her changing social, economic and political roles 1920–1970.* New York: Oxford University Press.

Coontz, S. (1992). *The way we never were: American families and the nostalgia trap.* New York: Basic Books.

Dailey, N. (1998). *When baby boom women retire.* Westport, CT: Greenwood.

Deckard, B. S. (1983). *The women's movement.* New York: Harper & Row.

Ford, C. B. (1999). *The girls: Jewish women of Brownsville, Brooklyn 1940–1995.* Albany: State University of New York Press.

Gannon, L. G. (1999). *Women and aging: Transcending the myths.* New York: Routledge.

Gould, J. Ed. (1999). *Dutiful daughters: Caring for our parents as they grow old.* Seattle: Seal.

Harrington, M. (1962). *The other America: Poverty in the United States.* Baltimore: Penguin.

Harvey, B. (1993). *The fifties: A woman's oral history.* New York: Harper Collins.

Hooyman, N. R. (1999). Research on older women: Where is feminism. *The Gerontologist,* 39:115–18.

Kaledin, E. (1984). *American women in the 1950s: Mothers and more.* New York: G. K. Hall.

Kessler-Harris, A. (1981). *Women have always worked.* Old Westbury, NY: The Feminist Press.

May, E. T. (1988). *Homeward bound: American families in the cold war era.* New York: Basic Books.

Mintz, S. & Kellogg, S. (1988). *Domestic revolutions: A social history of American family life.* New York: Free Press.

Rowbotham, S. (1997). *A century of women.* New York: Penguin.

Social Security Administration (SSA). (1999a). Income sources by age, sex, and marital status: Percent of aged units 55 or older with money income from specific sources 1998. *Social Security Bulletin,* Annual Statistical Supplement, Washington: Government Printing Office.

Social Security Administration (SSA). (1999b). Income from social security benefits by sex, marital status, race, and hispanic origin: percent of aged units 65 or older 1998. *Social Security Bulletin,* Annual Statistical Supplement. Washington: Government Printing Office.

Social Security Administration (SSA). (1999c). Income from private pensions or annuities by sex and marital status: Percentage distribution of persons aged 65 or older 1998. *Social Security Bulletin,* Annual Statistical Supplement, Washington: Government Printing Office.

Social Security Administration (SSA). (1999d). Table 6.D3, Number and average monthly benefit for wives and husbands, by age and sex 1998. *Social Security Bulletin,* Annual Statistical Supplement. Washington: Government Printing Office.

U.S. Census Bureau. (1998a). Current population survey, Table 2. Poverty status of people by family relationship, race, and Hispanic origin 1959–1990. Washington: Government Printing Office.

U.S. Census Bureau. (1998ab. Current population survey, Table 3.E1. Weighted average poverty thresholds for nonfarm families of specified size 1959–1998. Washington: Government Printing Office.

U.S. General Accounting Office (GAO). [1999]. *Social security: Criteria for evaluating social security reform proposals.* Testimony before the subcommittee on social security, committee on ways and means (March). Washington: Government Printing Office.

U.S. General Accounting Office (GAO). [1997]. *Social security reform: implications for the financial well being of women.* Statement by Jane L. Ross (April). Washington: Government Printing Office.

U.S. General Accounting Office (GAO). [1996]. *Social security: Issues involving benefit equity for working women* (April). Washington: Government Printing Office.

U.S. Senate. (1999a). Hearings before the special committee on aging (SSCA), (February). *Women and social security reform: Are individual accounts the answer?* 106th Cong. 1st sess., Washington: Government Printing Office.

U.S. Senate. (1999b). Hearings before the special committee on Aging (SSCA), (June). *The impact of social security reform on women* 106th Cong. 1st sess., Washington: Government Printing Office.

# Chapter 6

# *The End of Patriarchy: How Evolutionary Biology Explains Conflicts between Male and Female Behavior*

*Malcolm Potts MB, BChir, PhD, FRCOG*

## Introduction

I want to use evolutionary psychology to cover these topics.

Evolution is the outcome of random mutations, tested in the harsh world of natural competition. What Charles Darwin called the "war of nature" exists not only between species but between the two sexes of the same species.

Evolution is not about what is fair, moral or just, but about what works.

It really is adaptive for the male praying mantis to be eaten by the female during copulation because his body supplements her food supply and allows larger eggs to be laid which in turns means he transmits more of his genes to the next generation—evolution's ultimate metric. To facilitate this useful process the male can go on mating after his head has been eaten because evolution has ensured that the neurological control of copulation has migrated to the abdominal ganglia.

The image of a male copulating with its head bitten off is perhaps an appropriate starting place to explore patriarchy.

My article builds on the paradigm of evolutionary psychology which posits that certain human behaviors are universal—even blind people smile. Some universal predispositions, such as sexual jealously helped our ancestors to reproduce successfully.

I am not talking about biological determinism, but a rich interaction between genetics and social forces. In this multi-country study, male aggression is scored on the vertical axis and the level of monoamine oxidase and exposure to violence as a child on the horizontal. Low levels of monoamine oxidase—a brain enzyme—are associated with more pugnacious behavior. Bad parenting is a purely social variable. Both culture and genetics interact and almost 90% of brutal behavior occurs in those men unlucky enough to have a genetically low monoamine oxidase and a violent childhood.

Evolution has given us a large number of inherited predispositions that influence our behavior in unconscious ways. There is no correlation between height and ability but all American presidents save two have been of above average height, including George W Bush. However, former

Mexican president Vicente Fox is a full 6 inches taller than Bush. Politicians understand our Stone Age predisposition and Bush is standing on a box behind the podium.

# Sexual Agendas

Sarah Hdry, a prominent primatologist, has written:

*". . . two sexes caught in the bounds of irreconcilable conflicts. In only a few cases will the self-interest of consorts overlap"*[1]

Among birds it is possible for the male to sit on the egg and to feed the fledglings consequently many avian species, such as penguins, are monogamous.

Male mammals cannot share in incubating the egg or breast feeding. Inevitably, females invest more in reproduction than males do in producing sperm.

Evolution predicts that the sex that makes the most biological investment in the next generation will tend to be cautious in mating choices, while the one that makes least investment will be competitive and risk-taking.

Monogamous mammals are few and far between.

Darwin understand that

*". . . the male seems to owe his greater size to his ancestors having fought with other males during many generations."*[2]

Although males are little more than vehicles to carry testes, This bull elephant seal is the iconic mammalian patriarch, using size to fight off other males and inseminate as many females as possible.

It is in a woman's interest to be able to mate with the most attractive male available while also having any children at the optimum time in her reproductive life. It is to the advantage of the male to secure the greatest possible freedom in his own mating, while making sure any woman he impregnates is faithful to him and unable to exercise choice over the timing or number of her pregnancies.

It may have been mothers who bound their daughter's feet or hold them own for the cruelty of genital mutilation, but ultimately I see these obscenities as expressions of the male agenda to control female reproductive choices

Since evolutionary agendas are slow, evolving our inherited predispositions tend to adapt us not to a modern world of concrete and computers, but to a hunter-gatherer way of life stretching back to the Paleolithic and beyond.

Biology <u>cannot</u> tell us how to behave in the modern world and evolutionary insights in no way excuse cruel behaviors. It can provide insight into why we behave in certain ugly ways, and understanding is the first step in finding solutions.

If we value gender equity, or if we want to live in a more peaceful, sustainable world, then we need to strive to overthrown our patriarchal Stone Age traditions.

The Olympic discus record for men is 74 meters, for women it is 76 meters, <u>but</u> women throw <u>a one kilogram discus</u> while men must hurl a two kilo discus.[3] On average men are 15% larger than women and have greater upper body strength.

A biologist from Mars knowing nothing about us except our anatomy, would conclude, without any measure of doubt, that we are descended from a promiscuous or polygamous species where males fought for access to females.

Men and women are hard wired to look for certain physical features in a possible mate. This device tracks where a man's eyes go when looking a picture of a woman. Where he first looks is purely unconscious and takes place in milliseconds.[4]

Women store body fat on the hips and breasts in preparation for the calorific demands of pregnancy and lactation. Across the world, men prefer a woman with a waist/hip ratio of 0.7. We live in a culture where men are bombarded with images of nubile women, but even blind men choose the 0.7 ratio.

A low waist/hip ratio correlates with higher conception rates and it is hardwired into men's brains. In sports and in women's fashions, culture often exaggerates the shape evolution bequeathed us.

Women also make finely tuned unconscious decisions about men. Should they go with a tall, square jawed man who is highly competitive but may be unfaithful or even violent in the home, or is it better to fall in love with a softer, more gentle man, who is more likely to play a genuine role in nurturing any children and who may be less likely to chase after other women? The answer partly depends on the eternal environment.[5] If you live in Chicago, you might be wise to choose the squared jawed testosterone rich man best able to protect you. If you live in Rhode Island, then perhaps the softer, kinder man.

Evolution is the outcome of accidental mutations and mating behaviors, and takes many forms. Consider *Anticinus stuarti,* a tiny marsupial mouse. Each year in the fall, the males engage in an orgy of sex; they lose their fur, develop stomach ulcers and heart attacks—then they all die. The females live to the second year when they deliver equal numbers of male and female pups and the cycle starts again. A chance mutation which disposed of the males as soon as they completed their fertilizing function benefited the pregnant female by reducing competition for food during the lean winter months.

# Male Aggression

Testosterone is the primary hormone modulating male sexual activity. It also predisposes to violent, competitive, life-shortening behavior. Risk taking is biologically adaptive in males but not in females.

Revealingly, if you castrate male *Anticinus,* then they also live until the second year. We are also subject to evolutionary pressures and exactly as in marsupial mice; a castrated man lives longer than a man with intact testicles—in this case a remarkable 12 years longer. Not only does life seem longer for a eunuch—it *is* longer!

There are indeed good evolutionary reasons, as well as obvious cultural ones, why boys and girls behave differently. All parents who have a boy and a girl see this. When scientists offered young vervet monkeys toys such as police car and dolls,[6] the females picked up the dolls and cuddled them while the males banged the trucks against the cage floor.

We would have been astonished if Congresswoman Gabby Gifford had been shot by a woman instead of a man. In every country, men—especially testosterone filled young men—make up the majority of the convicted criminals.

Men kill other men—usually as the result of rivalries over status—nine times as often as a woman kills a man. Biologically, when a man murders another man over status or overt sexual rivalry, it is comparable to arming elephant seals with hand guns.

Male nastiness evolved precisely because of sexual competition, where aggression shaped the path to reproductive success.

One of the most viscerally disturbing examples of male aggression is when a child is murdered. In a small number of species, such as lions, gorillas and langur monkeys, where one male controls several females, when a new male takes over a 'harem', he systematically kills all the suckling young.

Like everything in evolution, this is not a conscious strategy, but those males who had a mutation coding for this infanticidal behavior would have left more genes in the next generation because killing the baby ended the anovulation associated with breastfeeding and made the female immediately available for impregnation.

Criminological data demonstrates that the relative risk of a non-biological father killing an infant of the women he has sex with is 60 times greater than that of a biological father. The effect lasts for precisely the time we would expect a women to breastfeed in a hunter-gather society. As every epidemiologist knows, a 60-fold risk is a compelling statistic and horrible as it may seem, men also seems to share the behavioral predisposition for infanticide.

But there is also another type of male violence we categorize as team aggression, where a group of adults in the prime of life attack and kill on individual from another troop or pack. It is profoundly different from murder.

Among the 5,490 different species of mammals, only four–chimpanzees, possibly wolves and hyenas, and ourselves.—systematically and deliberately kill their own kind. The motive is access to more resources, which ultimately translates into greater reproductive opportunities.

The animals that engage in team aggression are all territorial, highly social, intelligent and loyal to other members of their own species. Human beings and chimpanzees had a common ancestor about 7 million years ago. When Jane Goodall first observed team aggression among chimpanzees, she realized it was a form of "primitive warfare." The fossil record, archaeology, anthropology, and our contemporary world provide an unbroken sequence from tiny raids to 20th century wars touching every part of the globe.

The only intact corpse that survived from the Ice Age—discovered in the Alps in 1991—was initially thought to be a poor shepherd who had lost his way until it was shown he had three different human blood groups on his cloak and a flint arrow in his back.

In the highlands of New Guinea, where one million people literally lived in the Stone Age until the first contact with Europeans in the 1930s, about one firth of men are killed in raids by other men. (They really do wear penis sheaths.)

Jane Goodall found up to one third of adults chimpanzees were killed by other chimps. Among the Yanamamo in the Amazon, one in four adults has participated in killing another human being.

Team aggression evolved because those individuals with a mutation to go out and kill their neighbors ended up enlarging their territories, enabling them to reproduce more rapidly and leave more of its genes in the next-generation.

Modern wars can involve millions of men but ultimately they revolve around small raiding groups as in chimps or New Guinea. As a child, I lived near American air force bases. 26,000 volunteers were to die fighting over Germany. Their loyalty was to other members of the crew. They were the Band of Brothers Shakespeare extols in King Henry's great speech before the Battle of Agincourt on a wet day in October 1415.

For some men war is exciting. Women will fight courageously if they or their children are attacked. It may be adaptive to mate with a powerful warrior, but team aggression does not advance the female reproductive agenda. In the whole vast sweep of human history, I cannot find a single proven case where <u>women</u> banded together spontaneously and deliberately and sallied forth to kill human beings.

# Dehumanization

Courageous warriors are rewarded with Medals of Honor. Those who attack us we classify as cowardly murders. It was a small team of closely bonded men (two were brothers) who attacked America on 9/11.

As social intelligent animals, in order to systematically kill other members of our own species, I suggest we also needed to evolve a behavior to dehumanize—or 'dechimpanzeeize'—other members of our species. As Solzhenistsyn wrote, it is capacity that *"cuts through every human heart."*

# Patriarchs

Across history and across cultures, rich and powerful men have had more sex than those lower down in the social hierarchy. In pre-conquest Peru, the great Inca at the top of the social pyramid had the pick of the empire's women, while the serfs often went unmarried. Large harems were the order of the day for King Solomon, Turkish Sultans, and Chinese Emperors;[7] Osama bin Laden was the 17th child of a quintessential patriarch, who had 11 wives and 54 children.

The most obscenely cruel way for a man to control a woman's reproduction is to rape her. Eight per cent of the men in central Asia–and one in 200 worldwide—have identical Y chromosomes, suggesting that sometime in the last one thousand years, one man had a very large number of children. Genghis Khan was a brilliant but ruthless organizer. After a city was captured the commanders and common solders had equal rights to pillage, but every young woman had to be handed to the Great Khan. He boasted of the pleasure of violating other men's wives.

The most plausible explanation of the fact that about one in 200 men on this campus carry the same chromosome is that they are all descendants of Genghis Khan. Biologically he was the most successful man in history, yet hardly a role model for today's world.

The Mongols instilled fear into their enemies. After the Battle of the Kalka River in 1123 in what is now the Ukraine, the Mongol victors enjoyed a feast sitting on heavy planks placed over the defeated Russians as they slowly suffocated to death.

At one level, a pope is surely as different from a Mongol emperor as it is possible to be. But patriarchy takes many forms. The ability to dehumanize cuts through every human heart. Pius I became pope in 1848. He was short tempered and over confident. He made priests kiss his feet and almost caused a religious schism when he placed his foot on the head of the bishop of Antioch and ground it into the floor. It was Pius I who manipulated the First Vatican Council to proclaim the dogma of papal infallibility. He was so convinced of his infallible powers that when he saw a paraplegic on these Spanish Steps in Rome, in a Monty Python-like episode, he ordered the man "To rise up and walk". According to a by-stander, the "poor devil gave it a try and collapsed, which put the pope much out of sorts."[8] By declaring himself infallible, Pius sought top-down power over a docile, unquestioning church.

To disobey Genghis Khan meant death. For patriarchs, order trumps free discussion. When Hitler came to power in 1933 one German prelate, favorably compared Hitler's appointment as German chancellor with the declaration of papal infallibility half a century earlier—

> *"a decision for authority against discussion, for the pope against the cardinals and bishops, for the fuhrer Hitler against parliament."*[9]

Financial traders in London who juggle hundreds of thousands, or perhaps millions of dollars on a computer screen for many hours a day, also seem far removed from either Pope Pius or Genghis Khan. However, like all patriarchs their behavior is strongly modified by testosterone level. For some, as here, the higher the testosterone level the greater the profits. But testosterone also encourages risk-taking, whether on the battlefield or in front of a computer. it is the ultimate weapon of mass destruction and of and financial meltdown.

Competitive patriarchs have a strong sense of entitlement. Much of the work of Wall Street financers is <u>manipulating</u> money, not creating wealth.

Goldman Sacs turns a staggering 39% of its revenue into compensation for its staff. The average employee made $430,000 in 2010. The chief executive received $2 million in salary along with a $12.6 million bonus for running a company that in 2010 had to pay the Securities and Exchange Commission $550 million to settle charges of fraud.

The metaphor of bankers raping investors in the way Genghis Kahn raped his conquests is not inappropriate.[10]

# The Pill and Viagra

Genghis Kahn conquered territory with the sword; Pius I tried to conquer the thoughts of others by declaring himself God's mouth piece. Infallibility destroys the flexibility that is the hallmark of human behavior. It is a dogma that still casts a dark shadow over the lives of millions of women today.

Medicine has a patriarchal steak. As a young obstetrician in the 1960s I was an advocate for the reform of Queen Victoria's 1861 restrictive abortion law. I remember a meeting chaired by Sir John Peel, the Queen's gynecologist. As more and more arguments for a liberal law were made I could see Sir John becoming increasingly uneasy. Eventually he blurted out,

*"I don't like being told by the patient what to do."*

It was a revealing statement. Some of the emotion in debates about contraception and abortion is not driven by careful ethical analysis, but by a patriarchal desire of men to control women's reproduction.

The Harvard obstetrician John Rock, who led the clinical work on the first oral contraceptives, was a devout Roman Catholic who went Mass every morning. His 1963 book *The Time Has Come* argued that the Pill was morally acceptable because it merely extended the natural suppression of ovulation taking place during lactation.

Reproductive physiology, like some aspects of human behavior, evolved to adapt us to Stone Age environment where puberty occurred at 18 or older and pregnancies were spaced by long intervals of breast-feeding. Women in those few hunter gatherer societies that persisted until the 20th century, underwent the hormonal turmoil of ovulation without conception much less often than a modern woman. It seems the fewer menstrual cycles, the fewer reproductive cancers including breast cancer, but it is also true the more menstrual cycles the more uterine and ovarian malignancies.

The Pill was a brilliant invention, but it proved a serious challenge to the male drive to control female reproduction. Congress considered taking it off the market.

As a physician prescribing Pills in the 1960s, I was close to these intense controversies. I was delighted when the British Medical Research Council set up a study of 23,000 women using oral contraceptives and 23,000 controls. This study has gone on for 39 years and now includes 1.2 million women years observation. The results are stunning, confirming John Rock's analysis that oral contraceptives are natural. A relative risk of one means that you are no more likely and no less likely to die. A relative risk of 0.88 means you live longer than average.

The Pill is the only medicine that actually reduces the risk of dying from cancer.

It is not perfect (it neither raised nor reduces the frequency of breast cancer), but from an evolutionary perspective the hormone balance in a woman on oral contraceptives is more like our hunter gatherer ancestors than a modern women having hundreds of ovulatory cycles; taking the Pill, perhaps, is more natural than not taking it.

The Vatican established a Commission to study contraception and the majority agreed that the Pill was a theological acceptable method. But the infallible patriarch in the Vatican had no way to overturn a prior doctrine, even when manifestly wrong.

In July 1968 Pope Pius IV issued the encyclical *Humanae vitae*, condemning so called artificial contraception,

*". . . Similarly excluded is any action specifically intended to prevent procreation"*

John Rock and Catholics all over the world were shattered, theologians were dismissed, priests resigned and attendance at Mass dropped by 50 per cent.

*Humanae vitae* is not an infallible document, but Cardinal Wojtyla, who was to become Pope John Paul II, admitted that the reason for banning the Pill was not scientific or theological, but the framework of infallibility which prevented the Vatican admitting a mistake and moving forward.

> *If it should be declared that contraception is not evil, then we should have to concede that the Holy Spirit ... failed to protect ... a large part of the Catholic hierarchy from a very serious error,*

Compare *Viagra* and oral contraceptives. When the pill was developed by a private research lab in Boston, contraception was illegal in Massachusetts and. NIH was forbidden to support contraceptive research. No company wanted to market the new invention. There were no laws against studying male erections and when *Viagra* was discovered it was developed immediately as a block buster drug. Several hundred deaths had been linked to Viagra but unlike the Pill there have been no panic headlines, or Congressional hearings.

Patriarchal tendencies are universal. In 1967, the Ministry of Health and Welfare in Tokyo refused an application to market the Pill on the ground Japanese women were unlike Europeans. In 1990 they said oral contraceptives would accelerate AIDS. In 1998—with an obscurantism worthy of a medieval theologian–marketing was refused because artificial hormones in the sewage might feminize fish.

When Viagra was introduced into Japan, it received marketing approval in six months. No one asked what was happening to all the sexually excited fish in Japanese rivers. The asymmetry between the two drugs had become so grotesque that the Pill was also approved on Viagra's coattails—35 years after the initial application.

The male desire to enhance their erections while restricting access to the Pill is an act of simple patriarchy.

# Abortion

Safe abortion is perhaps the ultimate challenge to patriarchy.

Not all patriarchs are dictators but all dictators are patriarchs. Joseph Stalin reversed a previously liberal abortion law. Adolf Hitler forced German women to register their menstrual cycles in an attempt to prevent abortion. It was in Marshall Petain's Nazi dominated Vichy France that a woman was guillotined for performing abortions.

Yet, abortion is as much part of the modern world as the internal combustion engine or the cell phone. On average, every woman now alive will have one induced abortion.

Where abortion is illegal, traditional techniques of terminating a pregnancy are up to 1000 times more dangerous than modern surgical or medical procedures.

I have performed abortions and I have a PhD in embryology. I think the politics of abortion are not about morals but about patriarchy. The problem is not deciding whether abortion is right or wrong, but accommodating in a respectful way to a variety of sincerely held opinions on a complex topic.

In the United States several physicians have been murdered. As a result, first trimester abortion has become the first surgical procedure in history where the surgeon is more likely to die than the patient.

Roe v. Wade, the Supreme Court ruling making safe abortion available in all states, did not say abortion was right or wrong. It said something more profound, based on America's founding tradition of religious tolerance,

> "... we need not resolve the difficult question when life begins. When doctors, philosophers and theologians are unable to arrive at a consensus, the judiciary should not pass restrictive laws."

Religious assertions about when life begins are philosophically parallel to religious beliefs about life after death. Both are strongly held, but beyond the realm of science to prove or disprove. In a society which separates church and state, it should be no more surprising to have an abortion clinic in a city where many people are sincerely opposed to terminating a pregnancy than it is to have a mosque, a Catholic church, a Synagogue, or Mosque, all teaching different interpretations of eternal life.

I used to think that with the passage of time, there would be a slow and consistent erosion of hostility to fertility regulation, but it is of the nature of deep seated predispositions that if the acid of male hostility in contained in one place then it tends to leek out and corrode women's options in another.

Recently 600 bills have been introduced in state legislatures to restrict access to safe abortion The Republican majority in the House of Representatives is proposing legislation that would forbid a safe abortion to a 12 year old pregnant as a result of 'statutory rape.'[11] Last week in Baja Mexico a woman accused of having an abortion was sentenced to 23 years in prison,[12]

In America Catholic bishops oppose insurance coverage of contraception.[13] The real objection here goes back to St Augustine that sex is intrinsically sinful and therefore only justified if every act of intercourse is open to the possibility of procreation.

I suspect the temperature in rising in the abortion debate partly because the procedure is becoming simpler and safer. A woman can now end a pregnancy in her own home by taking a few tablets. Medical abortion will make the patriarchal control of abortion more and more difficult and, perhaps, ultimately, impossible.

Worldwide 200 million women wish to delay or never have another pregnancy but are not using any contraception, either because they have no access or face insurmountable barriers to its use. Meeting the unmet medical need for family planning has been highly successful in slowing rapid population where contraception and safe abortion have been realistically available. Family size has decreased rapidly even in illiterate communities living on less than a dollar a day. Yet the more patriarchal members of Congress have always worked hard to deny women overseas the right to decide if and when to have a child.

Patriarchs who deny women contraception, end up hoist by their own petard. In the mid-1980s I met with a younger more dynamic Hosni Mubarak to discuss family planning. At the time there were 50 million people in Egypt. Mubarak understood our population projections but we couldn't get him to understand that his top-down, over medicalized family planning program was insensitive to women's needs. Today, there are 80 million Egyptians; unemployment is rampant, instead of exporting wheat Egypt imports 60 per cent of its wheat, and food prices rose 50 to 70%. Egypt would be more stable today if a less patriarchal Mubarak had listened 30 years ago.

# Ways To End Patriarchy

It is easy to catalogue the injustices women have suffered down the ages, but are there any solutions? Is progress being made?

I want to suggest that the evolutionary perspective can help.

97% of Americans do not understand the power of Darwinian evolution; they deny themselves the perspective it provides into the wonder, beauty and mystery of the world around us, and the insights it opens on our behaviors—both good and bad.

We need to recognize that the world is getting less violent. Despite Darfur and Afghanistan, when we look at deaths from team aggression in relation to the total population, the world is more at peace today than it has ever been.

We should avoid over reacting to perceived threats. The military budgets of the industrialized nations equal the total income of the two billion people poorest people on the planet. The US contributes half this total.

In the Stone Age, if you found a member of your clan had been killed, you had every reason to fear an enemy behind the net bush. 9/11 killed one in 100,000 Americans. The average American in 2001 was more likely to be killed by a neighbor with a handgun than by an Al Qaeda terrorist. Nevertheless a survey one month after 9/11[14] showed respondents thought the 'average Americans had a one in two' chance of being harmed in a terrorist attack—a 50,000 fold overestimate.

Estimates of the number of Al Qaeda *jihadists* vary from a few thousand to 18,000. By the mid-nineties the US had spent as estimated one trillion dollars on the 'war on terror'—or $100 to $250 million per member of Al Qaeda. Never in the history of human endeavor has so much been spent on fighting so few.

I am not suggesting we should not worry about terrorist attacks but we need to learn to counter them in new ways. In every country that harbors or sponsors terrorists, women have a low status and little autonomy over their own lives. High birth rates contribute to massive unemployment. When you have few opportunities taking risks can be a sound reproductive strategy.

Investing in family planning can be sound counter strategy

When I first went to Afghanistan in 1970 there were half as many people as there today. The forces holding back family planning at that time were not lack of desire on the part of women, but patriarchal leaders.

We preach democracy but the freedom to decide when to have children is even more important than the freedom of the ballot box. The Pill is mightier than the sword. In the long run, injectable contraceptives and IUDs are more powerful weapons against local tyranny and global terrorism than Abraham's tanks or F16 fighter planes—and a lot less expensive!

It was women who discovered and marketed most traditional contraceptives and abortifacients, but it was men who wrote laws and preached theological arguments to restrict or condemn their use.

If we want to help others and also help ourselves we should work to set an example by taking the Pill off prescription in the USA. We have just seen the evidence about its safety: It is patriarchal men in pharmaceutical companies seeking to maximize profits who stop the Pill going over the counter next to aspirins in CVS pharmacies.

And speaking of commerce, why not ask your financial adviser his testosterone level? Or if that is difficult, choose a woman to invest the money that will go towards your pension. Woman were evolved to make more prudent long term decisions than men.

Lastly, and perhaps most importantly of all, we need to rejoice over the behavioral flexibility evolution has given us. Civilization at is best can overcome the worst of our Stone Age predispositions.

As I young boy in World War II, like ninety nine percent of people in Britain, I thought the Japanese were subhuman war criminals who deserved to be bombed out of existence. If I had had to write a thousand things that might happen at my age today, it would not have included being proud to have a Japanese/Iranian daughter in law and joyful to have a Japanese/Iranian/Scottish/American grandchild.

**Malcolm Potts**, MB, BChir, PhD, FRCOG, is a human reproductive scientist.
He is the first holder of the Fred H. Bixby-endowed chair in Population and Family Planning in the School of Public Health at the University of California, Berkeley and is currently founding director of the Bixby Center for Population, Health, and Sustainability.

# References

1. Hrdy, Sarah Blaffer. 1977. *The Langurs of Abu: Female and male Strategies of Reproduction.* Cambridge Mss: Harvard University pres. page 305.
2. page 619.
3. *http://en.wikipedia.org/wiki/Discus_throw.*
4. Watching the hourglass: eye tracking reveals men's appreciation of the female form. Barnaby J. Dion, Gina M. Grimshaw, Wayne L. Linklater, Alan F.Dion. *Human Nature* 2010 **21**; 355–370.
5. economist dec 14 2010. Robert Brooks Proc Royal Society.
6. Aleander, G. M. and Hines, M. 2002. In *Evolution and Human Behavior*, Vol. 23, pp. 167–483.
7. Betzig, L. L. 1986.
8. Hasler p. 124.
9. Hasler page 257.
10. Craig, Sussane Goldman chief gets bigger bonus and increase in salary. New York Times Jan 29, 2010. Page B4.
11. The new abortion rules New York Sunday Times January 30 Sunday opinion. Page 7.
12. ht*tp://www.reddesalud.org/news/act1_int.php?id=211* (accessed Feb 2, 2010).
13. Pera, Robert. Official consider requiring insurer to offer free contraceptives New York Times A 20 feb 2, 2011.
14. Jennifer S. Lerner, Roana m. Gonzalez, Deborah A. Samll and baruch Fischoff. Effects of Fear and Anger on Perceived Risks of Terrorism: A National Field Experiment. *Psychological Science* 14(20):144–150. 2003.
    Koenig, MA, Zablotska I, Lutalo T, Nalugoda F, Wagman J, Gray R. 2004. Coerced First Intercourse and Reproductive Health Among Adolescent Women in Rakai, Uganda. *International Family Planning Perspctives* 30, 156–163.

# Section III

## Adolescence and Sexuality

# Chapter 7

# *Facts on American Teens' Sexual and Reproductive Health*

*Guttmacher Institute*

## Sexual Activity

- Although only 13% of teens have had sex by age 15, most initiate sex in their later teen years. By their 19th birthday, seven in 10 female and male teens have had intercourse.[1]
- On average, young people have sex for the first time at about age 17,[2,3] but they do not marry until their mid-20s.[4] This means that young adults may be at increased risk for unintended pregnancy and STIs for nearly a decade or longer.
- Teens are waiting longer to have sex than they did in the recent past. In 2006–2008, some 11% of never-married females aged 15–19 and 14% of never-married males that age had had sex before age 15, compared with 19% and 21%, respectively, in 1995.[1]
- However, after declining substantially between 1995 and 2002, the proportion of teens who had ever had sex did not change significantly from 2002 to 2006–2008.[1]
- In 2006–2010, the most common reason that sexually inexperienced teens gave for not having had sex was that it was "against religion or morals" (38% among females and 31% among males). The second and third most common reasons for females were "don't want to get pregnant" and "haven't found the right person yet."[5]
- Among sexually experienced teens, 70% of females and 56% of males report that their first sexual experience was with a steady partner, while 16% of females and 28% of males report first having sex with someone they had just met or who was just a friend.[5]
- Seven percent of young women aged 18–24 who had had sex before age 20 report that their first sexual experience was nonvoluntary. Those whose first partner was three or more years their senior were more likely to report this than were other women in the same age-group.[1]
- Teens in the United States and Europe have similar levels of sexual activity. However, European teens are more likely than U.S. teens to use contraceptives generally and to use the most effective methods; they therefore have substantially lower pregnancy rates.[6]

Reprinted with permission: Guttmacher Institute, Facts on American teens' sexual and reproductive health, *In Brief,* New York: Guttmacher Institute, 2013, <http://www.guttmacher.org/pubs/FB-Teen-Sex-Ed.html>, accessed May 2013.

- Three percent of males and 8% of females aged 18–19 in 2002 reported their sexual orientation as homosexual or bisexual; the proportions reporting same-sex behaviors were similar.[7]
- The use of contraceptives during first premarital sex has been increasing, rising from 56% among women whose first premarital sex occurred before 1985, to 76% among those who first had sex in 2000–2004, to 84% among those whose first sex occurred in 2005–2008.[8]

## Contraceptive Use

- A woman who is sexually active and not using contraception has an 85% chance of becoming pregnant within a year.[9]
- The majority of sexually experienced teens (78% of females and 85% of males) used contraceptives the first time they had sex.[5]
- The condom is the most common contraceptive method used at first intercourse; 68% of females and 80% of males use it the first time they have sex. [5]
- In 2006–2010, some 96% of sexually experienced female teens had used a condom at least once, 57% had ever used withdrawal and 56% had used the pill. Smaller proportions had used other methods.[5]
- In the same period, one in five sexually active female teens (20%) and one-third of sexually active male teens (34%) reported having used both the condom and a hormonal method the last time they had sex.[5] Dual method use offers protection against both pregnancy and STIs.
- In 2006–2010, some 86% of female teens and 93% of male teens reported using contraceptives at last sex. These proportions represent a marked improvement since 1995, when only 71% of female teens and 82% of male teens had reported using a method at last sex. However, the proportions were unchanged between 2002 and 2006–2010.[5]
- Nearly one in five female teens at risk for unintended pregnancy (19%) were not using any contraceptive method at last intercourse.[8]

## Access to Contraceptive Services

- No state explicitly requires parental consent or notification for contraceptive services. However, two states (Texas and Utah) require parental consent for contraceptive services paid for with state funds.[10]
- Twenty-one states and the District of Columbia explicitly allow minors to obtain contraceptive services without a parent's involvement. Another 25 states have affirmed that right for certain classes of minors, while four states have no law. In the absence of a specific law, courts have determined that minors' privacy rights include the right to obtain contraceptive services.[10]
- In 2002, some 90% of publicly funded family planning clinics counseled clients younger than 18 about abstinence, the importance of communicating with parents about sex or both topics.[11]

- Nearly two million women younger than 20 were served by publicly supported family planning centers in 2005; these teens represented one-quarter of the centers' contraceptive clients.[12]
- In 2006, only 5% of American high schools made condoms available to students.[12]

# STIs

- Young people aged 13–24 made up about 17% of all people diagnosed with HIV/AIDS in the United States in 2008.[13]
- Although 15–24-year-olds represent only one-quarter of the sexually active population, they account for nearly half (9.1 million) of the 18.9 million new cases of STIs each year.[14]
- Human papillomavirus (HPV) infections account for about half of STIs diagnosed among 15–24-year-olds each year. HPV is extremely common, often asymptomatic and generally harmless. However, certain types, if left undetected and untreated, can lead to cervical cancer.[14]
- Two HPV vaccines—Gardasil and Cervarix are currently available, and both prevent the types of infections most likely to lead to cervical cancer. The Centers for Disease Control now recommends HPV vaccinations for both girls and boys, starting at age 11.
- In 2009, 44% of females aged 13–19 had received one or more doses of the vaccine against HPV; 27% had completed the recommended three doses.[17]
- All 50 states and the District of Columbia explicitly allow minors to consent to STI services without parental involvement, although 11 states require that a minor be of a certain age (generally 12 or 14) to do so. Thirty-one states explicitly include HIV testing and treatment in the package of STI services to which minors may consent.[18]

# Pregnancy

- Each year, almost 750,000 U.S. women aged 15–19 become pregnant.[19] Two-thirds of all teen pregnancies occur among 18–19-year-olds.[19]
- Overall, 68 pregnancies occurred per 1,000 women aged 15–19 in 2008. The 2008 rate was a record low and represented a 42% decline from the peak rate of 117 per 1,000, which occurred in 1990.[19]
- The majority of the decline in teen pregnancy rates in the United States (86%) is due to teens' improved contraceptive use; the rest is due to increased proportions of teens choosing to delay sexual activity.[21]
- Despite having declined, the U.S. teen pregnancy rate continues to be one of the highest in the developed world. It is more than twice as high as rates in Canada (28 per 1,000 women aged 15–19 in 2006) and Sweden (31 per 1,000).[22]
- In 2008, New Mexico had the highest teenage pregnancy rate (93 per 1,000); rates in Mississippi, Texas, Nevada and Arkansas followed. The lowest rates were in New Hampshire (33 per 1,000), Vermont, Minnesota, North Dakota and Massachusetts followed.[20]

- Eighty-two percent of teen pregnancies are unplanned; teens account for about one-fifth of all unintended pregnancies annually.[23]
- Fifty-nine percent of pregnancies among 15–19-year-olds in 2008 ended in birth, and 26% in abortion.[19]
- Black and Hispanic women have the highest teen pregnancy rates (117 and 107 per 1,000 women aged 15–19, respectively); non-Hispanic whites have the lowest rate (43 per 1,000).[19]
- The pregnancy rate among black teens decreased 48% between 1990 and 2008, more than the overall U.S. teen pregnancy rate declined during the same period (42%).[19]
- Most female teens report that they would be very upset (58%) or a little upset (29%) if they got pregnant, while the rest report that they would be a little or very pleased.[1]

# Childbearing

- Ten percent of all U.S. births are to girls aged 19 or younger.[24]
- Most births to teen mothers are first births. Eighteen percent are second or higher order births.[24]
- The share of births to teen mothers that are nonmarital rose from 79% in 2000 to 86% in 2009. Yet, over the last several decades, the share of all nonmarital births that are to teenagers has been declining, from 52% in 1975 to 21% in 2009.[24, 25]
- In 2009, some 39 births occurred per 1,000 women aged 15–19; this rate marks a 37% decline from the peak rate of 62 reached in 1991.[24]
- Six percent of teen mothers aged 15–19 received late or no prenatal care. Babies born to teens are more likely to be low birth-weight than are those born to women in their 20s and 30s.[26]
- Teen childbearing is associated with reduced educational attainment. Teen mothers are substantially less likely than women who delay childbearing to complete high school or obtain a GED by age 22 (66% vs. 94%).[27] Fewer than 2% of teens who have a baby before age 18 attain a college degree by age 30.[28]

# Fatherhood

- Most teen males report that they would be very upset (46%) or a little upset (34%) if they got someone pregnant, while the remaining 20% report that they would be pleased or a little pleased.[5]
- Teen fatherhood rates vary considerably by race. In 2006, the rate among black males aged 15–19 who became fathers (34 per 1,000) was more than twice that among whites (15 per 1,000).[29]
- The rate of teen fatherhood declined 25% between 1990 and 2006, from 24 to 18 per 1,000 males aged 15–19. This decline was far more substantial among blacks than among whites (38% vs. 18%).[29]

# Abortion

- Women aged 15–19 had 192,090 abortions in 2008.[**19**]
- The reasons teens most frequently give for having an abortion are that they are concerned about how having a baby would change their lives, cannot afford a baby now and do not feel mature enough to raise a child.[**30**]
- As of October 2011, laws in 36 states required that a minor seeking an abortion involve her parents in the decision.[**31**]

# References

1. Abma JC et al., Teenagers in the United States: sexual activity, contraceptive use, and childbearing, National Survey of Family Growth 2006–2008, *Vital and Health Statistics*, 2010, Series 23, No. 30.
2. Chandra A et al., Fertility, family planning, and reproductive health of U.S. women: data from the 2002 National Survey of Family Growth, *Vital and Health Statistics*, 2005, Series 23, No. 25
3. Martinez GM et al., Fertility, contraception, and fatherhood: data on men and women from Cycle 6 (2002) of the National Survey of Family Growth, *Vital and Health Statistics*, 2006, Series 23, No. 26.
4. U.S. Bureau of the Census, *America's Families and Living Arrangements*, Washington, DC: U.S. Government Printing Office, 2009.
5. Martinez G et al., Teenagers in the United States: sexual activity, contraceptive use, and childbearing, 2006–2010 National Survey of Family Growth, *Vital and Health Statistics*, 2011, Series 23, No. 31.
6. Santelli J, Sandfort T and Orr M, Transnational comparisons of adolescent contraceptive use: what can we learn from these comparisons? *Archives of Pediatrics & Adolescent Medicine*, 2008, 162(1):92–94.
7. Mosher WD et al., Sexual behavior and selected health measures: men and women 15–44 years of age, United States, 2002, *Advance Data from Vital and Health Statistics*, 2005, No. 362.
8. Mosher WD and Jones J, Use of contraception in the United States: 1982–2008, *Vital and Health Statistics*, 2010, Series 23, No. 29.
9. Trussell J, Contraceptive failure in the United States, *Contraception*, 2011, 83(5): 397-404.
10. Guttmacher Institute, Minors' access to contraceptive services, *State Policies in Brief* (as of October 2011), 2011, <http://www.guttmacher.org/statecenter/spibs/spib_MACS.pdf>, accessed Oct. 19, 2011.
11. Lindberg LD et al., **Provision of contraceptive and related services by publicly funded family planning clinics,** 2003, *Perspectives on Sexual and Reproductive Health*, 2006, 38(3):139–147.
12. Jones RK et al., Adolescents' reports of parental knowledge of adolescents' use of sexual health services and their reactions to mandated parental notification for prescription contraception, *Journal of the American Medical Association*, 2005, 293(3):340–348.
13. Centers for Disease Control and Prevention (CDC), HIV Surveillance Report, 2008, Vol. 20, 2010, <http://www.cdc.gov/hiv/topics/surveillance/resources/reports>, accessed Oct. 26, 2010.
14. Weinstock H et al., **Sexually transmitted diseases among American youth: incidence and prevalence estimates, 2000,** *Perspectives on Sexual and Reproductive Health*, 2004, 36(1):6–10.

15. U.S. Food and Drug Administration, FDA licenses new vaccine for prevention of cervical cancer and other diseases in females caused by human papillomavirus: rapid approval marks major advancement in public health, 2006, <http://www.fda.gov/NewsEvents/Newsroom/PressAnnouncements/2006/ucm108666.htm>, accessed Nov.19, 2010.

16. U.S. Food and Drug Administration, FDA approves new vaccine for prevention of cervical cancer, 2009, <http://www.fda.gov/NewsEvents/Newsroom/PressAnnouncements/2009/ucm187048.htm>, accessed Nov. 19, 2010.

17. CDC, National, state, and local area vaccination coverage among adolescents aged 13–17 years—United States, 2009, *Morbidity and Mortality Weekly Report*, 2010, 59(32):1018–1023.

18. Guttmacher Institute, Minors' access to STI services, *State Policies in Brief*, (as of October 2011), 2011, accessed Oct.19, 2011.

19. Kost K and Henshaw S, *U.S. Teenage Pregnancies, Births and Abortions, 2008: National Trends by Race and Ethnicity,* 2012, <http://www.guttmacher.org/pubs/USTPtrends08.pdf>, accessed February 6, 2012.

20. Guttmacher Institute, *U.S. Teenage Pregnancies, Births and Abortions*, 2008: State *Trends by Age, Race and Ethnicity*, New York: Guttmacher Institute, 2013.

21. Santelli JS et al., Explaining recent declines in adolescent pregnancy in the United States: the contribution of abstinence and improved contraceptive use, *American Journal of Public Health,* 2007, 97(1):150–156.

22. McKay A et al., Trends in teen pregnancy rates from 1996–2006: a comparison of Canada, Sweden, USA and England/Wales, *Canadian Journal of Human Sexuality*, 19(1–2):43–52.

23. Finer LB and Zolna MR, **Unintended pregnancy in the United States: incidence and disparities, 2006,** *Contraception*, 2011, doi: 10.1016/j.contraception.2011.07.013

24. Martin JA et al., Births: final data for 2009, *National Vital Statistics Reports*, 2011, Vol. 60, No.1.

25. Martin JA et al., Births: final data for 2000, *National Vital Statistics Reports*, 2002, Vol. 50, No. 5.

26. Martin JA et al., Births: final data for 2003, *National Vital Statistics Reports*, 2005, Vol. 54, No 2.

27. Perper K, Peterson K and Manlove J, Diploma attachment among teen mothers, Fact Sheet, Washington, DC: Child Trends, 2010,<http://www.childtrends.org/Files/Child_Trends-2010_01_22_FS_DiplomaAttainment.pdf>, accessed Mar.1, 2010.

28. Hoffman SD, By *the Numbers: The Public Costs of Adolescent Childbearing*, Washington, DC: National Campaign to Prevent Teen Pregnancy, 2006.

29. Martin JA et al., Births: final data for 2006, *National Vital Statistics Reports*, 2009, Vol. 57, No. 7.

30. Dauphinee LA, Guttmacher Institute, New York, personal communication, Mar. 23, 2006.

31. Guttmacher Institute, Parental involvement in minors' abortions, *State Policies in Brief* (as of October 2011), 2011 <http://www.guttmacher.org/statecenter/spibs/spib_PIMA.pdf>, accessed Oct. 19, 2011.

# Chapter 8

# *Facts on American Teens' Sources of Information About Sex*

*Guttmacher Institute*

## Sex, Pregnancy and Abortion

- Although only 13% of U.S. teens have had sex by age 15, most initiate sex in their late teen years. By their 19th birthday, seven in 10 teen men and teen women have had intercourse.[1]
- Between 1988 and 2006–2010, the proportion of never-married teens aged 15–17 who had ever engaged in sexual intercourse declined from 37% to 27% among females, and from 50% to 28% among males. During the same period, among teens aged 18–19, that proportion declined from 73% to 63% among females, and 77% to 64% among males.[2]
- The pregnancy rate among young women has declined steadily, from 117 pregnancies per 1,000 women aged 15–19 in 1990 to 68 per 1,000 in 2008. [3]
- The majority (86%) of the decline in the teen pregnancy rate between 1995 and 2002 was the result of dramatic improvements in contraceptive use, including an increase in the proportion of teens using a single method of contraception, an increase in the proportion using multiple methods simultaneously and a substantial decline in nonuse. Just 14% of the decline is attributable to decreased sexual activity.[4]
- Of the approximately 750,000 teen pregnancies that occur each year,[3] 82% are unintended[5]. Fifty-nine percent end in birth and more than one-quarter end in abortion.[3]
- In 2009, there were 39.1 births per 1000 women aged 15–19, marking a historic low in the birthrate. This rate represents a 37% decline from the peak rate of 61.8 in 1991.[6]
- The 2008 teenage abortion rate was 17.8 abortions per 1,000 women. This figure was 59% lower than its peak in 1988, but 1% higher than the 2005 rate.[3]
- Compared with their Canadian, English, French and Swedish peers, U.S. teens have a similar level of sexual activity, but they are more likely to have shorter and less consistent sexual relationships, and are less likely to use contraceptives, especially the pill or dual methods.[7]

Reprinted with permission: Guttmacher Institute, Facts on American teens' sources of information about sex, *In Brief,* New York: Guttmacher Institute, 2013, <http://www.guttmacher.org/pubs/FB-ATSRH.pdf>, accessed May 2013.

- The United States continues to have one of the highest teen pregnancy rates in the developed world (68 per 1,000 women aged 15–19 in 2008)—more than twice that of Canada (27.9 per 1,000) or Sweden (31.4 per 1,000).[8]
- Every year, roughly nine million new STIs occur among teens and young adults in the United States. Compared with rates among teens in Canada and Western Europe, rates of gonorrhea and chlamydia among U.S. teens are extremely high.[9, 10]

# Teens' Reports of Formal Sex Education

- In 2006–2008, most teens aged 15–19 had received formal instruction about STIs (93%), HIV (89%) or abstinence (84%). However, about one-third of teens had not received any formal instruction about contraception; fewer males received this instruction than females (62% vs. 70%).[11]
- Many sexually experienced teens (46% of males and 33% of females) do not receive formal instruction about contraception before they first have sex.[12]
- About one in four adolescents aged 15-19 (23% of females and 28% of males) received abstinence education without receiving any instruction about birth control in 2006–2008[12], compared with 8–9% in 1995.[13]
- Among teens aged 18–19, 41% report that they know little or nothing about condoms and 75% say they know little or nothing about the contraceptive pill.[14]

# School Health Policies and Programs

- In 2006, 87% of U.S. public and private high schools taught abstinence as the most effective method to avoid pregnancy, HIV and other STDs in a required health education course.[15]
- Sixty-five percent of high schools taught about condom efficacy and 39% taught students how to correctly use a condom in a required health education course.[15]
- Seventy-six percent of high schools taught about the risks associated with teen pregnancy as part of required instruction,[13] and 81% taught about the risks associated with having multiple sexual partners.[15]
- In 2006, public school districts were more likely to require pregnancy prevention to be taught in high schools than in elementary or middle schools (86% vs. 27% and 70%, respectively).[15]
- Similarly, public school districts were more likely to require instruction on STI prevention in high schools (87%) than at the elementary and middle school levels (33% and 77%, respectively).[15]

# Alternative Sources of Sex Information

- Adolescents consider parents, peers and the media to be important sources of sexual health information.[16]
- Seventy percent of male teens and 79% of female teens report talking with a parent about at least one of six sex education topics: how to say no to sex, methods of birth

control, STIs, where to get birth control, how to prevent HIV infection and how to use a condom.[11]

- Girls are more likely than boys to talk with their parents about birth control or "how to say no to sex."[11]
- Even when parents provide information, their knowledge about contraception or other sexual health topics may often be inaccurate or incomplete.[17]
- More than half (55%) of 7th–12th graders say they have looked up health information online in order to learn more about an issue affecting themselves or someone they know.[18]
- The Web sites teens turn to for sexual health information often have inaccurate information. For example, of 177 sexual health Web sites examined in a recent study, 46% of those addressing contraception and 35% of those addressing abortion contained inaccurate information.[19]
- Exposure to high levels of sexual content on television is associated with an increased risk of initiating sexual activity, as well as a greater likelihood of involvement in teen pregnancy.[20]

# Sex Education Policy

- Currently, 20 states and the District of Columbia mandate both sex and HIV education; one state mandates sex education alone, and another 13 states mandate HIV education.[21]
- A total of 37 states require that sex education include abstinence: Twenty-six require that abstinence be stressed, while eleven simply require that it be included as part of the instruction.[21]
- Eighteen states and the District of Columbia require that sex education programs include information on contraception; no state requires that it be stressed.[21]
- Thirteen states require that the information presented in sex education classes be medically accurate and factual.[21] However, a recent review of 13 commonly used abstinence-only curricula found that 11 had incorrect, misleading or distorted information.[22]
- Twenty-seven states and the District of Columbia require that sex education be age-appropriate.[21]
- In December 2009, Congress replaced the rigid Community-Based Abstinence Education Program with a new $114.5 million teen pregnancy prevention program to support evidence-based interventions, as well as other programs that have demonstrated promise.[23]
- In March 2010, Congress created through health care reform a five-year Personal Responsibility Education Program (PREP). Its stated purpose is to educate adolescents on both abstinence and contraception and to prepare them for adulthood by teaching such subjects as healthy relationships, financial literacy, parent-child communication and decision-making.[23]
- Through another provision in the health care reform legislation, Congress also renewed the Title V abstinence-only program for five years. This funding stream makes available $50 million annually for grants to the states to promote sexual abstinence outside of marriage.[23]

# Effectiveness of Sex Education Programs

- Strong evidence suggests that comprehensive approaches to sex education help young people both to withstand the pressures to have sex too soon and to have healthy, responsible and mutually protective relationships when they do become sexually active.[23]
- A November 2007 report found that "two-thirds of the 48 comprehensive programs that supported both abstinence and the use of condoms and contraceptives for sexually active teens had positive behavioral effects." Many either delayed or reduced sexual activity, reduced the number of sexual partners, or increased the use of condoms or other contraceptives.[24]
- There is no evidence to date that abstinence-only-until-marriage education delays teen sexual activity. Moreover, research shows that abstinence-only strategies may deter contraceptive use among sexually active teens, increasing their risk of unintended pregnancy and STIs.[23]
- A 2007 congressionally mandated study found that federally-funded abstinence-only programs have no beneficial impact on young people's sexual behavior.[23]
- Leading public health and medical professional organizations, including the American Medical Association, the American Nurses Association, the American Academy of Pediatrics, the American College of Obstetricians and Gynecologists, the American Public Health Association, the Institute of Medicine and the Society for Adolescent Health and Medicine, support a comprehensive approach to educating young people about sex.[23]
- Although there is no evidence indicating that federally-funded abstinence-only-until-marriage education is effective, a recent randomized controlled trial found that in specific cases, abstinence-only education programs that are specifically tailored to the local community and do not criticize contraceptives nor advocate abstinence until marriage can be effective in delaying sexual debut among younger teens.[25]

# Sources

1. Abma JC et al., Teenagers in the United States: sexual activity, contraceptive use, and childbearing, National Survey of Family Growth 2006–2008, *Vital and Health Statistics*, 2010, Series 23, No. 30.

2. Martinez G et al., Teenagers in the United States: sexual activity, contraceptive use, and childbearing, 2006–2010 National Survey of Family Growth. *Vital and Health Statistics*, 2011, Series 23, No. 31.

3. Kost K and Henshaw, *U.S. Teenage Pregnancies, Births and Abortions 2008: National Trends by Race and Ethnicity*, 2012, <http://www.guttmacher.org/pubs/USTPtrends08.pdf>, accessed February 6, 2012.

4. Santelli JS et al., Explaining recent declines in adolescent pregnancy in the United States: the contribution of abstinence and improved contraceptive use, *American Journal of Public Health*, 2007, 97(1):1–7.

5. Finer LB and Zolna MR, **Unintended pregnancy in the United States: incidence and disparities, 2006**, *Contraception*, 2011, doi: 10.1016/j.contraception.2011.07.013.

6. Ventura SJ and Hamilton BE, U.S. teenage birth rate resumes decline, *NCHS Data Brief*, 2011, No. 58.

7. Santelli J et al., Transnational comparisons of adolescent contraceptive use: What can we learn from these comparisons? *Archives of Pediatric Adolescent Medicine*, 2008, 162(1):92–94.

8. McKay A et al., Trends in teen pregnancy rates from 1996–2006: a comparison of Canada, Sweden, USA and England/Wales, *Canadian Journal of Human Sexuality*, 19(1–2):43–52.

9. Weinstock H et al., **Sexually transmitted diseases among American youth: incidence and prevalence estimates, 2000**, *Perspectives on Sexual and Reproductive Health*, 2004, 36(1):6–10.

10. Darroch JE et al., **Teenage sexual and reproductive behavior in developed countries: Can more progress be made?** *Occasional Report*, New York: The Alan Guttmacher Institute, 2001, No. 3.

11. Martinez G, Abma J and Casey C, Educating teenagers about sex in the United States, *NCHS Data Brief*, 2010, No. 44.

12. Unpublished tabulations of data from the 2006–2008 National Survey of Family Growth.

13. **Lindberg LD, Changes in formal sex education: 1995–2002**, *Perspectives on Sexual and Reproductive Health*, 2006, 38(4):182–189.

14. Kaye K et al., *The Fog Zone: How Misperceptions, Magical Thinking, and Ambivalence Put Young Adults at Risk for Unplanned Pregnancy*, Washington, DC: National Campaign to Prevent Teen and Unplanned Pregnancy, 2009.

15. Department of Health Services, Center for Disease Control and Prevention (CDC), *School Health Policies and Programs Study 2006 Pregnancy Prevention*, Atlanta: CDC, 2007.

16. Brown J, ed., *Managing the Media Monster: The Influence of Media (From Television to Text Messages) on Teen Sexual Behavior and Attitudes*, Washington, DC: National Campaign to Prevent Teen and Unplanned Pregnancy, 2008.

17. Eisenberg ME et al., **Parents' beliefs about condoms and oral contraceptives: Are they medically accurate?** *Perspectives on Sexual and Reproductive Health*, 2004, 36(2):50–57.

18. Rideout VJ et al., *Generation M2: Media in the Lives of 8- to 18-Year-Olds*, Menlo Park, CA: Kaiser Family Foundation, 2010.

19. Buhi ER et al., Quality and accuracy of sexual health information web sites visited by young people, *Journal of Adolescent Health*, 2010, 47(2):206–208.

20. Chandra A et al., Does watching sex on television predict teen pregnancy? Findings from a national longitudinal survey of youth, *Pediatrics*, 2008, 122(5):1047–1054.

21. Guttmacher Institute, Sex and STD/HIV education, State Policies in Brief, October 2011, <http://www.guttmacher.org/statecenter/spibs/spib_SE.pdf>, accessed Oct. 19, 2011.

22. Committee on Government Reform—Minority Staff, United States House of Representatives, The content of federally funded abstinence only education programs, 2004, <http://democrats.oversight.house.gov/images/stories/documents/20041201102153-50247.pdf>, accessed Aug. 18, 2011.

23. Boonstra H, Sex education: another big step forward—and a step back, *The Guttmacher Policy Review*, 2010, 13(2):27–28.

24. Kirby D, *Emerging Answers 2007: Research Findings on Programs to Reduce Teen Pregnancy and Sexually Transmitted Diseases*, Washington, DC: National Campaign to Prevent Teen and Unplanned Pregnancy, 2007.

25. Jemmott III JB et al., Efficacy of a theory-based abstinence-only intervention over 24 months: a randomized controlled trial with young adolescents, *Archives of Pediatric Adolescent Medicine*, 2010, 164(2):152–159.

# Chapter 9

# Oral Sex among Adolescents: Is It Sex or Is It Abstinence?

*Lisa Remez*

Over the past few decades, nationally representative surveys have accumulated a wealth of data on levels of adolescent sexual activity. Thanks to such surveys, we know how the proportion of 15–19-year-olds who have ever had intercourse has changed over the years. Similar data exist on age at first intercourse, most recent sexual intercourse and current contraceptive use.

Yet all of these measures focus on—or relate to the possible results of—vaginal intercourse. This is natural, given that attention to adolescent sexual activity arose initially out of concerns over the far-reaching problems associated with teenage pregnancy and childbearing. More recently, infection with sexually transmitted diseases (STDs), particularly with HIV, has fueled further public and scientific interest in teenage sexual behavior.

But to what extent does adolescent sexual activity consist of noncoital behaviors—that is, mutual masturbation, oral sex and anal intercourse—that are not linked to pregnancy but involve the risk of STDs? Some of these activities may also be precursors to vaginal intercourse. Yet, health professionals and policymakers know very little about their prevalence among teenagers.

There are several explanations for this dearth of information. One is the perceived difficulty of getting parents to consent to surveys on the sexual activity of their minor children (generally aged 17 and younger). Another is a generalized fear that asking young people about sex will somehow lead them to choose to have sex. The conflicts and passions usually surrounding the appropriateness of asking young people about sex, especially in public settings such as schools as compared with private households, become even more inflamed when the questions go into behaviors "beyond" intercourse.

Remez, L., "Oral Sex Among Adolescents: Is It Sex or Abstinence?" *Family Planning Perspectives* 32(6): 298–304. © The Alan Guttmacher Institute. Used With Permission.

Another reason is the federal government's reluctance to sponsor such controversial research into the full range of noncoital behaviors among adolescents.* For example, the highly charged political debate in 1992 over federal financing of comprehensive sexuality studies had a chilling effect on adolescent sexuality research.[1] The Senate's decision, prompted by pressure from a small group of conservative senators, to deny funding for the American Teenage Study of adolescent sexual behavior still reverberates in the scope of research on teenagers. (An amendment sponsored by Sen. Jesse Helms [R.-NC] prohibited the funding of that survey, along with one of adults, "in fiscal year 1992 or any subsequent fiscal year."[2] Despite warnings that ideology was dictating science, the conservative leadership succeeded in casting these endeavors as "reprehensible sex surveys" only undertaken "to legitimize homosexuality and other sexually promiscuous lifestyles."[3])

It has become increasingly clear, however, that the narrow focus on sexual intercourse in research that does get funded is missing a major component of early sexual activity. There is growing evidence, although still anecdotal and amassed largely by journalists, not researchers, that adolescents might be tuning to behaviors that avoid pregnancy risk but leave them vulnerable to acquisition of many STDs, including HIV.

The reports in the popular press that oral sex has become widespread among adolescents cannot be confirmed or refuted because the data to do so have never been collected. Moreover, adults do not really know what behaviors teenagers consider to be "sex" and, by the same token, what they consider to be its opposite, abstinence. All of this leaves health professionals and policymakers without the means to effectively address these issues.

The tendency to equate "sex" with intercourse alone represents long-standing cultural norms of acceptable sexual behavior and certainly applies to adults as well as to adolescents. It also reflects a deeply rooted ambivalence about talking about sex. Recent press reports, however, are forcing a reappraisal of the implications of this exclusive focus on coitus for research and data collection efforts, for STD prevention and treatment, and for the framing and interpretation of abstinence and risk-reduction messages.

This special report draws on interviews and correspondence with roughly two dozen adolescent and health professionals, including researchers, psychologists, abstinence program coordinators and evaluators, sexuality educators and epidemiologists, to explore some of these consequences. The report concentrates on oral sex, as opposed to other noncoital behaviors, because it is currently the subject of public debate in the media and in many schools. It reviews the limited information on adolescents' experience with oral sex, and looks at the even smaller body of evidence on what young people consider to be sex or abstinence.

---

*The exceptions are the National Survey of Adolescent Males, which asked 15–19-year-old males about their experience with oral and anal sex, and other studies that were not national in scope.

# Anecdotal Reports in the Media

The first hint in the popular press of a new "trend" in sexual activity among young people appeared in an April 1997 article in *The New York Times*.[4] That article asserted that high school students who had come of age with AIDS education considered oral sex to be a far less dangerous alternative, in both physical and emotional terms, than vaginal intercourse. By 1999, the press reports started attributing this behavior to even younger students. A July *Washington Post* article described an "unsettling new fad" in which suburban middle-school students were regularly engaging in oral sex at one another's homes, in parks and even on school grounds; this piece reported an oral sex prevalence estimate, attributed to unnamed counselors and sexual behavior researchers of "about half by the time students are in high school."[5*]

Other stories followed, such as a piece in *Talk* magazine in February 2000 that reported on interviews with 12–16-year-olds. These students set seventh grade as the starting point for oral sex, which they claimed begins considerably earlier than intercourse. By 10th grade, according to the reporter, "well over half of their classmates were involved."[6] This article laid part of the blame on dual-career, overworked "parents who were afraid to parent," and also mentioned that young adolescents were caught between messages about AIDS and abstinence on the one hand and the saturation of the culture with sexual imagery on the other. In April 2000, another *New York Times* article on precocious sexuality quoted a Manhattan psychologist as saying "it's like a good-night kiss to them" in a description of how seventh- and eighth-grade virgins who were saving themselves for marriage were having oral sex in the meantime because they perceived it to be safe and risk-free.[7]

In a July 2000 *Washington Post Magazine* cover story, eighth graders described being regularly propositioned for oral sex in school. The reporter echoed the assertion made in earlier articles that although overall sexual activity among older, high school-aged adolescents—as measured by the proportion who have ever had penile-vaginal intercourse—seemed to have recently leveled off or slightly declined, middle-school-aged students (aged 12–14) appeared to be experimenting with a wider range of behaviors at progressively younger ages.[8]

# What Teenagers Might Be Doing

How valid are these anecdotal reports? Unless and until data to verify them become available, we have only impressions to go on, and there is by no means a consensus among adolescent health professionals. Some believe the level of participation in oral sex and other noncoital behaviors is probably higher now than it was in the past, while others have a "hunch" that oral sex is no more common, just much more talked about.

---

*Around the same time, an *Iris Times* article reported on 14- and 15-year-old Dubliners who, after getting drunk on hard cider, gathered in local parks and paired off for oral sex. (See: Sheridan K, Our children and their sex games, *Irish Times,* July 17, 1999, p. 12.)

For example, according to Kathleen Toomey, director of the Division of Public Health in Georgia's Department of Human Resources, "anecdotal evidence and some recent data suggest that teenagers are engaging in oral sex to a greater degree than we had previously thought, but whether this represents a true increase is difficult to say, since we have no baseline data for comparison."[9] Susan Rosenthal, a professor of pediatrics and a pediatric psychologist at Cincinnati Children's Hospital Medical Center, notes that in her clinical practice, "girls are clearly talking about oral sex and masturbation (of their partners or by their partners) more frequently than I used to hear about, but whether this is because they talk more openly about it or are doing it more is unclear."[10] Deborah Haffner, a sexuality educator and former president of the Sexuality Information and Education Council of the United States (SIECUS), dismisses the press reports of oral sex among middle-school-aged adolescents as largely media hype, saying that only a very small number of young people are probably involved.[11]

Experts believe that the type of oral sex practiced by young teenagers is overwhelmingly fellatio, not cunnilingus. According to Deborah Tolman, senior research scientist at the Wellesley Center for Research on Women, that distinction is paramount: "We are not fainting in the street because boys are giving girls cunnilingus. Which is not to say that girls and boys never have that experience. They probably do, and just rarely do it again for a really long time, because of how girls feel about themselves and their bodies, how boys feel about girls' bodies, and the misinformation they have about each other's bodies."[12]

Many STDs can be transmitted by either fellatio or cunnilingus, although some are more easily passed than others. According to Penelope Hitchcock, chief of the Sexually Transmitted Diseases Branch of the National Institute of Allergy and Infectious Diseases, saliva tends to inactivate the HIV virus, so while transmission through oral intercourse is not impossible, it is relatively rare.[13] Other viral STDs that can be transmitted orally include human papillomavirus, herpes simplex virus and hepatitis B,[14] while gonorrhea, syphilis, chlamydia and chancroid are among the bacterial infections that can be passed through oral sex.[15]

In the absence of survey data on the frequency of oral sex, the question arises as to whether clinicians are seeing evidence of a rise in STDs that have been acquired orally. The answer depends upon the person asked. Some say they have seen no change in STDs acquired non-coitally, while others report that they are seeing both new types of infections and new types of patients—i.e., teenagers who have not yet initiated coitus but who come in with fears and anxiety over having acquired an infection orally.

Linda Dominguez, assistant medical director of Planned Parenthood of New Mexico and a nurse practitioner with a private practice, reports that at patients' requests, she is performing more oral swabs and throat inspections now than in the past.[16] She affirms that "I have more patients who are virgins who report to me that they are worried about STDs they may have gotten by having oral sex. There are a lot of questions and concerns about herpes, since they seem to know that there is some risk of 'top and bottom' herpes, as one of my patients put it."

Sharon Schnare, a family planning clinician and consultant in Seattle, remarks that she now sees many teenagers with oral herpes. She adds that "I have also found, though rarely, oral *Condylomata acuminata* [a sexually transmitted condition caused by the human papillomavirus] in teenagers."[17] Moreover, Hitchcock states that "several studies have shown that one-third of the isolates from genital herpes cases in kids right now are HSV1 [herpes simplex virus 1, the oral strain], which suggests a significant amount of oral intercourse is going on."[18] This suggestion is impossible to verify, however, because of the extensive crossover between the two strains. Moreover, trends are especially hard to detect because of past and current problems in the reliability of type-specific testing.

Pharyngeal gonorrhea is one STD that is definitely acquired through oral sex. A few cases of pharyngeal gonorrhea have been diagnosed in adolescent girls in Dominguez's family planning clinic in New Mexico[19] and in one region of Georgia through a community screening project among middle-school students to detect certain strains of meningitis bacteria carried in the throat.[20] In Georgia, the cases caught everyone off guard, according to Kathleen Toomey.[21] The infections were found only because throat swabs were being done for meningitis in a population that would not be considered "sexually active" in the traditional sense of the word.

Many researchers and clinicians believe that young adolescents who are having oral sex before they start coitus might be especially reluctant to seek clinical care. Moreover, adolescents virtually never use condoms or dental dams to protect against STD infection during oral sex, even those who know about the risk and worry that they might become infected.

However little is known about teenagers' experiences with oral sex, even less information is available on their involvement with anal sex, which also carries risks of STD infection, particularly of HIV. While teenage patients now seem much more comfortable talking about oral sex than they were in the past, the taboo against bringing up anal sex is still very much in place.

# Attitudes and Motivations

Experts say there are multiple, interrelated reasons for why adolescents might be turning to oral sex. Deborah Roffman, a sexuality educator at The Park School in Baltimore, asserts that "middle-school girls sometimes look at oral sex as an absolute bargain—you don't get pregnant, they think you don't get diseases, you're still a virgin and you're in control since it's something that they can do to boys (whereas sex is almost always described as something boys do to girls)."[22]

This sense of control is illusory, according to Roffman, because engaging in fellatio out of peer pressure or to gain popularity is clearly exploitative of girls who lack the maturity to realize it. The issue of just how voluntary oral sex is for many girls came up repeatedly, especially when the act is performed "to make boys happy" or when alcohol is involved. Roffman relates the experience of a guidance counselor who, after bringing up the topic of rape in this context of coerced oral sex, was told by female students that the term did not apply to their situation, because fellatio "is not really sex."

Teenagers seem to be especially misinformed about the STD risks of oral sex. Experts repeatedly mentioned their concerns over adolescents' perceptions of oral sex as less risky than intercourse,* especially in the context of teenagers' tendency to have very short-term relationships. Several observers mentioned the trap of AIDS education, which often teaches that HIV is transmitted through sexual intercourse, so adolescents think they are avoiding risk by avoiding sexual intercourse. Sarah Brown, director of the National Campaign to Prevent Teen Pregnancy, suggests what some adolescents might be thinking: "Okay, we get it. You adults really don't want us to have sexual intercourse, and you're probably right because of AIDS and pregnancy. But we're still sexual and we're going to do other things."[23]

Haffner's interviews with 11th and 12th graders reveal that they view oral sex as "something you can do with someone you're not as intimate with, while intercourse is, by and large, reserved for that special person."[24] This emotional differential between oral sex and vaginal sex—the assertion that oral sex carries few or no emotional ties—is acknowledged by many professionals who work with adolescents. Linda Dominguez quotes her adolescent patients as thinking "if you're going to avoid intercourse, you're going to resort to oral sex. You're going to do something that is sexual, but in some ways emotionally safer, before you give the big one away."[25]

Adolescent health professionals reinforced the view reported in the popular press that today's adolescents consider oral sex to be less consequential and less intimate than intercourse. "Oral sex is clearly seen as something very different than intercourse, as something other than sex," according to Susan Rosenthal. She also mentions a generational shift in thinking, noting that "if you were to query older women, oral sex might be perceived as something more intimate or equally intimate to vaginal sex (and which frequently happened later on in a relationship); for the teens, oral sex appears to be much less intimate or serious than vaginal intercourse."[26]

# Insights from Formal Research

How does the limited published research conducted on oral sex inform the current situation? Because of the difficulties in obtaining funding and consent for conducting this type of research among minors, many of these studies have necessarily relied on small, nonrepresentative samples of college-age students enrolled in human sexuality or psychology classes, which are hardly generalizable to the overall population. Perhaps the best, though still limited, dataset that includes adolescents dates from the early 1980s: In 1982, a marketing research firm collected data from a national panel of households in 49 states.[27] Douglas Kirby, currently of ETR Associates, directed this early research project; he recalls that "we were surprised that there was much more oral sex than we had anticipated."[28]

---

*For example, in a fall 1999 mall-intercept survey conducted by *Seventeen* magazine and the Henry J. Kaiser Family Foundation, 16% of 15–19-year-old males and females asserted that oral sex was "safe" because it protected against infection with an STD, while 48% labeled the practice as "safe" because it protected against pregnancy. Incidentally, 55% thought that oral sex was "gross," the same proportion who said they had ever done it. (See reference 45.) Moreover, in the *Seventeen*/Kaiser collaborative special section "Sex Smarts," the number-one sex myth listed in the "10 Sex Myths Exposed" was "oral sex is no big thing." (Forman G, 10 sex myths exposed, Sex Smarts Special Section, tearout in *Seventeen,* June 2000.)

Roughly one-fifth of the 1,067 13-18-year-olds surveyed in the early 1980s said they had ever had oral sex, and 16% of young women who had performed fellatio had never had vaginal intercourse.[29] To many adolescents, safer-sex in the pre-AIDS era presumably meant avoiding pregnancy. The practice of "outercourse," in fact, was suggested by at least one physician as early as 1972[†] as an alternative contraceptive method for young teenagers.[30] That physician, John Cobb, asserted that loosening the taboos around noncoital activity might "help significantly in the prevention of unwanted teenage pregnancy and of venereal disease."

Other nonrepresentative research done in the early 1980s focused on adolescents' sexual experimentation as a precursor or predictor of coitus. One longitudinal prospective study conducted in a southern city in 1980 and 1982 found that among a sample of black and white 12–17-year-olds, blacks proceeded more quickly to intercourse, while whites followed a predictable scenario of noncoital activities as substitutes or delay mechanisms.[31] Another study using the 1982 follow-up data set only (545 10th-12th graders) concluded that 24% of the virgins in the sample had had oral sex.[32] The corresponding proportion among those who had initiated coitus was 82%. In 1994-1995, a survey of 291 college undergraduates indicated that among those who were in a serious relationship, virgins were as likely as nonvirgins to have ever had oral sex (although nonvirgins were more likely to have had mutual oral sex).[33]

Few studies focus exclusively on individuals before they are "sexually active." One such effort assessed the range of precoital sexual activities among a volunteer sample of 311 non-virgin college undergraduates who were surveyed retrospectively, in the 1995–1996 academic year, about their experiences before their first coitus. Seventy percent of the males and 57% of the females reported having performed oral sex at least once before their first intercourse; the proportion ever receiving oral sex was the same for both genders (57–58%).[34]

Two early-1990s surveys based on total high school enrollment, instead of single-subject college classes, came out of efforts to evaluate condom availability programs for HIV prevention.[35] In 1992, baseline data collected for such a program in Los Angeles among 2,026 ninth-12th graders indicated that 29–31% of the virgins in this sample had engaged in masturbation with a partner, and 9–10% of those who had not yet had coitus had nonetheless had oral sex. Very few (1% of noncoitally experienced students) revealed that they had ever engaged in anal intercourse.[36] Another study from 1992, also designed to collect baseline data for a condom program evaluation, was conducted in suburban high schools in the New York City metropolitan area. The director of that study said it unexpectedly uncovered considerably higher rates of oral intercourse than of vaginal intercourse.[37]

---

†Twenty-five years later, this physician, in a letter to the editor, again advocated encouraging adolescents to practice outercourse (or heavy petting to orgasm without penetration) as a "cost-free, natural and effective way to prevent unwanted pregnancy and STDs while making love." This time, the message was updated with the warning that the advent of HIV meant that "of course, anal or oral intercourse is to be avoided." (See: Cobb JC, Outercourse as a safe and sensible alternative to contraceptives, letter to the editor, *American Journal of Public Health,* 1997, 87(8):1380–1381). Critics of this strategy, however, point to the fact that it has never been adequately evaluated and that since it involves promoting behaviors that are considered themselves predisposing factors for coitus, it may lead to intermittent, unprotected intercourse. (See: Genius SJ and Genius SK, Orgasm without organisms: science or propaganda? *Clinical Pediatrics,* 1996, 35(1):10–17.)

Finally, one nationally representative survey—the National Survey of Adolescent Males—asked about a full range of heterosexual genital activities in both 1988 and 1995. Although the overall proportion of 15–19-year-old males who had ever received oral sex did not change significantly from 1988 to 1995 (44% vs. 50%), this proportion more than doubled among blacks (from 25% to 57%).[38] Moreover, among virgin young men, the proportion ever having received oral sex increased from 10% to 17%, although this difference was not statistically significant. [Editors' note: For further details on these data, see pp. 295–297 & 304.]

Data collected in small-scale evaluations of abstinence education programs are an unexpected source of information on adolescents' current experience with oral sex. A few evaluation sites recently used questionnaires that asked about a variety of sexual activities in assessing how middle-school students interpret messages about behaviors to be abstained from. Thus, those who had had oral sex but not coitus could be distinguished from other groups. According to Stan Weed, director of the Institute for Research and Evaluation in Salt Lake City, the responses to these items indicate that "there is a percentage of kids for whom oral sex seems to be a substitute for intercourse; I'm guessing that, although it varies with the sample, for around 25% of the kids who have had any kind of intimate sexual activity, that activity is oral sex, not intercourse."[39]

# What Is Sex?

The many, even competing, agendas in the culturally loaded definitions of the term "sex" make sexuality research exceptionally challenging to conduct.[*] In early fall of 1998, the American public was riveted by President Bill Clinton's claim that he had not perjured himself because he "did not have sexual relations with that woman [White House intern Monica Lewinsky]"; he had, in fact, had something else—oral sex. At the time, according to a Gallup Poll, roughly 20% of adults also believed that oral sex did not constitute "sexual relations."[40] No one knows how many adolescents feel the same way. As Robert Blum, director of the Adolescent Health Program at the University of Minnesota puts it, "we know that there are many sexual practices other than intercourse that predispose young people to negative health outcomes. What we really don't know is, in an age of a focus on abstinence, how young people have come to understand what is meant by being sexually active."[41]

Limited data are available on college undergraduates' perceptions of what is meant by sexual activity. Among roughly 600 students enrolled at a Midwestern university surveyed in 1991, 59% did not believe that oral sex would qualify as sex and only 19% thought the same

---

*For gay men and women, for example, the arrow penile-vaginal intercourse definition is clearly irrelevant. In data recently collected from an Internet sample, adult homosexuals and bisexuals tended to label a greater number of activities as "sex" than did a comparable sample of heterosexuals. The researcher concluded that the implications of such semantic diversity "cannot be underestimated in conducting sexuality survey research, clinical sexual history taking or sex education." (See: Mustanski B, Semantic heterogeneity in the definition of "having sex" for homosexuals, unpublished manuscript, Department of Psychology, Indiana University, Bloomington, IN, 2000).

about anal sex.[42] Females (62%) were more likely than males (56%) to assert that cunnilingus and fellatio were not "sex."

What young adults consider to be "sex" also varies by contextual and situational factors, such as who is doing what to whom and whether it leads to orgasm. In data collected in early 1998 among a sample of college undergraduates who were read hypothetical scenarios and were asked to comment on them, 54% considered that a man would say fellatio did not qualify as sex and 59% that a woman would not consider cunnilingus to be sex;[43] these proportions were even higher once it was specified that oral sex had not resulted in orgasm. Correspondingly, in another study in which these students were asked which acts would define a sexual partner, they were less likely to say that a couple would consider one another as "sexual partners" if they had had oral sex than if they had had vaginal or anal intercourse.[44]

In the face of limited rigorous research in this area, magazines for teenagers serve as an important source of information on what adolescents think about oral sex. Impressions of oral sex are necessarily bound up with views on sexual intercourse, since one is usually cited as either a precursor or substitute for the other. According to a fall 1999 survey conducted by *Seventeen* magazine in which 723 15–19-year-old males and females were approached in malls, 49% considered oral sex to be "not as big a deal as sexual intercourse," and 40% said it did not count as "sex."[45] A summer 2000 Internet survey conducted by *Twist* magazine received 10,000 on-line responses from 13-19-year-old girls, 18% of whom said that oral sex was something that you did with your boyfriend before you are ready to have sex; the same proportion stated that oral sex was a substitute for intercourse.[46]

Adults and adolescents do not necessarily agree on what activities are now inferred by the word "sex." Individuals from across the ideological spectrum who were interviewed for this report acknowledged that the assumption of what "sex" encompasses has changed. As Tom Klaus, president of Legacy Resource Group in Iowa, which produces comprehensive pregnancy prevention and abstinence resources for educators, observes, "we thought we were on the same page as our kids when we talked about 'it.' The new emerging paradigm is that we can't be so certain that we are really talking about the same thing."[47]

# What Is Abstinence?

If adolescents perceive oral sex as something different from sex, do they view it as abstinence? Research conducted in 1999 with 282 12-17-year-olds in rural areas in the Midwest probed how adolescents who received abstinence education interpreted the term. students struggled to come up with a coherent definition, although older adolescents had less difficulty than younger ones. The wide-ranging responses covered ground from "kissing is probably okay" to "just no intercourse."[48]

Some of the students brought marriage into their definition of abstinence, and others asserted that it means going only as far sexually as one wanted to or felt comfortable with. The list of behaviors encompassed within virginity was long, and typically ended in statements such as "To me, the only thing that would take away my virginity is having sex. Everything else is permitted." (The very few recent abstinence program evaluations that assessed whether adolescents had engaged in sexual activities other than intercourse did not ask whether they did so under the assumption that they were being abstinent.[49])

In 1994–1995 data from 1,101 college freshman and sophomores in the South, 61% considered mutual masturbation (to orgasm) to be abstinent behavior, 37% described oral intercourse as abstinence and 24% thought the same about anal intercourse.[50] The authors surmised that pregnancy prevention came first in these students' perceptions, so behaviors unlinked to pregnancy then counted as abstinence. On the other hand, nearly one-quarter labeled kissing and bathing or showering together as "not abstinent."

Health educators themselves might be unclear about precisely what the term "abstinence" means. In a 1999 e-mail survey of 72 health educators, for example, nearly one-third (30%) responded that oral sex was abstinent behavior. A similar proportion (29%), however, asserted that mutual masturbation would not qualify as abstinence.[51]

Experts interviewed for this report acknowledged that defining what is meant by abstinence—and accurately communicating that definition to students—has become a crucial issue. While everyone agrees that the implicit meaning of the term is abstaining from vaginal-penile intercourse, especially since the concept is often taught as a "method" of avoiding pregnancy, the consensus stops there. What is the specific behavior that signals the end of abstinence and the beginning of sex?

Given the amount of federal and state money going into abstinence education, the lack of a consensus on whether and how to specify the behaviors to be abstained from warrants close examination. In 1996, Congress established a new abstinence-education program as part of its overhaul of welfare. Title V of the Maternal and Child Health Services Block Grant guarantees $50 million annually in federal support for five years (1998–2004) for abstinence-only education; since state and local governments are obligated to supply $3 for every $4 in federal funds, the total annual expenditure for government-supported abstinence education—which must promote abstinence until marriage—could reach almost $90 million each year.[52*]

Although Title V does not specify an age-range for these activities, the majority of the states that have received funding have targeted teenagers aged 17 and younger. The eight-point official definition in Title V specifies that programs teach "abstinence from sexual activity outside marriage as the expected standard for all school-age children,"[53] but the law does not delineate "sexual activity."

Several experts noted that the different purpose or intent of the teaching of abstinence—i.e., for public health reasons or for moral or religious reasons—will naturally produce a different set of activities to be abstained from. The lack of a consensus definition of abstinence is also a relatively new issue that current events are forcing to the forefront. As Barbara Devaney of Mathematica, a research agency conducting a national evaluation of Title V programs, points out, "at the time that the legislation was written, there was not much public controversy over what abstinence was; this was not yet on the radar screen."[54]

---

*The original Title V legislation had no provision for evaluation at the state level, but nearly every state has committed some funds—an average of 5% of their abstinence education monies. At the federal level, Congress allotted $6 million for a national-level evaluation in the Balanced Budget Act of 1997. (See: reference 52.)

This issue is especially thorny because some abstinence-only programs are committed to being as specific as possible so adolescents do not take away the wrong message about what abstinence is, while others insist that specifying those behaviors violates a child's innocence and amounts to providing a "how-to" manual. Tom Klaus affirms that the inability to specify what activities youth should abstain from is forcing a Catch 22—adolescents cannot practice abstinence until they know what abstinence is, but in order to teach them what abstinence is, they have to be taught what sex is.[55] According to Stan Weed, "there's no settled consensus in the abstinence movement. Some programs are willing to take it head on and say [oral sex] is not an appropriate activity, if you think this is a substitute, you're wrong; others are not even dealing with it."[56]

Amy Stephens of Focus on the Family, a Colorado Springs-based conservative religious organization, asserts that in its curriculum, *Sex, Lies and . . . the Truth,* "our definition is refraining from all sexual activity, which includes intercourse, oral sex, anal sex and mutual masturbation—the only 100% effective means of preventing pregnancy and the spread of STDs."[57] Stephens notes that the different faith communities will use language specific to their congregations (i.e., "chastity" in Catholic circles and "purity" in Christian Evangelical communities). In the official definition of abstinence used by the Chicago-based Project Reality, the "sexual activity" to be avoided until marriage "refers to any type of genital contact or sexual stimulation including, but not limited to, sexual intercourse."[58]

# Consequences and Implications
## Sexuality and Abstinence Education

Some adolescent health professionals believe that although the revelation of early oral sex has been shocking, it has had the positive effect of forcing a dialogue with adolescents about the full meaning of sexuality and of the importance of defining sex not as a single act, but as a whole range of behaviors. There is widespread agreement among educators from all along the ideological spectrum that the continuing lack of adult guidance about what sex really means contributes to the desensitized, "body-part" sex talked about in the press, whatever the real prevalence might be. They stress that teachers and parents need to do a better job at helping children interpret the context-free messages of sexuality they are bombarded with in the media, which now includes the still-evolving Internet. Some experts believe that programs are moving in the right direction by teaching adolescents how to identify bad or abusive relationships, but that there is still much work to be done to help them with intimacy and how to recognize good relationships.

The lack of guidelines on what activity is appropriate when is a common concern among professionals who work with adolescents. Educators who endorse comprehensive sexuality education support giving adolescents the criteria they need to decide when to abstain or when to participate across the full continuum of sexual behaviors. Abstinence proponents are wrestling with how to handle an evolving dilemma that pits those who stress the need to be as precise as possible in specifying the range of behaviors to be abstained from against others who insist that such specificity violates the core of abstinence-only education.

## Research and Evaluation

What is to be gained by broadening the range of behaviors asked about in surveys of sexual behavior? The simplest public health argument is that doing so would enable researchers to identify individuals whose behaviors place them at risk, so that more appropriate programs and policies can be developed. Many of these youth are now being missed by current survey instruments. By considering only adolescents who have ever had coitus, or only dividing them by whether they had that experience, "we don't get a full understanding of the range of adolescent activity and of the developmental and emotional processes involved," according to Mark Schuster, director, UCLA/RAND Center for Adolescent Health Promotion.[59]

It is also impossible to adequately assess how changes in sexual activity or in contraceptive behavior contributed to recent declines in adolescent pregnancy rates as long as information on sexual activity unlinked to pregnancy remains unavailable. For example, while different groups have attributed a greater or lesser share of the declines in pregnancy rates to increased abstinence,[60] how much of that "abstinence" corresponds to sexual activity other than intercourse is still unknown.

Another advantage to using a broader measure of sexual activity is being able to more fully measure the impact of various programs and curricula that address adolescent sexuality. As Sarah Brown stresses, "if, for example, we found that there was a curriculum that delayed the age of first vaginal intercourse, but increased the preponderance of oral sex, we should know that."[61]

Currently, the principal outcome measures used in evaluations of both comprehensive sexuality and abstinence-based programs are the standard ones of vaginal intercourse, pregnancy and contraceptive use. That holds true for the Mathematica national evaluation of Title V abstinence education programs. The project director, Rebecca Maynard, explains that after much debate, the group that devised the questionnaire settled on the stable outcome measure of intercourse for the first wave of follow-up, to assure that the evaluation was not measuring different definitions of sex, as opposed to different behaviors.[62]

Even if there is agreement on the need to expand the definition of sexual activity to create more accurate research and evaluation tools, getting those items onto survey instruments remains a concern. Some researchers assert that surveys need to be allowed to capture self-reports of these especially sensitive behaviors in the most private setting and mode of administration possible (i.e., using audio computer-assisted self-interviews rather than personal interviews). Others say that should national-level studies prove impossible because of the constraints of funding agencies, then small-area studies would be of value, especially in higher prevalence areas where there might be greater receptivity to gathering such data.

Other professionals are clearly worried about the prospect of gaining parental consent—what Brown terms "the 800 pound gorilla in the room"[63]—especially since many of the adolescents purported to be engaging in sexual activities other than intercourse are younger than 15, the minimum age usually included in traditional surveys. Stan Weed, who has experience drafting questionnaires in the new climate of ostensibly greater participation in oral sex, suggests that advance focus-group research can be helpful in countering objections to questions from parents and school administrators. If findings illustrate that the behavior is prevalent, for example, then the evaluation team can use that information to explain why those questions need to be asked.[64]

Although the well-known technique of asking 18-year-olds to report on their earlier experiences was also mentioned, some experts point out that parents' willingness to grant consent might have recently changed. Joyce Abma, a demographer at the National Center for Health Statistics, for example, is hopeful that "maybe we're in an era where people understand the dire nature of STD transmission and HIV. So if the message is that this could possibly contribute to both a better understanding of and eventual lessening of these serious health conditions, then there might be a greater possibility of cooperation."[65] This belief is echoed by others, who talk of the need to engage parents directly and to not necessarily assume that they would deny permission.

## *Clinical Care*

What are some of the health consequences of continuing to define sex so narrowly and to lack data on a wider range of behaviors? "As public health people, we need to think about how we can address prevention and education, when we don't even know which are the behaviors we are trying to 'prevent,' " Kathleen Toomey says.[66] She notes that the cases of pharyngeal gonorrhea were only uncovered among middle schoolers, who had not sought care otherwise, through a screening project for meningitis, adding "we're probably missing this because we are not routinely doing throat swabs and because we are not asking the right questions."

There is widespread agreement that oral STD risk in adolescent populations has yet to be adequately measured and screened for. This situation is exacerbated by the fact that many of the adolescent patients involved have not yet initiated coitus and thus are unlikely to visit a family planning or STD clinic. When they do, several practitioners assert, more detailed sexual histories, despite the extra time involved, are essential to prevent misdiagnosis and to understand what the patient, rather than the provider, means by "sexual activity." In the absence of an adequate screening protocol, unknowing clinicians might automatically assume that the patient has strep and prescribe antibiotics. The fact that many infections are asymptomatic further complicates the diagnosis when the mode of infection is not easily talked about.

The deeply rooted tendency to define sex as intercourse might not necessarily be working any more in reaching many adolescent patients at risk. How to counsel adolescents about lowering that risk is especially problematic, since many young people consider oral sex itself to be a form of risk reduction and are probably already reluctant (as are many adults) to discuss oral sex openly or to use dental dams or condoms. Many practitioners feel they have gotten very good at talking about penetrative risk, but that they now need to hone their skills at communicating with their young clients about other types of sexual activities—and to do so they need more information.

Qualitative and quantitative data on sexual behaviors other than intercourse are clearly needed to close the gaps in knowledge about practices that may expose young people to emotional and physical harm. Surveys have not yet been undertaken that would yield more useful data on the broad range of sexual behaviors young people might be engaging in. If such surveys are conducted and reveal that only a small percentage of adolescents are involved, "then we need not be alarmed," according to Laura Stepp, the *Washington Post* reporter who wrote some of the first stories on oral sex. "But if it's a considerable proportion, then we need to get out there with megaphones."[67]

# References

1. DiMauro D, *Sexuality Research in the United States: An Assessment of the Social and Behavioral Sciences,* New York: Social Science Research Council, 1995.
2. U.S. Congressional Record—Senate, Apr. 2, 1992, pp. S 4737 and S 4758.
3. Ibid., p. 4737.
4. Lewin T, Teen-agers alter sexual practices, thinking risks will be avoided, *New York Times,* Apr. 5, 1997.
5. Stepp LS, Parents are alarmed by an unsettling new fad in middle schools: oral sex, *Washington Post,* July 8, 1999, p. A1; and Stepp LS, Talking to kids about sexual limits, *Washington Post,* July 8, 1999, p. C4.
6. Franks L, The sex lives of your children, *Talk Magazine,* February 2000, pp. 102–107 & 157.
7. Jarrell A, The face of teenage sex grows younger, *New York Times,* April 2, 2000.
8. Mundy L, Young teens and sex: sex & sensibility, *Washington Post Magazine,* July 16, 2000, pp. 16-21,  29–34.
9. Toomey K, Division of Public Health, Georgia Department of Human Resources, Atlanta, GA, personal communication, Aug. 23, 2000.
10. Rosenthal S, Children's Hospital Medical Center, Cincinnati, OH, personal communication, Sept. 5, 2000.
11. Haffner D, personal communication, Oct. 4, 2000.
12. Tolman D, Wellesley Center for Research on Women, Wellesley, MA, personal communication, Aug. 18, 2000.
13. Hitchcock P, Sexually Transmitted Diseases Branch, National Institute of Allergy and Infectious Diseases, Bethesda, MD, personal communication, Aug. 21, 2000.
14. Edwards S and Carne C, Oral sex and the transmission of viral STIs, *Sexually Transmitted Infections,* 1998, 74(1):6–10.
15. Edwards S and Carne C, Oral sex and the transmission of non-viral STIs, *Sexually Transmitted Infections,* 1998, 74(2):95–100.
16. Dominguez L, Planned Parenthood of New Mexico, Albuquerque, NM, personal communication, Sept. 7, 2000.
17. Schnare SM, Seattle, WA, personal communication, Oct. 26, 2000.
18. Hitchcock P, 2000, op. cit. (see reference 13).
19. Dominguez L, 2000, op. cit. (see reference 16).
20. Toomey K, 2000, op. cit. (see reference 9).
21. Ibid.
22. Roffman D, The Park School, Baltimore, MD, personal communication, Oct. 12, 2000.
23. Brown S, National Campaign to Prevent Teen Pregnancy, Washington, DC, personal communication, Oct. 6, 2000.
24. Haffner D, 2000, op. cit. (see reference 11).
25. Dominguez L, 2000, op. cit. (see reference 16).
26. Rosenthal S, 2000, op cit. (see reference 10).
27. Coles R and Stokes G, *Sex and the American Teenager,* New York: Harper and Row, 1985.
28. Kirby D, ETR Associates, Santa Cruz, CA, personal communication, Sept. 12, 2000.
29. Coles R and Stokes G, 1985, op cit. (see reference 27).
30. Cobb JC, Nonprocreative sexuality as an alternative to contraception, in *Advances in Planned Parenthood, Vol. VIII, Proceedings of the Tenth Annual Meeting of the American Association of Planned Parenthood Physicians,* Princeton, NJ: Excerpta Medica, 1973.

31. Smith EA and Udry R, Coital and non-coital sexual behavior of white and black adolescents, *American Journal of Public Health,* 1985, 75(10):1200–1203.

32. Newcomer SF and Udry JR, Oral sex in an adolescent population, *Archives of Sexual Behavior,* 1985, 14(1):41–46.

33. Werner-Wilson RJ, Are virgins at risk for contracting HIV/AIDS? *Journal of HIV/AIDS Prevention & Education for Adolescents & Children,* 1998, 2(3/4):63–71.

34. Schwartz IM, Sexual activity prior to coitus initiation: a comparison between males and females, *Archives of Sexual Behavior,* 1999, 28(1):63–69.

35. Schuster MA, UCLA/RAND Center for Adolescent Health Promotion, Santa Monica, CA, personal communication, Sept. 13, 2000; and Koplewicz H, Department of Pediatric Psychiatry, New York University School of Medicine, personal communication, July 18, 2000.

36. Schuster MA, Bell RM and Kanouse DE, The sexual practices of adolescent virgins: genital sexual activities of high school students who have never had vaginal intercourse, *American Journal of Public Health,* 1996, 86(11):1570–1576.

37. Koplewicz H, 2000, op. cit. (see reference 35).

38. Gates GJ and Sonenstein FL, Heterosexual genital sexual activity among adolescent males: 1988 and 1995, *Family Planning Perspectives,* 2000, 32(6):295–297 & 304.

39. Weed S, Institute for Research and Evaluation, Salt Lake City, UT, personal communication, Oct. 24, 2000.

40. Gallup short subjects, *The Gallup Poll Monthly,* No. 396, Sept. 1998, Survey GP 9809035, Sept. 21, 1998, Q. 15, p. 47.

41. Blum R, Adolescent Health Program, University of Minnesota, Minneapolis, MN, personal communication, Aug. 8, 2000.

42. Sanders SA and Reinisch JM, Would you say you "had sex" if . . .?, *Journal of the American Medical Association,* 1999, 281(3):275–277.

43. Bogart L et al., Is it "sex"?: college students' interpretations of sexual behavior terminology, *Journal of Sex Research,* 2000, 37(2): 108–116.

44. Cecil H et al., Classifying a person as a sex partner, unpublished manuscript, University of Alabama at Birmingham, School of Public Health, 2000.

45. News release, *Seventeen* News: National survey conducted by *Seventeen* finds that more than half of teens ages 15–19 have engaged in oral sex, Feb. 28, 2000.

46. Birnbaum C, The love & sex survey 2000, *Twist,* Oct./Nov. 2000, pp. 54–56.

47. Klaus T, Legacy Resource Group, Carlisle, IA, personal communication, Sept. 21, 2000.

48. Bell HA, Just because you see their privates doesn't mean you're not a virgin: adolescents' understanding of sexual terminology, unpublished thesis, Iowa State University, Ames, IA, 2000.

49. Weed S, 2000, op. cit. (see reference 39).

50. Horan PF, Phillips J and Hagan NE, The meaning of abstinence for college students, *Journal of HIV/AIDS Prevention & Education for Adolescents & Children,* 1998, 2(2):51–66.

51. Mercer JG, Defining and teaching abstinence: an e-mail survey of health educators, unpublished thesis, North Carolina State University, Raleigh, NC, 1999.

52. Pfau S, *Abstinence Education in the States: Implementation of the 1996 Abstinence Education Law,* Washington, DC: Association of Maternal & Child Health Programs, 1999.

53. Section 912, (2)(A)-(H), Public Law 104–193, Welfare Act, 104th Congress, Aug. 22, 1996.

54. Devaney B, Mathematic Policy Research, Inc., Princeton, NJ, personal communication, Aug. 22, 2000.

55. Klaus T, 2000, op. cit. (see reference 47).

**56.** Weed S, 2000, op. cit. (see reference 39).

**57.** Stephens A, Focus on the Family, Colorado Springs, CO, personal communication, Sept. 9, 2000.

**58.** Sullivan K, Project Reality, Golf, IL, personal communication, Nov. 6, 2000.

**59.** Schuster MA, 2000, op. cit. (see reference 35).

**60.** Darroch JD and Singh S, *Why Is Teenage Pregnancy Declining? The Roles of Abstinence, Sexual Activity and Contraceptive Use,* Occasional Report No. 1, New York: Alan Guttmacher Institute, 1999; and Jones JM et al., *The Declines in Adolescent Pregnancy, Birth and Abortion Rates in the 1990s: What Factors Are Responsible?* Fanwood, NJ: Consortium of State Physicians Resource Councils, 1999.

**61.** Brown S, 2000, op cit. (see reference 23).

**62.** Maynard R, Mathematica Policy Research, Inc., Princeton, NJ, personal communication, Sept. 22, 2000.

**63.** Brown S, 2000, op cit. (see reference 23).

**64.** Weed S, 2000, op cit. (see reference 39).

**65.** Abma J, Reproductive Statistics Branch, National Center for Health Statistics, Hyattsville, MD, personal communication, Oct. 11, 2000.

**66.** Toomey K, 2000, op. cit. (see reference 9).

**67.** Stepp LS, *Washington Post,* Washington, DC, personal communication, Oct. 11, 2000.

# Chapter 10

# The Young Men's Clinic: Addressing Men's Reproductive Health and Responsibilities

*Bruce Armstrong*

Interest in men's health, including their sexual and reproductive health, has been growing over the past two decades. The 1994 International Conference on Population and Development in Cairo and the 1995 Fourth World Conference on Women in Beijing both recognized the effect of men's behavior on women's health, highlighted the importance of shared responsibility and sparked interest in developing interventions to increase male involvement in reproductive health programs.[1] A 2002 report by The Alan Guttmacher Institute emphasized that the sexual and reproductive health concerns of men are important in their own right, not only because males play important roles as fathers and sexual partners.[2] The National Survey of Adolescent Males, the Youth Risk Behavior Survey, and studies and reports sponsored or produced by other organizations have significantly contributed to the growing body of knowledge about men's sexual and reproductive health concerns, beliefs, attitudes and behaviors.[3]

Since 1997, the Office of Family Planning in the Office of Population Affairs at the Department of Health and Human Services has funded diverse community-based programs to learn how to engage with and provide reproductive health services to males.[4] This special report describes sexual and reproductive health services and how they have evolved at one of those programs—the Young Men's Clinic, an ambulatory clinic for adolescent and young adult males in New York City.

## The Young Men's Clinic

The clinic is a component of a reproductive health program jointly operated by the Center for Community Health and Education at Columbia University's Mailman School of Public Health and New York-Presbyterian Hospital. It is located in the upper Manhattan community of Washington Heights, which has the highest concentration of Hispanic residents in New York City.[5] Created in 1987, the Young Men's Clinic is the only facility in the city

Armstrong, B. "The Young Men's Clinic: Addressing Men's Reproductive Health and Responsibilities," *Perspectives on Sexual And Reproductive Health,* 35(5), 220–225. © The Alan Guttmacher Institute. Used With Permission.

specifically tailored to address the sexual and reproductive health needs of adolescent and young adult men, and has been recognized for many years as an important model of the delivery of community-based health care services to young males.[6]

The Young Men's Clinic provides medical, social work, mental health and health education services at two clinic sessions each week. Services are provided in the clinical space used by the Center for Community Health and Education's reproductive health program, which serves adolescent and adult women at more than 25,000 visits each year. Between 28 and 35 men are served at each session. Use of the clinic has almost tripled since 1998: Some 1,452 men made 2,522 visits in 2002, compared with 506 men who made 908 visits in 1998.

The target age range for the clientele of the Young Men's Clinic is 13–30. Seventy-five percent of patients are 20–29, and 46% are 20–24 (the male age-group with the highest rates of gonorrhea and chlamydia[7]). Ninety-five percent are Hispanic (the majority of whom identify themselves as Dominican); 3% are black. Approximately half of the men are employed either full- or part-time. Only 25% of patients receive Medicaid benefits, and 3% have some form of private insurance.

## *History*

The Young Men's Clinic evolved out of the adolescent family planning program that has been operated by the Center for Population and Family Health (now the Heilbrunn Department of Population and Family Health) since 1976. Both the scope and the use of services have shifted with fluctuations in funding and with increased knowledge about the needs of young men.

Use of reproductive health services by males was generally low during the 1970s (few of the male involvement demonstration projects sponsored by the Office of Population Affairs during that period attracted many males.) However, the emergence of HIV and AIDS, concerns about rising teenage pregnancy rates, and increases in the proportion of teenage births that were nonmarital prompted renewed interest in developing strategies to reach young men during the early 1980s.

Knowledge of young men's sexual and reproductive health needs and behaviors was limited during the mid-1980s, and the available information was typically obtained from women. To increase knowledge of factors that female and male Hispanic adolescents perceived as barriers to using contraceptives and family planning clinics, researchers from the Center for Population and Family Health conducted and videotaped focus groups with youth from the community.[9] Several of the male participants said they were reluctant to visit a clinic close to their homes because they did not want to be identified as sexually active ("What if my aunt sees me!"). Participants also believed that family planning clinics are for women only, and that talking about birth control is not "manly" ("Men are supposed to know these things"; "Women expect you to take charge"). Embedding sexual and reproductive health care within a broader menu of services was endorsed as one way of reducing men's embarrassment over being seen at the clinic ("If I could limp in like I hurt my ankle playing basketball, I'd tell the doctor I had a drip").

The focus groups triggered a substantial (and unexpected) level of interest among the young men. Several returned to the hospital to watch the videotaped sessions (which were followed by discussions about HIV and condoms), and suggested other recreational activities that could be taped and used to connect men to services. Videotaping was extended to include break dancing in the streets, performances at school talent shows and basketball games in local parks. These activities attracted young male performers and athletes to the hospital clinic, and most young men enthusiastically participated in discussions about HIV and sexually transmitted diseases (STDs) after viewing their videotape.

These young men also functioned as gatekeepers, linking faculty at the Center for Population and Family Health to adults at community-based organizations. As common missions, interests and needs were identified, partnerships were forged between the burgeoning "men's program" and agencies that were deeply rooted in the community. For example, leaders of community-based organizations accompanied young men from their programs to the health discussions. In return, faculty and students at the Center for Population and Family Health chaperoned dances and cosponsored basketball tournaments (purchasing T-shirts, and refereeing and videotaping games). Training in cardiopulmonary resuscitation was arranged at the hospital for a local scout troop, and the scouts reciprocated by distributing flyers about the new program throughout the community.

Building on the connections established by the focus group youth and partner organizations in the community, faculty conducted in-depth interviews with high school football coaches, Little League baseball coaches, clergy and other adult "key informants" to hear what sexual and reproductive health services young men needed and how services should be designed. The consistent message that emerged from these interviews was that young men in Washington Heights had little access to routine physical examinations that were needed for participation in school, sports and work.

Informed by these responses and encouraged by the success of the videotaping outreach initiative, the Center for Population and Family Health applied to the Office of Population Affairs in 1987 for a "special initiatives" grant and received $20,000 to expand services for young men at the family planning clinic. This supplemental funding was used to develop a Monday evening clinic session exclusively for males. Pediatrics residents provided services under the supervision of an attending physician, and faculty from the Center for Population and Family Health trained first-year medical students to provide health education. With the advent of the new evening sessions, the Young Men's Clinic shifted forma street outreach and health education program to a clinical model that was complemented by occasional outreach activities.

## Current Service Model

The Young Men's Clinic currently provides a limited package of such health care services as physical examinations for school and work and treatment of sports injuries, acne and other conditions. The clinic's main focus is addressing the sexual and reproductive health needs of young men—e.g., screening and treatment of STDs, confidential HIV counseling and testing, and condom education and distribution. An attending physician, a nurse practitioner and a master's-level social worker make up the core clinical team. Family medicine resident physicians augment the medical staff during six months of the year. Medical and public health students from Columbia University provide health education services under the supervision of public health faculty. Although the majority of patients at the Young Men's Clinic speak English, 90% of the salaried clinical and support staff speak both Spanish and English.

Medical students complete psychosocial histories and provide health education at initial and annual visits. Sessions are tailored to each individuals' concerns and developmental level. "Teachable moments" are maximized so that men have opportunities to discuss how to use condoms, communicate with their partner about contraception, perform testicular self-examinations and maintain a regular schedule of visits to the clinic (e.g., for regular STD screening). Young men with significant psychosocial needs (e.g., referrals for mental health or employment services) are referred to the social worker.

Public health students design health education activities that they conduct in the waiting room. Discussions focus on STDs and other health issues that concern men (e.g., hernias and stress management), as well as beliefs related to the outcomes of and widespread acceptance of such preventive health behaviors as limiting the number of sexual partners and supporting a partner's use of a contraceptive method.

To create a male-friendly environment, clinic staff show sports and entertainment videos when group activities are not being conducted, and distribute magazines such as *Sports Illustrated* and *Men's Health*. Paintings of men engaged in health-promoting behaviors (e.g., holding a baby) are placed in strategic locations throughout the clinic, and photographs of distinguished men of color (e.g., Secretary of State Colin Powell and former Surgeon General David Satcher) are displayed on the clinic's Wall of Fame.

The social worker provides mental health and social services during clinic sessions and short-term case management services throughout the week. Some of these services do not require young men to revisit the clinic. For example, the social worker provided more than 800 telephone consultations in 2002. Consultations typically are brief (10 minutes or less) and focus on health education (e.g., symptoms of herpes), decision-making (e.g., how to help a girlfriend decide on a contraceptive method), interpersonal skills (e.g., how to talk to a partner about getting tested for STDs) and finding necessary services at other agencies (e.g., support groups for gay adolescents). Even though telephone counseling is not a reimbursable service, logs capture the full range and volume of this important activity, and summary statistics are reported to funders.

# Outreach

The increasing number of clients visiting the Young Men's Clinic challenges the notion that men are hard to reach and demonstrates that young men will engage in programs that are accessible, affordable, culturally sensitive, rooted in the community and tailored to their needs. The following outreach interventions were designed to ensure that the clinic has high visibility in the community:

- A social marketing cartoon series that portrays men as competent, caring and involved in health-promoting activities has been developed. Cartoons are printed in English and Spanish on brightly colored cards and distributed through several channels. Story lines address emergency contraception, urine-based chlamydia screening, male support for female contraceptive use, hernia, and referral services at the Young Men's Clinic. A cartoon about dual protection against pregnancy and STDs is being developed. Information about the clinic (location, days and hours of operation, and telephone number) is embedded in each script.

- Medical and public health students are sent to community events such as evening basketball games. Wearing colorful clinic T-shirts, students distribute cartoons and engage men in "life space interviews" about clinic services.

- The results of formative research at the clinic in 2001 suggested that young men delay seeking health care because they fear hearing bad news. In addition, concerns were frequently expressed about the confidentiality of test results and about pain associated with laboratory tests (especially penile probes). A seven-minute digital video about urine-based screening was produced to address these concerns. In the video, satisfied patients give "testimonials" about the clinic and describe the benefits of being tested ("I sleep better at night knowing everything is all right"). The clinic's attractive facility is shown while merengue music plays in the background. Copies of the video are distributed to community-based organizations and downloaded onto computers at school-based clinics run by the Center for Community Health and Education.

- The social worker leads discussions in the family planning clinic to help women link their partners to the Young Men's Clinic. Cartoons are distributed and discussed, and women are encouraged to make appointments for their partners. After these groups were instituted, the proportion of new male patients who were referred by family planning patients increased sharply, from 25% in 1999 to 53% in 2001.

- Although most residents of Washington Heights have limited financial resources, close family and friendship networks provide invaluable support. These networks also create entry points for introducing information about men's sexual and reproductive health services. A standard talking point during waiting room groups, for example, focuses on what men can do to take care of their sexual and reproductive health, their partner's health and the health of their children. Telling friends about the clinic is proposed as one possible action. Tapping into these networks appears to be an effective strategy: Some 25% of the men who came to the Young Men's Clinic for the first time in 2001 said they had heard about the clinic from another patient; in addition, almost two-thirds of the men who made revisits in 2000 and 2001 reported that they had told another man about the clinic since their last visit.

## Funding

The Young Men's Clinic has been supported over the years by a patchwork of funding that has included in-kind institutional contributions (e.g., the clinic facility, volunteer students and Columbia faculty), private foundation and state grants, patient fees and third-party Medicaid reimbursement. The clinic has never received funds from either New York-Presbyterian Hospital or Columbia University.

Administrators from the Center for Community Health and Education strongly believe that to prevent transmission of STDs in women and reduce the incidence of unintended pregnancy, men must be included in reproductive health services. Since 1987, when medical services for young men were introduced, some funds from the family planning operating budget have been committed to cover medical, social work and support staff at the Young Men's Clinic.

Title X funding specifically designated for men's services was first received in 1998, when the clinic was designated as an Office of Population Affairs male demonstration project. The Young Men's Clinic received funding from the New York Community Trust that same year. These additional funds enabled the clinic to hire a part-time medical directory and a full-time social worker, and to expand to two sessions each week. But although these funds provided a more secure financial base, they did not cover the total cost of operating the clinic.

The total annual operating expenses for the Young Men's Clinic are approximately $311,000, excluding administrative overhead and indirect expenses, such as rent for the clinic facility. Of that amount, $150,000 comes from the Office of Population Affairs through the New York State Department of Health, and approximately $88,000 from Medicaid billing and out-of-pocket patient fees. Other grants and funding sources provide $73,000. Uninsured patients who are 19 or older pay a nominal fee based on income, pursuant to Title X guidelines. A new Medicaid entitlement benefit that covers family planning and reproductive health care services for men and women with incomes less than 200% of the federal poverty level (Family Planning Benefit Program) has been in place in New York State since October 2002.

# Organizing Concepts

## *Empowering*

The Young Men's Clinic attempts to empower men to adopt and sustain behaviors that improve their health and the health of their partners. This is challenging because many of the clinic's patients, like other low-income young men of color, experience environmental and structural barriers to meeting their most basic needs on a daily basis. Many are recent immigrants, and few have jobs that provide a living wage or employer-sponsored health insurance. Shifting eligibility requirements for Medicaid coverage since the institution of welfare reform in 1996 have left many confused, fearful and distrustful of medical and other service providers.[10]

To improve staff members' ability to increase young men's self-efficacy and engage them as partners in their own health care, the clinic trains them to help young men identify and use personal and environmental resources to make changes in their lives (e.g., initiating condom use); avoid responding to patients in a manner that sounds blaming, threatening or minimizing and that diminishes men's motivation to take action; and communicate confidence that men can change their behavior and affect their environment. For example, when completing a psychosocial history with an adult who has never finished high school, staff are trained to ask "How did you decide to leave school before you graduated?" rather than "Why did you drop out?" When providing health education about genital warts, staff help young men save face by telling them "It's okay; many men haven't heard about viruses like this one" instead of "You should know about this by now; it's a common infection."

## Teachable Moments

Parents, teachers and health care providers regularly miss opportunities to talk with young men about sexual health concerns and fail to provide them with the knowledge and skills they need to protect themselves.[11] As a result, many young men are uninformed about sexual and reproductive health, unfamiliar with the health care system, uncomfortable talking with physicians and reluctant to seek help even when they have symptoms.[12] A visit to the Young Men's Clinic may present one of the few opportunities men have to discuss sexual and reproductive health.

The clinic maximizes teachable moments so that young men have multiple opportunities to ask questions, obtain information, learn skills and think about their behaviors. Graduate students leading group activities in the waiting room focus conversations on factors that are associated with using condoms and with partner communication (e.g., concerns that condoms will affect sexual pleasure). Students inject these issues into discussions so they can be explicitly explored (e.g., asking whether women *always* feel insulted if a man wants to use a condom).

Downtime in the waiting room is also used to inform men about cancers of the male reproductive tract, describe how the testicles are examined during a comprehensive physical, demonstrate testicular self-examinations and provide guidance about what to do if symptoms are observed (i.e., call the clinic). Encouraging men to perform testicular self-examinations and to use the Young Men's Clinic as their medical home raises men's awareness of their reproductive health, establishes a baseline of what is normal and creates opportunities for expressing concerns that may warrant attention (e.g., symptoms of herpes or genital warts).

## Collaboration

Healthy People 2010 states that developing community partnerships is one of the most effective ways to improve the health of communities.[13] The Young Men's Clinic collaborates with several governmental, nonprofit and community-based organizations to leverage resources and create a comprehensive package of services. A linkage with the New York City Department of Health, for example, allows the clinic to offer urine-based screening for chlamydia and gonorrhea to every patient at no cost to the clinic. (The prevalence of chlamydia among clinic clients was about 11% in 2002. All of the men who tested positive were successfully treated with a single dose of azythromycin.)

EngenderHealth, an organization that provides technical assistance related to reproductive health throughout the world, funded the clinic's social marketing cartoons. Family medicine residents have increased the number of in-kind medical providers and facilitated referrals to the family medicine outpatient clinic when diabetes and other chronic conditions are diagnosed. A Harlem Health Promotion Center health educator is assigned to the Young Men's Clinic and provides smoking cessation services during clinic sessions.

# Challenges and Responses

Although the substantial increase in clinic use since 1998 is encouraging and provides evidence that men are willing to participate in sexual and reproductive health care, the success of the Young Men's Clinic has created some of its most vexing problems. marketing activities and informal word-of-mouth outreach by satisfied male and female users of the family planning and reproductive health programs run by the Center for Community Health and Education have dramatically increased the clinic's visibility, but the growing demand for services is outpacing the clinic's capacity. Some 5–10 nonemergency walk-in patients have to be turned away and rescheduled at every clinic session. Although the clinic has adapted by collaborating with government and community-based agencies, enlisting graduate students to provide health education services, maximizing recovery of reimbursable revenue and seeking additional sources of funding, the financial challenges facing the clinic are formidable.

The Young Men's Clinic serves men who are the least likely to be insured and the most likely to be disconnected from health care. Men in their 20s are too old for the State Children's Health Insurance Program (SCHIP) and are rarely eligible for Medicaid. moreover, many of the clinical, counseling and health education services men need are not reimbursable.[14]

The clinic also serves a large number of immigrants, both legal and undocumented. New York State court decisions have restored full Medicaid eligibility to legal immigrants who were eligible for Medicaid before the state implemented federal welfare reforms, but undocumented adults still do not qualify for coverage except for prenatal and emergency services.[15] The policy at programs of the Center for Community Health and Education, including the Young Men's Clinic, is that no one is denied services because of inability to pay. This includes undocumented immigrants. The clinic administration and staff believe that any other position would be unethical. Moreover, health care costs would ultimately be driven up if men had to be treated at emergency rooms and their partners had to be hospitalized with pelvic inflammatory disease and other complications of untreated chlamydial infections.

As at most male involvement programs in the Untied States, especially those serving low-income, uninsured, minority communities, securing adequate and stable funding to provide and (given the high level of interest and need) expand services has been the most pressing dilemma. Few funding sources target men's sexual and reproductive health.[16] The decision to allocate scarce resources to men's services is difficult for managers of Title X-funded programs because of the rising costs of providing services and inadequate Medicaid reimbursement rates. Moreover, despite Title X's extraordinary success in helping to prevent millions of unintended pregnancies over the last 30 years, funding for the program has not kept pace with inflation. The growing federal budget deficit and pressures on states to balance budgets have created even greater financial uncertainties.[17]

Limited funding in the face of the high demand for services has constrained the capacity of the Young Men's Clinic to implement several important activities, including the expansion of health education services at community venues. During the summer of 2003, however, the clinic applied for funding to launch a community-based health education and condom distribution intervention at 14 community-based organizations in Washington Heights and neighboring Harlem, and for an additional medical provider to serve newly recruited patients. If this intervention is funded, a health educator will deliver a three-session group curriculum that uses the social marketing cartoons and digital video. A slide program that walks men through a typical clinic visit by showing digital photos of staff (e.g., receptionists), space (e.g., the lab) and activities (e.g., taking blood pressure) will also be used. Men will be encouraged to visit the clinic for STD screening. Building on the success of the In Your Face school-based intervention, developed by the Center for Community Health and Education,[18] the health educator will escort each young man who visits the Young Men's Clinic through his initial visit.

Although formative evaluations have informed the development of culturally sensitive outreach interventions such as the video and cartoons, and process evaluations (e.g., patient flow analyses, chart reviews and patient satisfaction surveys) have identified service delivery problems so that corrective action could be taken, funding constraints have limited the clinic's ability to conduct rigorous outcome evaluations. The clinic is currently seeking funding to support systematic evaluations of clinic interventions (e.g., the effectiveness of waiting room group activities on knowledge, beliefs and behaviors), as well as outcome studies that measure changes in condom use and partner communication among clinic users.

# Conclusions

The sexual behavior of adolescent males has changed for the better in recent years.[19] Nevertheless, more progress is needed to achieve not only the Healthy People 2010 goal of eliminating health disparities, but also increased condom use among adolescents who are sexually active, and lower rates of pregnancy and chlamydial infection.[20] It is particularly important to increase primary and secondary prevention efforts that target men in their early 20s, who are more likely than younger males to engage in risky sexual behaviors and to have adverse reproductive health outcomes.[21] Achieving reductions in sexual risk-taking among men in their early 20s similar to those observed among adolescent males could contribute to further declines in unintended pregnancy and STD rates among young women.

The Young Men's Clinic is successfully engaging young men of color who are poorly served by the U.S. health care system. To improve young men's access to comprehensive and integrated sexual and reproductive health care throughout the country, health organizations and community-based agencies will increasingly need to pool resources, strengthen linkages and craft strategies for incorporating sexual and reproductive health into services. Most important, public and private funding specifically earmarked for men's services must be increased.

# References

1. United Nations (UN), International Conference on Population and Development, Programme of Action, <www.iisd.ca/linkages/Cairo/program/p04009.html>, accessed Apr. 15, 2003, and UN, Fourth World Conference on Women, Beijing Declaration and Platform for Action, <www.un.org/womenwatch/daw/beijing/platform>, accessed Apr. 15, 2003.

2. The Alan Guttmacher Institute (AGI), *In Their Own Right: Addressing the Sexual and Reproductive Health Needs of American Men,* New York: AGI, 2002.

3. Sonenstein FL et al., Changes in sexual behavior and condom use among teenaged males: 1988 to 1995, *American Journal of Public Health,* 1998, 88(6):956–959; Grunbaum JA et al., Youth risk behavior surveillance—United States, 2001, *Morbidity and Mortality Weekly Report Surveillance Summary,* 2002, Vol. 51, No. SS-04, Rich JA and Ro M, *A Poor Man's Plight: Uncovering the Disparity in Men's Health,* Community Voices Publication Series, Battle Creek, MI: W.K. Kellogg Foundation, 2002, No. 476; Sonenstein FL, ed., *Young Men's Sexual and Reproductive Health: Toward a National Strategy,* Washington, DC: Urban Institute, 2000; and Sandman D, Simantov E and An C, *Out of Touch: American men and the Health Care System, Commonwealth Fund Men's and Women's Health Survey Findings,* 2000, <http://www.cmwf.org/programs/women/sandman_men'ssurvey2000_374.asp>, accessed Apr. 1, 2003.

4. Male Advocacy Network, *Components That Work in Male Reproductive Health and Education Programs,* Washington, DC: Male Advocacy Network, 2002.

5. Citizens' Committee for Children of New York (CCC), *Keeping Track of New York City's Children,* New York: CCC, 2002.

6. Armstrong B et al., Involving men in reproductive health: the Young-Men's Clinic, *American Journal of Public Health,* 1999, 89(6):902–905; Steinhauer J. At a clinic, young men talk of sex, *New York Times,* Sept. 6, 1995, pp. B6–7; Stolberg SG, Men's reproductive health care gets new emphasis, New York Times, Mar. 19; 2002, p. B6; Sonenstein FL et al., *Involving Males in Preventing Teen Pregnancy: A Guide for Program Planners,* Washington, DC: Urban Institute, 1997; AVSC International, Selected U.S. reproductive health clinics serving men: three case studies, New York: AVSC International, 1997; and Hanson M, ed., *Maternal and Child Health Program Design and Development: From the Ground Up: Collaboration and Partnership: A Casebook,* New York: Columbia University School of Social Work, 1997.

7. Centers for Disease Control and Prevention (CDC), *Sexually Transmitted Disease Surveillance,* 2001, Atlanta: CDC, 2002.

8. Schulte MM and Sonenstein FL, Men at family planning clinics: the new patients? *Family Planning Perspectives,* 1995, 27(5):212–216 & 225.

9. Darabi KF, Barriers to contraceptive use and clinic utilization among Hispanic teenagers in New York City, New York: William T. Grant Foundation, 1985.

10. Adams A and Armstrong B, Connecting the disconnected: involving male minority youth in reproductive health, unpublished document, Columbia University, Mailman School of Public Health, New York, 1999.

11. Porter LE and Ku L, Use of reproductive health services among young men, 1995, *Journal of Adolescent Health,* 200, 27(3):186–194; Kaiser Family Foundation and *Glamour, Survey of Men and Women on Sexually Transmitted Diseases,* Menlo Park, CA: Kaiser Family Foundation, 1998; Lindberg LD, Ku L and Sonenstein FL, Adolescents' reports of receipt of reproductive health

education, 1988–1995, *Family Planning Perspectives,* 2000, 32(5):220–226; and Holtzman D and Rubinson R, Parent and peer communication effects on AIDS-related behavior among U.S. high school students, *Family Planning Perspectives,* 1995, 27(6):235–240 & 268.

12. Sandman D. Simantov E and An C, 2000, op. cit. (see reference 3).

13. U.S. Department of Health and Human Services (DHHS), *Healthy People 2010: Understanding and Improving Health,* second ed., Washington, DC: U.S. Government Printing Office, 2000.

14. Sonenstein Fl, 2000, op. cit. (see reference 3).

15. Bachrach D and Lipson K. *Health Coverage for Immigrants in New York: An Update on Policy Developments and Next Steps.* New York Commonwealth Fund, 2002.

16. Sonenstein FL, 2000, op. cit. (see reference 3)

17. Gold RB, Nowhere but up: rising costs for Title X clinics, *Guttmacher Report on Public Policy,* 2002, 5(5):6–9; Dailard C, Title X family planning clinics confront escalating costs, increasing needs, *Guttmacher Report on Public Policy,* 1999, 2(2):1–3; Gold RB, Title X: three decades of accomplishment, *Guttmacher Report on Public Policy,* 2001, 4(1):5–8; and Dailard C., Challenges facing family planning clinics and Title X, *Guttmacher Report on Public Policy,* 2001, 4(2):8–11.

18. Tiezzi L et al., Pregnancy prevention among urban adolescents younger than 15: results of the "In Your Face" program, *Family Planning Perspectives,* 1997, 29(4):173–176 & 197.

19. Sonenstein FL et al., 1998, op. cit. (see reference 3); and Grunbaum IA et al., 2002, op. cit. (see reference 3).

20. DHHS, 2000, op. cit. (see reference 13).

21. Ku L et al., Risk behaviors, medical care, and chlamydial infection among young men in the United States, *American Journal of Public Health,* 2002, 92(7):1140–1143; Bradner CH, Ku L and Lindberg LD, Older, but not wiser: how men get information about AIDS and sexually transmitted diseases after high school, *Family Planning Perspectives,* 2000, 32(1):33–38; Ku L, Sonenstein FL and Pleck JH, Young men's risk behaviors for HIV infection and sexually transmitted diseases, 1988 through 1991, *American Journal of Public Health,* 1993, 83(11):1609–1615; and Ku L, Sonenstein FL and Pleck JH, The dynamics of young men's condom use during and across relationships, *Family Planning Perspectives,* 1994, 26(6):246–251.

# Section IV

# Sexuality Education

# Chapter 11

# What's the Good of Taking a Human Sexuality Class?

*John P. Elia*

Sexuality permeates many aspects of our lives. In fact, we are confronted with personal and global aspects of sexuality on a daily basis. Concerns about sexuality extend from our personal lives, in terms of integrating and managing our own sexuality, to a more global level. On a broader societal level, there are a plethora of sexual issues that confront us on a daily basis. For instance, mass media is more often than not saturated with sexual imagery. Everything from high-tech computer games to news reports contains some form of sexuality. Additionally, sexuality is part of the national conversation regarding matters of health and politics. The same-sex marriage issue is being slugged out in the highest court in the land. While the Boy Scouts of America very recently permitted out gay boys the opportunity to participate and advance in the organization, the Boy Scouts continues to deny openly gay adults to serve as leaders. The issue of whether The Affordable Care Act (known as "Obama Care" in common parlance) should require employers to offer contraception as a part of health care insurance plans is still being sorted out.

Mental health professionals have long claimed that having intimate and sexual connections with others is center stage for most people. Even though this is the case, there is little to no formal education that addresses this topic in elementary and secondary school curricula. Sexuality education at the high school level focuses mostly on the physical and biomedical aspects of sexual health and how to avoid pregnancy or how to dodge sexually transmitted infections (STIs). What underlies most sexuality education efforts is a mere offering of the "facts" about sexual health and how to avoid the potential calamities of sexual behavior. As well intentioned as teachers are, sexuality education ends up being a mere conveyance of the facts with ever-present attention on avoiding unwanted pregnancies, STIs, sexual assaults, etc.

The *good* of taking a general survey human sexuality class or a course that deals in some ways with sexual matters needs to go beyond the discourse of disaster to offer a more balanced approach. In fact, coursework in human sexuality—particularly broad, survey courses—potentially has much good to offer. In this essay, I will identify a number of good qualities that such coursework is likely to offer, such as

- fostering appreciation for the breadth and depth of human sexuality;
- providing a balanced—even sex-positive—perspective;

- promoting and increasing sexual literacy;
- fostering physical, emotional, and social sexual health;
- promoting sexual self-understanding; and
- promoting sexual and social justice.

While this essay does not pretend to offer a comprehensive discussion about all of the good that a broad-based survey course in human sexuality can provide, it does articulate some initial thoughts about the broad-based academic, personal, and social value of such coursework.

# Fostering Appreciation for the Breadth & Depth of Sexuality

Perhaps the most significant benefit of taking a general survey course in human sexuality is learning to appreciate the breadth and depth of human sexuality as a field of study as well as the broad implications sexuality has for our lives. In terms of the breadth of the field, sexuality studies spans from art to theology—and includes every discipline in between. A well-developed sexuality course makes use of information from a variety of disciplines (e.g., art, biology, communication studies, history, political science, public health, philosophy, psychology, and sociology) and introduces students to conceptual frameworks and theoretical foundations. Virtually every field of study can contribute to our understanding of sexual matters. For example, the field of art can help us understand the sexual aesthetics of both fine and performance arts. Biological science helps us understand reproductive anatomy and physiology and the physiological aspects of sexual functioning in general. Communication studies helps to sharpen our understanding of interpersonal communication, discourse analyses, and media studies related to sexuality.

Delving into the history of sexuality can serve to inform us about how U.S. society has evolved the collective values it has about sexuality and why we are not more sex positive. Historical inquiry can help to answer these questions. Philosophy can help us, for example, consider ethical dimensions of sexuality. Questions regarding the value of monogamy, reproductive technologies, and sexual consent fall into the philosophical realm.

Political science introduces us to the political aspects of sexuality and how the politics of sexuality is omnipresent. The politics of abortion, the politics of sexual identity in one's personal life and in organizations, and the politics of health care related to sexual issues (such as Obama Care and medical coverage of contraception) are fervently debated political matters.

Turning to public health can help us understand how sexually transmitted infections (STIs) spread in communities and how communities manage health-related sexual issues. Akin to public health, health education offers a framework for understanding, achieving, and maintaining the physical, emotional, and social aspects of sexual health. Sociology provides us with a framework for societal aspects of human sexuality and examines such issues as stigma and social/sexual justice.

While this is neither an exhaustive list of disciplinary contributions to sexuality studies nor a complete inventory of all of the sexually-related issues covered within the disciplines listed above, it is hoped that the above-mentioned examples provide the reader with an idea of how a general survey human sexuality course is enriched by an interdisciplinary approach and how such an approach provides students with a deep appreciation for how vast and rich human sexuality is, not to mention how integral it is to the human experience.

# Providing a Balanced and Sex-Positive Approach

Instruction about sexual matters has historically been offered from a health and hygiene and mechanical perspective. In other words, formal instruction has focused on preventing sexually transmitted infections (STIs) and has promoted heteronormativity (heterosexuality is the dominant culturally expected sexual norm linked with marriage and reproduction) as the best and most respectable form of sexual relationship. The general underlying message has been that avoiding disease and other problems brought about from sexual relations is the primary purpose of sexual instruction in formal educational settings. Sexuality has been portrayed as dangerous and likely to cause problems. Simply put, sexuality has historically been characterized from a negative perspective. For example, sexuality education has not included discussions of desire and pleasure. These positive aspects of sexual expression have been conspicuously absent from the sexuality education landscape. Sexual expression has many positive elements: it is an expression of love; it is a form of stress reduction; it offers a release from sexual tension; it is a means of self-expression; it creates a sense of adventure; it promotes pair bonding; it enables reproduction; it is a form of creativity; etc. A general survey course can mark how human sexuality is often looked at with suspicion and begin to deconstruct the negativity and work toward building a sex-positive approach putting more focus on the good aspects of sexual expression. Ultimately, however, both the positive aspects and the potentially negative consequences of sexual activity need to be covered.

# Promoting and Increasing Sexual Literacy

A general survey human sexuality course should necessarily have as one of its major charges to promote and increase sexual literacy. Sexual literacy, in large part, comprises having knowledge about the factual aspects of human sexuality as well as possessing the skills and ability to access resources required to have a fulfilling sex life whether that be with oneself or one's partners. It is also important to note that sexual literacy goes beyond the individual and the sexual experiences with one's partners and extends to the larger social world. Unfortunately, sexual illiteracy in American culture has been pervasive. In my view, sex negativity has pushed the possibility of open, honest, and factual discussions about sexual matters underground, and what has resulted is even more sensationalism about sexuality in the media and even in our own minds. Let's face it, many of us may well think that we are "good" with sexuality and believe now that we are into the twenty-first century, all of the traditional, conservative trappings of the Judeo-Christian sexual ethics—which have promoted a narrow range of acceptable sexual practices and lifestyles anchored in heterosexuality that involves marriage and reproduction—are behind us. But is this the case?

It is true that U.S. society has loosened up a bit regarding sexuality, and strides have been gained along the lines of human rights and mainstream communication about sexual issues.

Some examples include the advent of the birth control pill in 1960; the sexual liberation movement of the 1960s; removal of homosexuality as a *de facto* mental illness in the early 1970s; Roe v. Wade in the 1970s, which resulted in the right for women to choose whether to terminate pregnancies; development of LGBT studies and human sexuality studies courses at many colleges and universities in the United States beginning for the most part in the 1970s; widespread communication about safer sex practices beginning in the 1980s; and the development of Viagra in the 1990s, which spurred communication about sexual functioning and desire for men and opened the proverbial door even wider about how to communicate about sexuality. These are just a small sample of recent embattled historical events that have given rise to the national conversation about sexual matters. Such critical and thoughtful engagement helps promote sexual literacy in general.

However, despite some advancement in bringing sexual issues into the public sphere, in many ways we have a long trek ahead regarding fully integrating a good understanding of the multifaceted aspects of the human sexual experience. Many young people, for example, learn about sex from their friends and media sources, and much of what they learn is likely to be misinformation (Crooks & Bauer, 2011). It is critical that deep learning about sexual matters lead to actions of advocacy for an increasingly sex positive community and society. Formal sexuality education needs to occur for such deep and important learning to take place in general.

A general survey course can contribute quite a lot to increasing sexual literacy. This sort of educational experience ideally should happen from elementary school through college/ university level to ensure sexual literacy. At its best, sexual literacy leads to a better, more fulfilled life in terms of helping individuals most immediately with their own sex lives as well as encouraging them to engage intelligently in the wider societal discussion about sexual topics. Sexuality expert Jonathan Alexander (2008) puts it best when he observes ". . . literacy about sexuality as a highly significant personal, social, and political topic is crucial for students to understand some of the more important debates and issues of our time" (p. 4). Put another way, "Research on sexuality education suggests that effective programs [courses] should promote sexual literacy—going beyond dispensing knowledge to include development of personal and social skills" (Santelli & Hirsch, 2007, p. 116). The development of sexual literacy, then, is one of the most significant outcomes of a general survey human sexuality course. In many ways, sexual literacy is connected to gaining and maintaining good sexual health.

# Fostering Physical, Mental and Social Sexual Health

According to the World Health Organization (2013), *sexual health* is defined as ". . . a state of physical, mental and social well-being in relation to sexuality. It requires a positive and respectful approach to sexuality and sexual relationships, as well as the possibility of having pleasurable and safe sexual experiences, free of coercion, discrimination and violence." Students in a comprehensive human sexuality course are often afforded a fair amount of time during the semester/quarter to examine not only many components (e.g., physical, mental, and social aspects) of sexual health, but also how these components relate to one another.

The physical aspect of health dominates most people's thinking about health and wellness. Furthermore, physical maladies and how to fix them often come to mind. In the sexual realm, a lot of folks think about some of the most daunting physical issues confronting them, such as sexually transmitted infections (STIs), testicular cancer, ovarian cancer, breast cancer, sexual assaults, urinary tract infections, etc. While it is clearly important that students of human sexuality learn about the various assaults to physical sexual health and possible prevention strategies, it is also critically important to study ways of enhancing physical sexual health such as maintaining good nutrition, getting an adequate amount of sleep, maintaining good physical hygiene, and doing Kegel exercises on a regular basis to strengthen the pelvic floor muscles, which are helpful to achieve more powerful orgasms and prevent urinary incontinence. It is also important to acknowledge that some individuals live with chronic medical conditions and others have temporary and permanent physical challenges. People should enjoy sexual experiences as much as possible no matter what their physical limitations might be. It is critical that general human sexuality courses deal with a wide range of physical aspects of sexual health.

The mental health aspect of sexuality is vital to address in a sexuality class in terms of an individual's attitudes about her or his sexuality as well as one's attitudes toward others' sexualities. As discussed earlier, sex negativity is still very much a part of our reality. There is a lot of sexual shame, guilt, and uneasiness people carry and internalize. Sexuality courses should address the impact of sex negative attitudes on individuals and begin to explore ways of enhancing mental/emotional sexual health. Being self-loving and possessing good self-esteem and pride about one's sexuality are critically important to achieving and maintaining good mental sexual health. Being able to communicate about one's sexuality to close friends and family members is part of achieving good mental sexual health as well.

The social aspect of sexual health is as critically important as the physical and mental aspects. Understanding how social attitudes and behaviors regarding sexuality impact individuals and vice versa is imperative. Hegemonic heterosexuality is valued and held in high esteem in U.S. society at the expense of other forms of sexuality. This has created what is known as heteronormativity, and in turn, sexual prejudice has resulted. Renowned social psychologist Gregory Herek (2000) defines sexual prejudice as ". . . negative attitudes toward an individual because of her or his sexual orientation" (p. 19). Sexual prejudice is perhaps more commonly known as *biphobia* and *homophobia*. Of critical importance is that students of human sexuality truly understand the varying degrees of sexual prejudice (from slurs and jokes about sexual minority people to murdering them, and everything in between) and the negative health impacts this prejudice has on individuals and communities. Prejudice and oppression have long been known to have deleterious effects on health and wellbeing. Of foremost value in the classroom setting is that students understand what undergirds such sexual prejudice, the negative impact it has not only for sexual minority individuals but also for their friends and family members, and how it wreaks havoc on social life in general.

# Promoting Sexual Self-Understanding

A general survey human sexuality course plays a significant role in sexual self-understanding. This form of self-understanding ranges from an appreciation of one's sexual anatomy and physiology to insights one has about reactions to lectures, class discussions, readings, and guest speakers. In other words, this sexuality class is fertile ground for gathering fact-based information about a wide range of sexual matters as well as engaging in introspection and self-reflection about one's sexual attitudes and values. It is important to be honest with ourselves as we reflect on our own prejudices and uneasiness about sexual issues. For instance, if you have a negative or positive reaction to someone who reveals that he or she is non-monogamous, what is the basis for your reaction? What does this say about your own sexual value system? Have your perspectives about a variety of sexual matters evolved over the years? If so, what do you attribute to such a change in your sexual views, attitudes, tastes, and values? Do you feel comfortable with your own sexuality or your reactions to the sexual views, attitudes, tastes, and values of other individuals? Is your own sexual lifestyle congruent with your sexual values? These questions and a plethora of others can be posed and answered in the context of a general, survey human sexuality course.

# Promoting Sexual and Social Justice

There is a disturbing amount of sexual and social injustice in the United States. There is a hierarchy of sexuality. Some people are respected and valued more in general based on their sexual tastes and lifestyles. Heterosexual individuals who are married and have children are valued most. This flies in the face of a society such as ours that allegedly stands for democracy and supports diversity and plurality. In fact, there are many ways in which individuals are discriminated against based on their sexuality. An expert in sexuality studies, Gert Hekma (n.d.), asserts "Denial of institutional and social equality and participation to sexual minorities . . . occurs in such areas as education, parental rights, health care, labor markets, housing, taxing, pensions and insurance, partner benefits, political representation, and immigration laws, to name only some of the major terrains" (para. 14). Many students, particularly those who are less acquainted with sexual minority issues, are unaware of the disparity of treatment of those who are considered sexual *others*.

Perhaps the most prominent issue in the news today concerns same-sex marriage. It is interesting and sad that the road to marriage equality for same-sex couples has been so long, bumpy, and fraught with embittered debate. In many ways, it has become a circus! It is amazing that same-sex marriage is being so deeply contested. At this time, the U.S. Supreme Court is deciding on both the legality of same-sex marriage and the constitutionality of the Defense of Marriage Act (DOMA). If there were more sexual and social equality and justice, same-sex marriage would not be an issue at all. Another issue has to do with gays and lesbians in the U.S. military. Just recently the "Don't Ask, Don't Tell" federal policy was lifted. These are just two examples of how people are treated unequally based on sexual orientation.

A human sexuality course often examines why people are treated better or worse based on their sexual orientations, sexual tastes, and sexual lifestyles. Young, single individuals are often pressured to be coupled and committed. We have all heard about, or experienced, going to a family reunion and being questioned about if we are dating and/or who we are dating and when marriage is going to occur. If we are married then questions are asked about when we will be having children. There is a lot of pressure for individuals to conform to the heteronormative standard in which being married and having children are part of societal expectations.

It is important that we know we should not be coerced to live any particular sexual lifestyle. This is one of the tenets of the Sexual Bill of Rights.

Sexual (in)justice also comes into play with disabled individuals, the aged, and others who are generally written off as sexual beings. The disabled are often dismissed as sexually "out of commission" and are viewed and treated as second-class sexual citizens. Those who are elderly are treated as if they cannot or should not be sexual. If older people are sexual, they are likely to be derided or disciplined in one way or another. Many individuals, for a variety of reasons, are written off sexually speaking. As students of human sexuality, we must look at the injustices from which many individuals suffer along sexual lines and look toward interventions to correct these injustices so literally everyone can enjoy sexuality without social disapproval.

## Conclusion

This brief essay provides some observations about the potential good to be gained by taking a college/university general survey human sexuality course. Given that misinformation about sexuality is so pervasive, the merits of studying human sexuality from a variety of disciplinary perspectives are many. The breadth and depth of human sexuality from academic and personal standpoints are truly something over which to marvel. In the end, such a course offers students meaningful knowledge that can be applied to their academic studies and/or to their personal lives as evolving sexual beings. Perhaps equally important is righting the wrongs that have been suffered by individuals who do not, for whatever reason, fit the image of those who are viewed as acceptable sexual citizens. The hope of any instructor of such a human sexuality course is that her or his students will become more sexually literate, will have more satisfying and fulfilled sex lives, and will be agents of social change to challenge the social and sexual injustices that are ubiquitous in the United States.

## References

Alexander, J. (2008). *Literacy, sexuality, pedagogy: Theory and practice for composition students.* Logan, Utah: Utah State University Press.

Crooks, R., & Baur, K. (2011). *Our sexuality* (11th ed.). Belmont, CA: Wadsworth Publishing.

Hekma, G. (n.d.). Sexual citizenship. glbtq: an encyclopedia of gay, lesbian, bisexual, transgender and queer culture. Retrieved from http://www.glbtq.com/social-sciences/sexual_citizenship,2.html

Herek, G. M. (2000). The psychology of sexual prejudice. *Current Directions in Psychological Science.* 9(1), 19–22.

Shtarkshall, R. A., Santelli, J. S., & Hirsch, J. S. (2007). Sex education and sexual socialization: Roles for educators and parents. *Perspectives on Sexual and Reproductive Health.* 39(2), 116–119.

World Health Organization (2013). Health topics: Sexual health. Retrieved from http://www.who.int/topics/sexual_health/en/

John P. Elia, PhD, is professor and associate chair of health education at San Francisco State University. Additionally, he is editor-in-chief of the Journal of Homosexuality. Correspondence may be sent to him at: jpelia@sfsu.edu

# Chapter 12

# What Would Make Sex Good For You?

*Ivy Chen, MPH*

In the last seventeen years of teaching sexuality health education professionally to teens and college students, I have evolved from a primarily biological curriculum to one that is more personal. Though accurate information and knowledge about basic sexual and reproductive anatomy, pregnancy, birth control and sexually transmitted information are still very much important components of my programs, I strive to make each piece of information as relevant as possible to my audience. Over the years, the heart and soul of the programs that I teach are the activities involving sexual decision-making and healthy romantic relationships.

There is a need and an opportunity to guide healthy sexual decision-making for young people. According to statistics, both young men and women have sex for the first time, usually meaning sexual intercourse, at age 17 [1]. This later high school age means that there is time to help a young person set standards for themselves if these discussions happen in early high school or even in 8th grade. This discussion can certainly still be useful for older teens or young adults in college. A recent study had declared that a person's first sexual experience, whether it was a positive or negative experience, colors the way they feel about sex, potentially for many years after [2]. While this seems very intuitive to me, a number of teens that I have taught just expects the first time to be awkward, something to "just get it over with". One of the goals that I have is for my students to take the information learned from class and feel that they have the power to create a positive sexual experience for themselves, especially for their first time.

When I lead the discussion about setting standards, I say "my wish for you is that whenever you decide to have sex, whether it is your first time or any time, I want it to be good for you!" Rather than the proverbial "wolf in sheep's clothing", this is more of a sheep in wolf's clothing. In other words, we will be talking about high standards of preserving health and safety but the discussion is wrapped in the edgier coating of "good sex". Often directed at young people, the media has been selling their version of good sex, which often is over-glamourized, unplanned, depicted without risks and misleading. Sex education needs to reappropriate what actually constitutes "good sex".

Sometimes we start with a contrast and define what "bad sex" is. There is an old saying, "sex is like pizza; even when it's bad, it's still pretty good". That is simply not true, on both counts. Pizza *can* be bad, whether it is the cardboard crust or the stale toppings, but I digress on the pizza. Sex can certainly be bad. When I ask my students what would constitute "bad sex", the various answers include

- Sex without consent.
- Sex one regrets having.
- Sex that is not pleasurable or is painful.
- Sex that is interrupted, like by parents.
- Sex you do not remember having, because of being drunk or high.
- Sex that results in something physically unwanted, like a sexually transmitted infection or an unintended pregnancy.
- Sex that may give someone a negative reputation, particularly if a partner shared intimate details or start rumors.
- Sex that affects a relationship negatively, making it "weird" between the two people, possibly because they were not ready for some of the emotions associated with the activity. This result can be ironic for people who may try to use sex as a shortcut to intimacy.

Now, **what would make sex good for you**? The answers students give can often be organized into four categories:

1. **An Appropriate Partner:** In answering the question "what would you want in order to have good sex?", a teen student may say, "uh, someone to do it with?" Yes, but who would be an appropriate sexual partner? There are two main sub-questions to examine:
   a. *What qualities do you want in a partner?* The list of what students say they want in a romantic partner can vary, with answers that include "good-looking, smart, funny, can cook, smells good, liked by my parents, has money, likes sports, etc." However, in terms of a healthy relationship, the qualities in a partner that are very important are respect, honesty, trust and good communication.
   b. *What is the status of your relationship*? The majority of young people (70% of females and 56% of males) have their first sexual experience with a steady romantic partner [1]. Therefore, a substantial part of our discussion revolves around issues in a healthy long-term relationship. However, the spectrum of who constitutes an appropriate partner can range from a stranger/one night stand to a friend-with-benefits to a girl/boyfriend to a spouse. Of the reasons why teens who have not had sex say that they are waiting, the top reasons include their values/morals and that they "haven't found the right person yet." [1]
   Some teens may underestimate the emotions that having a sexual experience with a "friend" may engender. The lack of definition and expectations that are associated with hooking up with a friend may cause confusion or frustration.
   Some students object to the use of the word "relationship" when talking about a one night stand, which they do not consider a relationship. A relationship is a connection made with another person. A one night stand is usually a very short and perhaps not very emotionally-intimate relationship, but is nonetheless a relationship that still has some degree of responsibility to the other person.
2. **Location:** Let's pick a venue. In the media, there seems a popular portrayal of sex in public places, like restrooms or elevators. In reality, sex mostly happens on a bed.

Why? Beds are located in bedrooms, in houses or hotels, which meet several criteria for a good location for sex:

    a. *Private:* Privacy is a difficult thing for many young people to get, whether they live at home with their family or in a dorm or shared house. Lack of privacy may lead some teens to have sex in cars. Beds are usually in room with a door with a lock, ensuring privacy.

    b. *Comfortable:* Beds are usually soft, spacious and comfy. Backseats of many cars are cramped, has a low roof and with lumpy seat belt buckles sticking out. Bathrooms usually have cold, hard tile. Even when a student suggests a seemingly romantic place for sex such as "Hawaii on the beach at sunset", there are other practical issues like all that sand that would be very uncomfortable in various body orifices.

    c. *Clean:* Compared to a public restroom or an alley way, bedrooms are usually cleaner.

    d. *Safe:* Indoor spaces are generally safer. Sometimes, there could be issues with nature or the elements such as unwittingly having sex on top of poison oak or getting sunburned. Some teens do not realize that they can be arrested for having sex in public if caught. There are other stories about couples who roll off a tall roof while having sex and die. While they may be urban legends, the stories certainly serve as cautionary tales about bad sex venue choices.

3. **Equipment:** While the term "equipment" might invoke images of a helmet or knee-pads, few people actually use that during sex. What I mean are the various items that a person might need to be prepared for a sexual experience.

    a. *Safer Sex Material:* When asked the question about what is needed to be ready for sex, the most common answer is condoms. In addition to a condom, other safer sex material include other birth control, perhaps flavored condoms or dental dams for protected oral sex, and maybe even gloves or finger cots. Artificial lube may make sex safer by preventing condom breakage and microscopic tears in the vagina or rectum. Male condoms can also make sex better by decreasing the intensity of the sensation slightly so that he can last longer. Therefore, something that makes sex safer can also increase pleasure by preventing him from coming too soon. Lastly, safer sex material can help to make sex better by providing more peace of mind.

    b. *Props to Set the Mood:* When a person recounts a particularly memorable or romantic sexual experience, the scene is usually very sensual. Sensual literally means fulfilling the senses of touch, sound, sight, smell and taste. Therefore, the whole experience is not just about genitals touching. There may be candlelight, sexy music, a lavender bubble bath, rose petals on the bed, chocolate-dipped strawberries, etc.

    c. *Adult Toys:* When I lead a discussion with college students, I include this category. For a person 18 or older, they may purchase and use sex toys. There are numerous safety issues here as well, including using a new condom on a toy that is going into a different partner's body to prevent transmission of STIs. Young people may need to be warned not to turn other objects into impromptu sex toys. Open glass bottles may create suction if inserted into the body and later difficult to remove. Phallic shaped fruits and vegetables may have insecticide or herbicide on the outside peel that could be absorbed into the thin moist epithelium of the rectum or vagina. Objects that do not have a flange, a flared base, can be pulled up into the body, especially up the anus. Other than the embarrassing and expensive trip to the emergency room, objects that are improperly used as sex toys can be very risky.

4. **Information:** "What would you want to know before you feel ready for sex?"

   a. *Consent:* Acquiring permission from the partner for any sexual act is important. Some people may not realize that a person who is drunk or under the influence of a substance is not legally able to give consent for sex. People who are unconscious, either passed out or asleep, cannot give consent. For high school students, I also give information about the age of consent and statutory rape. Even in this discussion about having sex, I always tell students that there is always a choice to abstain or say no to anything that they do not want to do.

   b. *Sobriety:* In our society, alcohol is associated with social or romantic situations like dates or weddings. Alcohol may even be thought of as an aphrodisiac, though in reality, alcohol slows down body processes such as orgasm and can make getting an erection or lubrication more difficult. Alcohol use can certainly alter our decision-making process, causing more risk-taking behaviors such as unprotected sex. The role of alcohol in date- rape is prominent, and a person can pressure their date to drink perhaps with the intention to incapacitate the other person. Many young people may not know their level of tolerance for alcohol and get drunk faster than anticipated. Though some teens may think that being an adult means they get to drink and have sex, I tell them that being an adult really means making good decisions and taking responsibility for those decisions. Many older teens whom I teach, who are on the brink of having sex for the first time, insist on sobriety.

   c. *Sexually Transmitted Infections:* Often, the first answer they give for what info they want to know before having sex is "whether or not my partner has an STD." The truth is that many sexually transmitted infections may be asymptomatic [3]. Therefore, a person can be infected and can pass it onto a partner unknowingly. The fair thing to do is for both partners to get tested before having sex and/or to consistently use condoms. What I have to address is the undertone of "I need to protect myself from you." Because most sexual experiences do occur in the context of a stable relationship, the kinder and wiser thing to do is to think as a team and protect both partners' health.

   d. *Pregnancy Prevention:* Though many teens and young adults imagine becoming parents someday, they usually do not want a pregnancy as a result of the sex they may be having currently. I can fill an entire separate article with all the myths I have heard about how "you can't get pregnant if. . . ." Sample myths include not getting pregnant if two people have sex while standing up, have sex in a pool or hot tub or douching the vagina after sex with Diet Coke. Even withdrawal, pulling out the penis before ejaculation, is not genuine birth control due to the presence of sperm in the pre-ejaculatory fluid. Young people not only need to know how to use real birth control methods correctly, but they also often need to know how to access sexual and reproductive health care services. Many of the most effective birth control methods are by prescription only. Many teens may not realize that they have the right to a confidential relationship with their doctor and can get on prescription birth control without their parents' permission or knowledge. Though I highly encourage parents to talk with their kids about sex and be involved in their teens' decision-making, I also want young people to know that they have the power to act and decide on their own behalf.

e. *Pleasure:* One of the main motivations why people have sex is because it can be pleasurable. The media usually over-sensationalize this aspect but many sex education programs ignore it altogether. When someone thinks about "good sex", the first thing that occurs to people is pleasure, hopefully mutual pleasure. Some young people have resigned themselves to the idea that the first time will definitely be awkward, especially if both partners are virgins because "nobody knows what they're doing". Some people feel performance anxiety. Especially with heterosexual couples, the male may feel like he has to be active and "give" her an orgasm, as if it is something presented in a box with a big red bow on it. I emphasize that people are responsible for their own pleasure, to explore what feels good to themselves and to communicate that to partners. Even if someone loves their partner, a person simply cannot read minds. Giving and receiving pleasure can be learned, and usually gets better with practice and open communication between the partners. Information about the areas of the body that are particularly sensitive and stages of sexual responses can also be taught.

This is a quite a checklist for having "good sex"! Values clarification and planning help to minimize regrets and maximize satisfaction from the decision to have sex. In fact, setting high standards can delay sexual involvement until it is right for the young person. In the long run, comprehensive sex education can help to produce more responsible relationships and a healthier sexual well-being [4]. I invite you to answer the question "what would make sex good for you?" for yourself, perhaps discuss with friends or partner. You are also welcome to use this activity to facilitate a discussion with teens or students in your live.

# For your reference, here's a handy summary

"What would you need or want for sex to be GOOD for you?"

1. **Who Would be An Appropriate Partner?**
   a. *What qualities do you want in a partner?*
   b. *What is the status of your relationship?*
2. **What is a Good Location for sex?**
3. **What Equipment Would You Want to Have With You?**
   a. *Safer Sex Material?*
   b. *What Props to Set the Mood?*
   c. *(Optional) Adult Toys?*
4. **What Information Would You Want to Have to Feel Ready For Sex?**
   a. *About sexually transmitted infections?*
   b. *About pregnancy prevention?*
   c. *About giving and receiving pleasure?*
   d. *About consent and sobriety?*

# References

1. **Guttmacher Institute,** Facts on American Teens' Sexual and Reproductive Health, *In Brief Fact Sheet*. February 2013 <http://www.guttmacher.org/pubs/FB-ATSRH.html>
2. Abrams, Lindsay. **Study: How We Lose Our Virginity Shapes Our Entire Sexual Lives.** *The Atlantic.* January 29, 2013
3. **Guttmacher Institute,** Facts on Sexually Transmitted Infections in the United States, *In Brief Fact Sheet*. June 2009 <http://www.guttmacher.org/pubs/FIB_STI_US.html>
4. **Guttmacher Institute,** Facts on American Teens' Sources of Information About Sex. *In Brief Fact Sheet*. February 2012 <http://www.guttmacher.org/pubs/FB-Teen-Sex-Ed.htmltmacher.org/pubs/FIB_STI_US.html>

# *Studs, Sluts, Virgins and Wimps: What's Missing From Sexual Health Education*

*Donnovan Somera Yisrael*

In January 1992, it was my very first week on the job as a sexual health educator doing HIV/AIDS workshops in middle and high schools in San Mateo County, a very large county to the south of San Francisco, California. I was at a school to watch a more experienced presenter and "learn the ropes." He wrote the letters 'A', 'I', 'D' and 'S' on the board. Then he asked the students what each letter of the acronym stood for, briefly corrected or elaborated on the definitions they offered, plopped himself down on the top of the teacher's desk in the front of the class and asked: "Any Questions?" There was more, I think, but not much more. I had my work cut out for me.

In the curriculum that was handed down to me, there were, more or less, three modules: Day 1—game show type activity to quiz the students on the basic facts/biology/transmission of HIV/AIDS, Day 2—presentation from a person living with HIV or AIDS, Day 3—Agree/Disagree activity to help students wrestle with ethical decisions (e.g. "Women who are HIV positive should not have children.") and discriminatory beliefs about people living with HIV/AIDS (e.g. "I would share a drink with someone who is HIV positive.") Done well, all of these modules are really important in helping people begin to understand HIV/AIDS, but as I would learn later, they were "necessary but not sufficient" if the main purpose of such educational workshops was to actually prevent the spread of HIV. So as I learned to lead each module, I was also working to improve them, asking basic questions like: "What is the point of this activity? Does this activity help students be better able to protect/prevent themselves from getting infected with HIV?"

After a year of working with this curriculum, I was fortunate to get a health educator position with the YWCA of The Mid-Peninsula (located in Santa Clara County, the next county to the south) which had an AIDS Prevention Program. This change in jobs allowed me to compare the YWCA curriculum with the one I was working with in San Mateo County, which, in turn, was based on the curriculum being used by San Francisco Unified. The point of all of this is that I felt like we were using a "state of the art" curriculum at that time because it was based on the one being used in San Francisco, one of the epicenters of the HIV/AIDS epidemic.

And then, in the classroom, something interesting began to happen. Randomly, like lava bubbling up out of the ground, questions (usually from a young female) would raise issues that I was not prepared to answer. In other words, my curriculum did not address these concepts.

---

Reprinted by permission of Donnovan Somera Yisrael.

For example, after doing our bit on transmission and telling the students to use condoms, a young female would raise her hand and say something to the effect of "... well how come boys can buy condoms, carry them around and brag about how they are having sex (even if they aren't) and we girls are going to feel pretty bad if grandma's best friend sees us buying condoms at the drugstore or if our birth control falls out of our purse at church ..." or "Why do boys get 'props' for having sex and girls get called sluts ..." In my head, I flipped the pages in my binder to find the answers. I received no training on this and it was not in my curriculum or any curriculum that I could find.

Simultaneously while doing HIV/AIDS presentation in local high schools, I was asked to co-teach a 1-unit course at Stanford University on volunteerism/activism regarding HIV/AIDS, which was called Project SAVE (Stanford AIDS Volunteer Educators). One of the guest lecturers that we brought in (other than Rachel Maddow's Rubberware Parties) was Rafael Diaz, a professor who gave up a tenured post at Stanford to study a population (through the University of California, San Francisco) which he was very passionate about: Latino gay men.

In his lecture for our class, Professor Diaz began to tell us what he'd discovered in his qualitative and quantitative research with Latino gay men. He spoke of "sexual silence" which refers to the fact that if a latino gay man wanted to stay with his family and community of origin, then he would have to remain closeted about his sexual orientation. The other side of the coin being that if he wanted to "come out" about his sexual orientation, he would have to leave his family. The language he noted in his presentation was rich and striking: "People might say, what a whore, you carry a condom in your car."

Slides from Dr. Diaz's presentation:

**Explicit and Covert Messages Latino Gay Men Receive**
Homosexuality . . .

- makes them not truly men and not normal
- meant they would grow up alone, without children
- is dirty and sinful which leads to sexual guilt and shame
- shameful to their families and loved ones
- meant that if they stayed they would have to live in a "sexual silence"
- meant that in order to live openly they would have to leave their families
- This oppression promotes the use of substances during sex (for coping, comfort and escape) which directly lowers the odds of safer sex.

(Diaz and Ayala 2001)

**Latino Gay Men on Safer Sex** (Implicit Theories)

- "It's like the heat of the moment, you get lost in that, you just want to do it all right there and then." "... couldn't think, I was too horny. . ."
- ... men felt very strongly that condoms disrupted the magic of an intimate sexual moment: Participant: It (a condom) just destroys the moment . . ."
- "People might say, what a whore, you carry a condom in your car."
- Some men spoke about the need to feel the warmth of a boyfriend's or potential lover's body, flesh-to-flesh, in order to feel truly connected.

"I was very much in love and I wanted to feel him closer"

Not only did Dr. Diaz's presentation begin to answer those unexpected questions that would bubble up in class, but it lit a fire of passion under me in my work in sexual health and health empowerment that fuels my career to this day, over 20 years later. In one short class session, Dr. Diaz was able to validate for me that the "lava" that was randomly bubbling up in our middle and high school classrooms was, indeed, valid and needed to be addressed. Furthermore, knowing what I know now, these phenomenon which would be studied in fields such as sociology or anthropology (as opposed to biology or even psychology) are at the root, the source of why people allow themselves to be at risk or even actively engage in behaviors that put them at risk for HIV and other negative consequences of risky sexual behavior.

While I was not doing presentations for out gay men, I *was* hearing about very similar "cultural scripts" (what we came to call them when, serendipitously, I did research with Dr. Diaz when he was at UCSF a few years later) or cultural messages about sex, sexuality, dating, romance, and gender roles. Latino girls in San Jose, CA would ask questions about the much older boys that would court them, implicitly or explicitly describing dynamics which included traditional gender roles, power, coercion, feelings of obligation, etc. and that was just one specific group. It ends up that every person is/was in some way vulnerable to the pressures (rewards and punishments) from the particular group or culture they lived in. This may seem very obvious now, but remember, there was no module in our HIV/AIDS curriculum addressing cultural pressures/role models.

Working alongside Carolyn Laub (who went on to found the Gay-Straight Alliance Network), my colleague at the time, we endeavored to find an activity that would help us to intentionally bring up these very powerful and ubiquitous cultural dynamics to help young people to identify them and see how they were disempowering them in regards to sexual health, as well as in so many other ways related to romance, sex, gender and even violence.

Very often we would "piggyback" our week-long workshops with our friends at Planned Parenthood who would cover birth control and other STIs in depth. To our fortune, one of their presenters showed us an activity which would become the vehicle we needed. Planned Parenthood was using an activity to very quickly get youth to discover that there is a double-standard when it comes to males, females and sex. We saw much more potential in this activity and so we borrowed it (with permission of course).

I should mention that Planned Parenthood had given it an awkward and meaningless title: "SIM, SAM, SIF and SAF" which stood for Sexually Inactive Male, Sexually Active Male, and so on. Realizing that the power of gender roles and cultural scripts that encourage or discourage behaviors comes directly from the language (or more specifically, the shame that the language imparts), I was not going to miss the opportunity (for both marketing of the workshop and education) to utilize the power of language in the title. The title we came up with was "Studs, Sluts, Virgins and Wimps." Later, I added "Pimps, Wimps, Whores and Bores." Due to the sheer number of words I've collected in the last 20 years, not to mention the combinations, the possible titles are endless. It would be very descriptive to call this presentation: "Feminist Perspectives on Comprehensive Sexual Health Education," but I am not sure that we would draw the same audience (quantity or quality) as "Studs, Sluts, Virgins and Wimps."

The activity itself is very basic: a two-by-two matrix with the variables "male" and "female" at the top (the gender binary) and 'sex' and 'no sex' on the side. (See appendix for instructions and discussion points). After a bit of set-up, the workshop facilitator asks the audience to shout out whatever comes to mind when they hear the following: words or adjectives describing a sexually active male, a male who has NOT had sex, a female who has NOT had sex and a female who has had sex. It should be noted that there are two other categories that don't have space in the 2×2 matrix but have become an important part of the activity:

**Question:** If a male has a partner (may be having sex) but is deemed overly submissive or nice to his partner what might he be labeled?
**Answer:** "Whipped" or "Pussy Whipped"

**Question:** If a female is not sexually active but is sexually attractive, what might she be called?
**Answer:** "Tease" or "Cock Tease"

There is a lot of nervousness and then laughter as people hesitate and then begin to shout out these terms, most of which are not suitable for the dinner table. With almost every term they offer, I make a point which gets them to start critically deconstructing a system to which all are exposed but which most do not think about, much less critique. Jumping back and forth between comedy and seriousness, I open them up, have them laugh at themselves and society and then lower the boom: do we all really want to stand behind what our language *really* means? For example, after we are done filling in the last box, the "slut" category, I tell the audience that in almost two decades of doing this talk I've collected *well* over 600 labels (mostly in English and Spanish) and descriptive terms for this category alone. And then I challenge them to find a comparable list of such highly derogatory terms (in quality or quantity) for any group of people in our society, even for those who we can all agree have done horrible things. No one can/has met this challenge. And then I remind them that we hoist this list upon females for the simple fact of their sexual behavior or desire. There is silence. For maybe the first time, they begin to see the problematic nature of this cultural system and the oppression that it perpetuates to all involved (male, female, gay, straight, etc.), admittedly in different ways and at varying levels of magnitude.

In doing this workshop for youth, college-aged students and parents now for approaching 20 years, I can easily make enough points in setting up and debriefing the activity to fill two hours. In brief, the overall goal of this workshop is to get audience members to stop simply accepting and participating in "The Game" (which we came to call it for simplicity and to suggest that one can decide not to "play") by linking the values espoused in "The Game" to unhealthy sexual behaviors and the shaming of others, which leads to all manner of unhealthy behaviors (e.g. violence, alcohol use/abuse in sexual situations, bullying, etc.) Said another way, there are two systems with two very different sets of values, and thus behavioral outcomes. "The Safer Choices" seek to lower our odds of negative sexual consequences by recommending three strategies: 1) Knowing when it is *not* a good time to have sexual intercourse and being able to follow through with that decision [note: 'abstinence' has many problematic connotations], 2) having access to and using barrier methods which limit the sharing of bodily fluids and 3) *both* testing for STIs and having only one sexual partner who is also tested. "The Game" on the other hand, if you take its values and pressure out to their logical end encourage: 1) not talking about sex [different reasons for males and females], 2) using alcohol on oneself and others [See Appendix for notes from my workshop: "Blame It On the A-a-a-a-a-alcohol"] and 3) not carrying and using condoms. Obviously, if sexual health is our goal, the power and pervasiveness of "The Game" is highly problematic.

To this day, I scan anything related to sexual health to see if the authors have integrated an understanding of gender roles and cultural scripts into their analyses and efforts. All too often I find this dimension missing. So while I've presented "The Game" so often that I could do it in my sleep, I know that I won't stop anytime soon. Luckily, I am rewarded each and every time I facilitate this eye opening, critical thinking experience for an audience as I realize that each person who hears this workshop can never again hear sexist jokes, banter or stories in the same way again.

Donnovan Somera Yisrael joined the staff at Stanford University's Vaden Health Center in 1998), where he has been involved as a teacher, presenter and consultant on health issues since 1993. His present position as The Manager of Emotional and Sexual Health Programs allows him to address a wide variety of health issues that affect young people, including: alcohol abuse, sexual health, sexuality/sexual identity, sexual assault, relationship abuse, body image, emotional health/intelligence and grief/loss. Donnovan's perspective on health education attempts to answer the question: "What in the culture/social environment leads to a specific health risk behavior or health outcome?"

# *The Game—Donnovan Somera Yisrael*

**Materials**: A chalkboard and chalk or a few sheets of easel paper and marking pens.

**Time:** This activity should take at least 45 minutes. Ideally, you have a full hour. Discussion time may approach infinity so make sure to get your main points across.

**Overview:** "The Game" is an interactive discussion. The main goal of this activity is for students to first see and then become critical of the complex system of values and rules (most of which are gender-based) which regulate our sexual behavior. These values and rules are contained in and perpetuated through "scripts" (called "cultural scripts" or "sexual scripts"). Although many of the "scripts" in "The Game" are not new, students are given a structure on which they can map what they observe in the world. This structure also shows how the many "scripts" in the game relate to each other, forming a complex web of often conflicting values and rules. It is the students themselves who describe the culture by brainstorming (uncensored) all of the words that they know and use to talk about sexually active and non-sexually active males and females. It is the job of the presenter to help students to dig deeper into the language to expose the underlying values and contradictions. Using storytelling to characterize both male and female experiences, the facilitator will ultimately lead the class into a discussion about how "The Game" and its rules prevent even a well informed person from implementing the "Safer Choices." To close (depending upon time, this may be a whole activity in itself), the students will discuss what it means to play "The Game" and, most importantly, how we can resist doing so. The presenter of this activity must have a willingness to listen and learn from the audience as well as perform and tell stories.

## Setting up "The Game"

Elicit the "Safer Choices" from the class. **What strategies can you use to prevent yourself from getting an STD?** List them on the right side of the board and discuss.

On the left side of the board draw a stick figure to represent the students. Underneath the figure, write "you". On top write "the facts" to signify that this person knows all of the facts and information regarding the prevention of HIV infection. **Ideally, each of you will be able to use the "Safer Choices" when they are necessary in your life**. Draw an arching line from the top of the stick figure to the "Safer Choices" **Is it possible, even though you know how to**

**protect yourself from HIV, that you or your friends will fail to choose one of the "Safer Choices"?** Said another way, **Is it possible that one of you will have unprotected sex with a person who has not been tested for HIV? Why?** List the reasons that students come up with and discuss briefly.

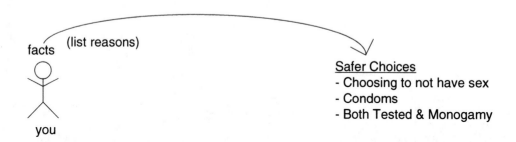

Safer Choices
- Choosing to not have sex
- Condoms
- Both Tested & Monogamy

facts  (list reasons)

you

# Redefining "Peer Pressure"

**People say that there is a lot of pressure to have sex and yet when you ask them to describe a time when they were pressured by a peer, they can't. What does sexual peer pressure actually look like?** Make up absurd examples of overt peer pressure (e.g. A bully walks up and says hey wimp, smoke this cigarette. . .) **Does it usually happen this way?** (Facilitate discussion)

## *Make this point*

People **do** experience overt peer pressure (e.g. Drink! Drink! Drink!) but most often pressure creeps into our minds in subtle and insidious ways. We forget that we can feel pressure even when the pressuring person isn't even talking directly to us. (Tell stories about sexually inexperienced teenagers at parties or in the locker room listening to others talk about sex and feeling pressure.) Because it is so subtle, often we don't even label it as "peer pressure". When the term "peer pressure" is used, it often fails to acknowledge the internal workings of that pressure. Such as: What is going on in the persons head after they hear a pressuring comment? Does the person believe what they are being told? Do they go home that night and repeat the pressuring messages over and over. This is where "peer pressure" starts sounding a lot like "self-pressure".

### "The Game"

1. Draw a large 2×2 matrix (figure 2) on the board.
2. Write "male" and "female" across the top.
3. Write "sex" and "no sex" down the left side.
4. For this activity, it is very important that the students do not censor their language. For a limited time only, in response to the following questions, you can use any words that pop up into your heads even if those words aren't usually appropriate in classrooms,

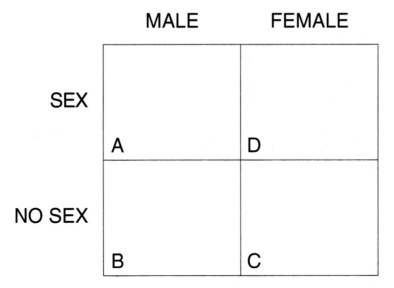

places of worship or around one's grandparents. The words that the students produce are written in the appropriate boxes. (see figure 2) The order in which the following questions are asked is very important.

box **A**: **What are the names that a male gets called if he is sexually active?**

box **B**: **What are the names that a male gets called if he is not sexually active?**

box **C**: **What are the names that a female gets called if she not sexually active?**

box **D**: **What are the names that a female gets called if she is sexually active?**

5. For each box ask: **Does the person who is called these names hear them as complements or "put-downs"?** Put a (+) next to complements and a (−) next to insults.

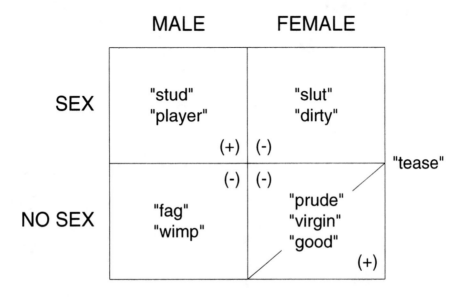

# Discussion Questions

- Looking up at the diagram we have constructed together, does anyone have any initial observations that they would like to share?
- Next, we are going to discuss what it is like growing up as a male versus growing up as a female. What are the rules of "the game" if you are a male? What are the rules of "the game" if you are a female?
- Are there any winners in this "game"? How is "the game" more than just a double standard? How do girls lose "the game"? How do guys lose "the game"?
- How does "the game" make it difficult for guys and girls to use the Safer Choices in every sexual situation?

# "The Game" vs. the "Safer Choices": How Females Lose

**Choosing Not to Have Sex**

- At a certain age (which seems to get younger and younger), girls are made to feel like **"prudes," "uptight,"** or immature if they have not had any sexual experiences (includes kissing, touching, dating, etc.).
- People tell youth that sex (like cigarettes) is for adults. Some youth turn the logic on its head and think that if they have sex it will make them an adult or more mature. This logic is incorrect. If you are immature and have sex, you will simply be a sexually active immature person.
- Females are taught to make others, especially men, happy. Put another way, females learn to be afraid to make men angry. This takes away a female's power when she tries to say "no" to sexual pressure.
- Females are only taught that they should say "no" to sex. Like the dynamics in the story "The Boy Who Cried Wolf," the lack of a healthy "yes" to sex/sexuality takes power away from a female's "no." (Belief in this assertion does NOT indicate that the writer validates its use as a defense for rape.)
- Women are told by the world that having a boyfriend/husband is the ultimate goal. He is a source of money, protection, transportation, self-esteem, and completeness. In this context, pleasing/fear of losing your man becomes extremely important and if your boyfriend wants sex it is going to be very difficult to say "no."
- **The Britney Spears Syndrome**–Even though you are not supposed to be having sex, you are supposed to talk like you are, dress like you are, act like you have, and be able to attract men using your body parts/suggest that you will have sex with them. Having "attractive" body parts is "Girl Power" (Thank you Spice Girls!). And if you do all of this you will attract a nice boy like Justin Timberlake. This is not usually what happens to young girls who follow this ethic. Essentially, "Girl Power" is the ability to "turn heads" and "turn on" men. The problem is that these females are called **"teases."** And according to the very widely accepted (absolutely NOT by this writer) logic of the **"tease,"** they deserve what they get.

## Protection

- A female who buys, has, or carries condoms risks being seen as a **"slut."**
- Unlike with birth control, a female must get her partner to agree to use condoms.

- A girl learns very early on that she should not talk about sex. She has not had any role models who talked about sex or any practice talking to someone about sex.
- A girl learns that it is not okay for her to know about sex (unless she is a peer educator). If she does, she must not show it. The implication is that knowing about sex means you are doing it and "girls shouldn't be doing it."
- Females are taught to make others, especially men, happy. Put another way, females learn to be afraid to make men angry. If he doesn't want to use a condom, a female is less likely to have been trained to stand her ground.
- One of the scripts in "The Game" is that one way to prove our love for someone is to trust them, even if that trust has not yet been earned: "I love you so much I'll do anything (take large risks) for you." In this context, condoms signify a lack of trust and thus a lack of love. Fear of losing the partner plays a big role in this scenario.

### Monogamy with Testing

- The love script says "I love you so much that I would do anything for you." That includes trusting the other person before that person has earned the trust. Asking someone to get tested is seen as a lack of trust and thus a lack of love.

# *"The Game" vs. the "Safer Choices": How Males Lose*

### Choosing not to have sex

- It can be said that males don't even have this choice at all. If a male is not having sex, it can't possibly be because he has chosen not to. The assumption is that there must be a problem: he is gay, he is ugly, he is scared, he is religious, or he is impotent.
- Sex has somehow become a rite of passage/initiation into manhood for boys. Choosing not to have sex is choosing not to be a man. Males are asked to undergo great risk to prove and maintain their manhood/masculinity.

### Protection

- One of the main scripts in "The Game" for men is that they have uncontrollable libido (sex drive). Once they get going, they can't stop for anything, including putting on a condom.
- In "The Game," penetration is the ultimate goal of sex. It defines the loss of virginity. Penetration is not possible without an erection. Using condoms adds an "inconvenient" step to the act of sex which people say **"ruins the mood/moment."** One possible reason for this is because it forces people to really think about what they are doing and keeps people from being **"swept away."** In addition, condoms do result in a slight loss

of sensitivity. (The use of lubrication and eroticizing safer sex can be effective here.) Anything that, in anyway, threatens the erection, threatens a male's masculinity and threatens **"the man."**

- Real men are supposed to be ready, willing and able to take risks. They are taught to shun protection: helmets or condoms. Men are supposed to have **"no fear."**
- Men learn to brag about scars and injuries. As incredible as it may sound, anecdotal stories show men bragging about getting girls pregnant and even getting STI's like herpes, gonorrhea and crabs. These negative consequences become proof of one's manhood.

## Monogamy with Testing

- A monogamous male is teased about being **"pussy-whipped"** if there is any suggestion that he changes his plans for his partner's sake or is "too" loving and attentive. It is said that his girlfriend is a **"ball and chain"** or that she **"wears the pants. . . "**
- A **"pimp"/"player"** must have multiple partners. He is characterized in a number of ways: 1) his sex drive is so tremendously powerful that he can't let a viable sexual partner past him, 2) he is so good looking that the girls can't leave him alone (and a "real man" is not going to refuse sex) and/or 3) he is **"suave" or "smooth"** and has **"got skillz"** and thus **"gets lots of game/play from the ladies."**

- Boys learn to brag and joke about sex but they (like the females) do not get any modeling or practice discussing sex and related issues in a serious way. Testing requires the initiation of a frank sex-related discussion. Monogamy requires the ongoing negotiation of a relationship.

- A **"real man"** would not wait to have sex. He would **"hit that"** as soon as possible. Waiting 3 months is not even a consideration for a male who is playing "The Game."

Updated 05/23/05

# Blame It On the A-a-a-a-alcohol: Why We Use Alcohol in Sexual Situations

*Donnovan Somera Yisrael, MA ('89)*
*Manager of Relationship and Sexual Health Programs*
*Health Promotion Services (HPS)*

## Discussion Questions and Points

*Why do we use alcohol? What purpose does it serve?*

*According to "The Game" why might **males** use alcohol?*

- To prove masculinity/manhood (i.e.risk-taking behavior)
- A man must be able to prove that he is fearless (alcohol turns off our fear/inhibitions/common sense.)
- Men must be able to "hold" their alcohol (Over the past few decades this has become equally a female issue)
- To deal with pain or loss (Men are taught to be ashamed of their sadness and pain. It is turned into anger. Alcohol is used to numb feelings, yet, ironically alcohol suppresses our inhibitions allowing repressed feelings to come out.)
- To express emotions (e.g. late night after a break-up)
- Others?

*According to "The Game" why might **females** use alcohol?*

*In general, why do we use alcohol in sexual situations?* (a.k.a. Why do "drunken hook-ups happen?")

- Relax self
- Deal with shyness
- Bars/Parties with alcohol have always seemed to be the ways to meet people for romantic purposes.
- Change identity
- Let loose
- Increase confidence
- Decrease inhibitions
- Others?

*Why might males use alcohol in sexual situations* (according to "The Game")?

- To give himself "courage" (a.k.a."liquid courage") to face fear/ possible rejection/ deal with personal insecurity/ artificially boost confidence. As the default asker/aggressor/initiator in romantic and sexual situations the male may use alcohol to deal with the pressure to be the "player"/"pimp" even when he is not ready or does not desire to perform that role.
- To deal with performance anxiety/personal insecurity - Men are the doers in sex. They must perform and their body parts must perform. Ironic, because of alcohol depressant effects can lead to erectile difficulties
- To facilitate getting sex by getting another person drunk and thus dropping their inhibitions and defenses. It may be that a sober person is viewed as threatening (i.e. eyes open, lights on, no swept away feeling, vulnerability). That is, alcohol is used to deal with our fear of intimacy.
- To give oneself "beer goggles" because not hooking up at all may be worse than hooking up with someone that either you or society does not view as attractive.
- To deal with sexual orientation issues
- Others?

*Why might **females** use alcohol in sexual situations* (according to "The Game")? (IMPORTANT NOTE: It is not logical or ethical to use any of the following reasons as rational for perpetrating sexual assault on a female. That is, because a female may need an excuse to act sexually does not mean that she necessarily wants to have intercourse. And even if she does this does not mean she want to have sex with anybody/everybody who walks up. )

To enable oneself:

- To be sexy
- To be sexual
- To have sex (e.g. "it's supposed to hurt")
- To have an excuse/alibi for doing something that may be embarrassing or looked down upon by society. To be able to blame alcohol.
- To be "swept away"–to avoid/ takes away responsibility (i.e. blame alcohol or the other person for initiating sexual behavior). Alcohol can be called "Swept Away in a Bottle"
- To purposefully unpremeditated sex.
- Related script: Condoms=Pre-meditation
- To "get with" the bad boy (heterosexual female)
- To deal with sexual orientation issues
- Others?

Updated 05/10/10

# Chapter 14

# Why I Teach About Pleasure

*Kate McCombs, MPH*

During my final presentation of my Master's thesis at University of Melbourne's School of Population Health, I said the word "clitoris" about half a dozen times.

After presenting my methods slides and before my conclusion, I did a female condom demonstration on my hand, indicating how the clitoris could be directly stimulated with the external ring. I talked about orgasm, pleasure, and even masturbation to an audience of doctors, epidemiologists, and other public health students. While the presentation was well-received, it certainly stuck out like a sore thumb among the talks on childhood nutrition, malaria, and tuberculosis.

In my experience working in Public Health, I have often noticed that there is a great divide between conversations about "sexual health" and discussions around pleasure. More often than not, discussions around pleasurable sex are relegated to *Men's Health* magazine or sex blogs. In the academic world of public health, we can talk all day about how HIV (human immunodeficiency virus) attaches to a CD4 cell, but as soon as we start talking about orgasm, or why people might not want to use condoms because of diminished sensation, the conversation can get quiet remarkably quickly.

I am certainly not the first person to recognize this omission of pleasure. In 1988, Michelle Fine wrote a seminal piece called "Sexuality, schooling, and adolescent females: the missing discourse of desire" calling for more discussion around pleasure in sexuality education (1). Despite Fine's call to action (and many subsequent ones), public health—and even sexual health—discussions rarely address the fact that people sometimes make risky health choices because those behaviors feel good. If sexual health promotion fails to address *why* people are engaging in a particular health behavior, it is less likely that the message will connect with that target audience. As someone who works for a university's public health department and as an editor for a sex-positive blog, I observe this pleasure/health divide on a regular basis. Magazines and blogs are filled with advice about how to have hotter sex while the discourse in academia tends to focus on STIs (sexually transmissible infections) and unplanned pregnancy.

To my delight, there has been a small but growing body of sexual health literature that advocates for the inclusion of pleasure messages in STI and HIV prevention education. When it came time for me to decide on a topic for my Master's thesis, there was no question: I was going to read everything I could get my hands on that talked about pleasure-inclusive sex ed. It's a

Reprinted by permission of Kate McCombs.

kind of education that I deliver, most often in workshops for university-aged students, and I've found that it connects with participants' life experience in a way that the use-condoms-or-else approach does not.

The term "pleasure-inclusive" describes approaches that include information about desire, sexual sensation, and enjoyment in their discussions about safer sex. Several studies describe the importance of pleasure in motivating people's safer sex decision-making, and a few report increased uptake of safer sex practices after pleasure-inclusive sex education delivery (2–5). By highlighting the ways in which pleasure-focused activities can reduce STI and HIV risk, pleasure inclusion can serve to be a way to "sell" a safer-sex message, especially to target groups that are oversaturated by, and tuned-out from, the prevention message.

Even the World Health Organization (WHO) acknowledges pleasure's place in holistic sexual health. The WHO defines sexual health as "a state of physical, mental and social well-being in relation to sexuality" (6). The WHO continues to state that sexual health "requires a positive and respectful approach to sexuality and sexual relationships, as well as **the possibility of having pleasurable and safe sexual experiences,** free of coercion, discrimination and violence" (emphasis mine) (6).

Despite the fact that a) sex is the primary route of HIV transmission (4), b) pleasure is one of the primary reasons that people have sex (7), and c) it is included in the WHO definition of "sexual health," pleasure is rarely discussed in STI and HIV prevention initiatives. The vast majority of the current literature is gray and/or qualitative, so it's not clear to what extent we can apply the findings of these studies to the general population. However, there is enough data to inspire optimism about the power of this kind of education to connect with target audiences and perhaps to influence their safer sex behavior.

In this piece, I'll explain further what pleasure-inclusive education looks like and why it's an important addendum to STI and unplanned pregnancy prevention education. I'll also look at the acceptability of these approaches to health educators, funding bodies, and target audiences and explore what factors act as barriers and facilitators to this kind of education.

# Why Talk about Pleasure?

When I first started researching and delivering pleasure-inclusive sex ed, I was met with a variety of responses. Some people don't understand why pleasure is relevant, while others just question how that approach would ever be acceptable in a largely sex-negative culture. Occasionally, in an effort to understand pleasure inclusivity, I get: "you mean like putting a condom on with your mouth?" While that sort of strategy is used in some programs targeted to adults, it is certainly not the only type of education that seeks to marry pleasure and health. In fact, many of the pleasure-inclusive programs I've come across focus extensively on women's pleasure—as both a consent and satisfaction-increasing strategy.

It's been suggested to me on more than one occasion that pleasure in a sex ed context could be awkward since many of those teaching the subject would be so uncomfortable with the material. I think there is a lot of truth to this assumption, and I often worry about how often people with sex-negative (or even just sex-uncomfortable) perspectives are tasked with teaching sex ed to young people. Whether the content of that sex ed is purely about STIs or includes pleasure messages, the attitudes of the person delivering that education is a difficult-to-control variable. Many people are uncomfortable talking about sex—even with the people they're having it with—and it's important to create more safe spaces to discuss sexuality in order to reduce the stigma, shame, and embarrassment that often accompany sex discussions.

When I talk to people about the importance of pleasure messages in STI and unplanned pregnancy prevention approaches, they sometimes ask what pleasure has to do with health. Well, on the face of it, perhaps not much. But after sharing the WHO's opinion on the subject, I respond by describing the research about what a huge factor pleasure is in motivating people's sexual decisions. Leaving out pleasure from discussions about condom use would be like talking about healthy eating without talking about taste.

Clearly, this approach is controversial and in many contexts would be difficult, if not impossible, to implement. Despite the fact that pleasure education can be an effective tool for promoting health and other goals of comprehensive sexuality education, it's often met with resistance in more conservative environments and in any context where the intention is not clear. However, it is also interesting to note that a significant percentage of the current literature on pleasure-inclusivity is based on programs implemented in developing countries (2,3,8–10). There's even an example of a Christian church delivering pleasure-inclusive sex education as part of their HIV prevention program in Mozambique (11). This particular program focused on increasing fidelity among heterosexual married couples, and while it may not be as inclusive and systematic as I would like, it illustrates how pleasure and health promotion can be brought together—even within conservative environments.

Often the discussions around the role of pleasure in STI prevention—even among its advocates—are vague about what specific topics this includes. To clarify, I describe below a number of the key pieces of pleasure-based knowledge that I think are conducive to both health and satisfaction.

# Linguistically Precise Terms for Body Parts

Teaching the difference between "vulva" and "vagina" may seem semantic, but I (and many other sex educators) argue that this is an incredibly important distinction to make. If a woman only know the whole genital area as "vagina," she has fewer linguistic tools to describe exactly how she wants to be stimulated in a sexual situation. In her book *Because It Feels Good*, sex researcher Debby Herbenick describes how knowing the names of the different parts of the vulva are important for health as well as pleasure (12). She notes that if a woman tells a medical practitioner that she has pain in your vagina, he or she will do an internal examination. If the discomfort is actually on her labia, for instance, she may not get the medical attention she needs.

Australian sex educator Linda Kirkman illustrates the importance of the vulva/vagina distinction in an activity she uses in her university lectures. She asks students to pick a spot on the back of their hand, then has them direct the person next to them to that spot using only the word "arm." While one could say up, down, to the left, etc., this activity illustrates how negotiating pleasure can be much more challenging (and time-consuming) when you don't have a comprehensive vocabulary tool kit.

The location and function of the clitoris is particularly pivotal. Since most women do not orgasm from vaginal stimulation alone, it's important for them to be aware of the clitoris's role in female pleasure. Male pleasure, even when not discussed explicitly, is nearly always present in reproductive penile-vaginal sex. Many sex educators (myself included) are concerned that the general lack of acknowledgment of the clitoris in some sex ed spaces gives women the impression that penile-vaginal sex is the default when in fact, most women need additional stimulation to experience orgasm. While I also argue that an excessive orgasm-focus can be damaging, people are still entitled to and can benefit from anatomical knowledge about the loci of orgasm.

# Masturbation Is Normal and Healthy

For an activity that is STI and unplanned pregnancy-free, masturbation is remarkably controversial. Surgeon General Jocelyn Elders was asked to resign after she commented that it was normal, healthy, and perhaps should be taught due to the reasons previously described. I don't believe Dr. Elders was calling for a comprehensive how-to in schools, but rather she wanted to ensure that young people know that masturbation is a perfectly acceptable way to experience pleasure and learn about one's body.

There's a lot of widespread cultural shame and silence around the topic of masturbation. Even when it is discussed, it's often framed as something people only do when they're not getting laid. It's important for people to know that it's normal to masturbate, even within a sexually-satisfying relationship. The benefit of this knowledge is two-fold: people have more realistic information about normal sexual practices and masturbation becomes more than just a second-tier replacement for partner sex. Provided that it doesn't become a compulsive habit that impairs your ability to function socially (something that's rare, to say the least), masturbation can be a healthy adjunct to a satisfying sex life. It's an excellent way to learn about one's body in a risk-free environment, and learning to communicate what stimulation one enjoys can encourage communication within relationships.

# Using Lubricant Makes Condoms Feel Better

It never ceases to amaze me how many people don't know about using lubricants with condoms. Latex and non-latex alternatives like polyisoprene and polyurethane can dry out easily, making sex less comfortable and micro-tears in the genital tissue more likely. Yes, most condoms come pre-lubricated but extra lubrication increases pleasure and reduces the risks of tearing. Pleasure-inclusive condom promotion should include information about what lubricants are condom-compatible. Anything oil-based (like petroleum jelly or baby oil) can degrade latex and polyisoprene, so it's preferable to encourage the use of water- and silicone-based products. It also bears mentioning that lubricating both sides of the barrier can increase pleasure. As sex educator Gareth Durrant says, "Lube is a lot like beauty; while it's great to have it on the outside, it's a whole lot better when it's on the inside as well."

# Pleasure Is about More Than Just Orgasm

When I teach workshops on pleasure physiology and eroticizing safer sex, I like to begin by asking people to name non-sexual, non-genital things they find pleasurable. I often get responses like "getting a massage" or "eating chocolate." Their responses often remind me of the scene in *Amelie* when Audrey Tautou's character waxes lyrical about the joys of cracking the top of a crème brûlée.

I facilitate this activity, not only to break the ice in a workshop on a taboo-riddled topic, but also to get people thinking about being present with pleasure. Sexual pleasure isn't just about orgasm. Sex educators and therapists are constantly encouraging people to "enjoy the journey, not the destination" because many of the sexual challenges adults face can be traced to a goal-obsessed approach. In most pop-culture sexual education, there is a huge emphasis on bigger, longer, and more frequent orgasms. This is not to say that orgasms should be side-lined, but I do think people should feel permission to enjoy consensual pleasure without an excessive goal-focus. Education about orgasm is important, but fixation on an outcome can undermine climax as well as the overall satisfaction of a sexual exchange.

A colleague of mine, Jacki Brown, who teaches about sexuality and disability, attended one of my workshops and commented on my pleasure-isn't-just-orgasm approach. She described how learning about non-orgasm-focused approaches to sexual pleasure was particularly useful for people with disabilities. Since some people with disabilities are not able to experience orgasm, focusing on other types of pleasure can make for more positive experiences. Her words really stuck with me, as I had not considered that this approach had this inclusivity aspect.

## Pleasure Is Not Just about Penile-Vaginal Sex

Traditional sex education tends to focus exclusively on penile-vaginal sex and, occasionally, oral and anal sex. While these activities tend to be the riskiest in regards to STI and HIV transmission and pregnancy, there are a host of other sex behaviors that are pleasurable but much lower risk. Mutual masturbation, sharing fantasies, erotic massage, etc. all carry little to no health risk. Acknowledging that these forms of sexual expression can be valid additions or alternatives to penetrative intercourse can be a way to encourage safer sex.

Some researchers argue that this aspect of pleasure-focused education has the potential to overcome much of the heteronormativity in traditional sex ed (13,14). If sex ed is purely focused on baby-making or pregnancy prevention, it excludes the students who don't identify as heterosexual. Even for people who will have reproductive sex in their lifetimes, relatively few of their sexual encounters will be motivated by procreativity.

When I discuss pleasure-inclusive approaches with other sexual health educators, their first concern is about acceptability. Questions like "How do you convince department heads to run programs like that?" and "Is it OK for public health organizations to transmit that kind of knowledge?" are common. There are no easy answers, of course, but in the literature on pleasure-inclusive approaches there are several factors that influence acceptability.

Acceptability has been defined as "a quality which makes an object, person, event, or idea attractive, satisfactory, pleasing, or welcome . . . [and] the acceptability of a given phenomenon may differ according to the source, context, and timing of the evaluation (15)." Throughout the literature on pleasure-inclusive sex education, two primary themes emerge that influence the acceptability of this approach; 1. cultural-appropriateness and community involvement and 2. marketing and language. Many of the programs described in the literature reflect both of those themes.

# Cultural-Appropriateness and Community Involvement

Logically, programs that include pleasure-based messages are more acceptable when they are suited to and appropriate for the target population. In order to establish cultural acceptability, communities must be consulted and included to ensure that programs are relevant and desirable. Ensuring that the target population is included in program development is important across all sectors of public health but is especially crucial when exploring highly taboo issues like sexuality. Not only does consulting a target group prior to implementation make programs more acceptable, it also increases sustainability.

It is well accepted that "sex sells," but health promoters rarely capitalize on that truism to promote safer sex. More often than not, STI prevention messages are overly-clinical and disease-focused and may not address the desire and pleasure that is more alive in people's consciousness when they actually make sex decisions. Even when someone has access to barrier methods, information about how to use them, and a relationship in which he or she can negotiate their use, a person's intention to practice safe sex when they are unaroused may shift once they are actually in a sexual scenario. Concern about disease, pregnancy, and risk may not be as alive for them once they are in a non-rational mental space.

One of the key factors in increasing acceptability is age-appropriateness. I suspect that sometimes when I tell people I teach pleasure-inclusive sex education, they assume I'm teaching middle schoolers about the Kama Sutra. Suffice it to say, this is not the case. I primarily teach over 18s, which broadens the scope of what I can present in terms of pleasure. As with all types of sex education, making sure messages are appropriate for the target age group is crucial. For high school students, accompanying messages about correct condom use with information about lubricants would be appropriate. Even for younger students learning about puberty, it is appropriate for them to know what masturbation is and that it's something normal that people do in private (if they choose to do it). It also bears mentioning that there's no evidence to suggest that including age-appropriate pleasure messages encourages sexual behavior.

# Marketing and Language

Many pleasure-inclusive STI prevention programs utilize pleasure to make the safety message sexy. Some research suggests that this approach makes those messages more memorable and, as a result, more likely to influence behavior change (2,4,10). Most public health studies and interventions use relatively clinical language to communicate safety messages. Many of the pleasure-inclusive programs make a point of addressing the disparity between health education language and the language people use in their erotic encounters. They argue that in order to be effective, STI and HIV prevention education need to reflect the language that the target group uses when negotiating their sexual practices.

Traditional sexual health promotion uses marketing approaches that characterize people as victims of STIs, which further perpetuates the stigma around STI testing and diagnosis. We see another perspective in many pleasure-inclusive programs, which seek to market barrier methods as a way to encourage pleasure and overcome any diminished sensation that can result from barrier use. For example, some STI prevention programs capitalize on the fact that the external ring of a female condom can be used to stimulate the clitoris during intercourse (2,4). Unlike the male condom, this STI prevention method is controlled by women *and* can result in more sexual pleasure. Some enthusiasts of this strategy argue that if women can understand their pleasure responses and can negotiate those with a partner, it increases their ability to negotiate safer sex with a partner (3,4).

# Conclusion

My primary goal for this piece is to inspire greater discussion about the role that pleasure plays in motivating risk behavior. The rationale for acknowledging and talking about pleasure is not to encourage people to "have more sex," as the perception sometimes seems to be. Rather, it is to prompt people to consider why they have sex, what they enjoy about sex, and how taking precautions has the potential to make sex better, whether through the knowledge that risks have been mitigated or through the enjoyment of the physical experience itself. Safer sex decisions are more complicated than simply knowing the risks of STIs or how to use a condom.

While these pieces of knowledge are important, pleasure is not superfluous—it is a key motivator for sexual decision-making. Pleasure certainly influences unsafe sexual practices but can also be an entry point into discussions that encourage risk-reduction behavior. People are motivated by pleasure. If public health practitioners are able to connect with this universal aspect of humanity, it could further their message.

With the growing need to implement sound STI and HIV prevention strategies, it is crucial that our target groups' needs be considered, both in content and in delivery. The research on this type of delivery suggests that target groups find pleasure-inclusive approaches acceptable and desirable. While there is a great need for more research regarding the acceptability of these approaches, the current research does strongly suggest that this is a worthwhile area of study. The existing literature inspires optimism about this unconventional approach, but such innovation requires an increased evidence base to better advocate to stakeholders.

Pleasure is clearly a fundamental source of human motivation and should be an important component of programs that seek to change behavior, especially when the behavior, like sexual activity, is so strongly motivated by pleasure. Knerr and Philpott, two of the most prolific researchers and advocates in the area of pleasure-inclusive STI and HIV prevention, argue that "the results of this kind of approach . . . go beyond improving sexual health, to enabling women and men to experience healthier, happier lives (11)." Pleasure is integral to the human experience, and in order to have a holistic approach to public health, we must not exclude it in the discourse.

Kate McCombs, MPH is a sex educator, blogger, and speaker, specializing in sex-positive approaches to sexual health promotion. She's the managing editor for MySexProfessor.com, a sex education blog, and is the founder of Sex Geekdom, a community for sex educators, researchers, and other sex geeky folks. You can find her on twitter @katecom or at katemccombs.com.

# References

1. Fine M. Sexuality, schooling, and adolescent females: the missing discourse of desire. Harvard Educational Review. 1988;58:29.
2. Knerr W. The Global Mapping of Pleasure: A directory of organizations, programmes, media and people who eroticize safer sex. The Pleasure Project The Realising Rights Research Consortium; 2008.
3. Knerr W, Philpott A. Promoting Safer Sex Through Pleasure: Lessons from 15 Countries. Society for International Development. 2009;52:95–100.
4. Philpott A, Knerr W, Maher D. Promoting protection and pleasure: amplifying the effectiveness of barriers against sexually transmitted infections and pregnancy. Lancet. 2006;2028–31.
5. Scott-Sheldon LA. Eroticizing creates safer sex: a research synthesis. The Journal of Primary Prevention. 2006;27:619.
6. WHO. Health Topics: Sexual Health [Internet]. 2011 [cited 1915 Jan 1]. Available from: http://www.who.int/topics/sexual_health/en/
7. Meston CM, Buss DM. Why Humans Have Sex. Archives of Sexual Behaviour. 2007;36:477–507.
8. Mkumbo K. What Tanzanian young people want to know about sexual health; implications for school-based sex and relationships education. Sex Education. 2010;10:405–12.
9. Garcia S, Yam E, Firestone M. "No party hat, no party": successful condom use in sex work in Mexico and the Dominican Republic. Reproductive Health Matters. 2006;14:53–62.
10. Gysels M, Pool R, Nyanzi S. The adventures of the Randy Professor and Angela the Sugar Mummy: Sex in fictional serials in Ugandan popular magazines. AIDS Care. 2005;17:967–77.
11. Knerr W, Philpott A. Putting the sexy back into safer sex: The Pleasure Project. IDS bulletin. 2006;37:105.
12. Herbenick D. Because it Feels Good. New York, NY: Rodale Books; 2009.
13. Allen L. Beyond the birds and the bees: constituting a discourse of erotics in sexuality education. Gender and Education. 2004;16:131–67.
14. Lamb S, Listig K, Graling K. The use and misuse of pleasure in sex ed. Sex Education. 2013;13:301–18.
15. Marshall JF. Acceptability of fertility regulating methods: Designing technology to fit people. Preventive Medicine. 1977;6:65–73.

# Chapter 15

# *Strategies for Communicating About Sexuality with Your Kids or Teens*

*Ivy Chen, MPH*

Over many years of teaching sexuality education in the San Francisco Bay Area, I have collected many effective strategies from parents about communicating with their kids about sexuality. I am grateful for their input, and I am sharing some of their best suggestions with you.

- *Though these tips are presented as parents talking/interacting with their own children, many of these tips can be implemented by any adult to the kids and teens in their lives. A kid can never have enough caring adults in their lives, so if you are a cool auntie or uncle, older cousin, older sibling, or trusted family friend, you can use these communication tips too.*

1. **Keep Your Answers to About Two Sentences**
   When a kid asks a question about sex or reproduction, many parents think, "OK, here comes the Big Talk." Then the parent launches into a long discussion until the kid's eyes glaze over. The most natural way to handle the questions is to address the question being asked at face value and try to condense your answer into about two sentences. This brevity is particular important for younger kids, whose attention span may be short, and who often simply just wants a word defined or wants a quick factual answer. If parents keep their answers short, this pattern invites a conversation with their children rather than a long one-sided lecture. One of the best strategies that I have heard was from a parent who shared that she "puts on her imaginary lab coat" whenever her 10 year old daughter asks a question about sexuality. The imaginary lab coat helps her to put on a scientist's persona and focus on a few biological facts when answering questions.

2. **Get Your Kid to be Your Ally**
   Many parents may not be comfortable discussing sexuality issues with their kids, but many feel like they have to appear to be the authority on the subject. If you start out by admitting to your kids that you are nervous talking to them about sexuality, and that they need to encourage you, they are more likely to be empathetic and share in the discussion rather than feel as if you are lecturing to them.

A mother, whose daughter I had taught from 6<sup>th</sup>-8<sup>th</sup> grades, wanted to be the one to talk with her daughter about sex but was extremely nervous. She confessed to her daughter that while she was speaking about sex, she was probably going to turn red, start sweating, and probably would not be able to look her in the eye. In fact, she was so flustered that the only way she could finish talking was to turn her chair around to talk to the wall rather than look at her daughter! Nonetheless, she got through that first conversation about sex with her daughter's encouragement, and the subtext that her daughter received was that mom made it a priority to talk with her about sex despite mom's fears and discomfort. They have had many subsequent conversations, which had gotten easier with practice.

3. **The Car is a Great Place to Talk About Sex**
When you are driving, you are focused on the driving and looking ahead. If a kid asks a sexuality question, then many parents find it easier to talk about sex when not making direct eye contact. Driving carpool also seems to provide parents with plenty of details about the puberty and relationship drama that is happening among your kid's friends. Kids and teens are much more open when their own parent is not present, so the driver may get an earful. Lastly, driving around with your child allows a parent to comment on the multiple billboards and the way the media portrays sexuality, masculinity, femininity, and beauty. You might also comment on a news story on the radio that touches upon some aspect of sexuality whether the news is talking about same-sex marriage, a new birth control method, or a political candidate's stance on abortion rights. If you listen to pop music, there is plenty to dissect with the graphic sexual lyrics in many songs. As you comment, you are just "thinking out loud", not requiring your kids' input but they are definitely listening.

4. **Continue the Cuddling with Your Kids**
Parents may be less physically demonstrative with their kids as they grow into teens. Particularly, dads tell me they are less comfortable hugging their developing daughters. Although teens can be more aloof than when they were kids, this is a normal developmental phase during which they are separating and individuating from their parents. Teens may experience a "push-pull" relationship with their parents where they want to be babied one moment and then treated like an adult the next. Though sometimes challenging, I encourage parents to be steadfast in offering affectionate touch to their kids in the forms of cuddles, hugs, kisses, etc. Parents should help teens acknowledge the difference between affectionate touch and sexual touch. Teens who are deprived of affectionate touch from a safe source, such as family, may seek out any human touch, including riskier sexual touch.

5. **Give Your Teen a Choice in Physical Affection**
One of the principals I work with shared this great tip:
After years of telling her teenage son to be respectful of other people's boundaries and to have others respect his boundaries, she decided that it was important for her to practice what she preached with him. Rather than smothering him with hugs that he

sometimes resists, she said to him, "Son, I love you, and I want to demonstrate that every day to you in a physical way, but I want you to tell me what you're comfortable with for each day." On that first day, he said, "OK, I'm good with a fist-bump." Though a little disappointed, she respected the request. A couple of days later, he approached her and said, "Today, I'd really like a hug."

6. **Continue Childhood Night-Time Rituals**
   a. **Tuck-in time:** Bed time is often when kids/teens reflect on the events of the day. This is when kids are more likely to ask you a question, especially when the lights are dimmed, they are tired and their defenses are lowest. If you are present to tuck them in and perhaps prompt them with the question, "anything you want to chat about before you go to sleep?", they may bring their issues up.
   b. **Good Night Kiss:** Parents may phase out the good-night kiss as their kids get older, but continuing the ritual will pay dividend as kids get older. You may be able to negotiate curfew with the good-night kiss. If your teen wants to stay at a party that ends at midnight but you want them home earlier, you could say, "you know I got to sleep at 11pm, and I need my good night kiss from you before I sleep." Teens will take this message better if parents explain the subtext that they can only go to sleep soundly knowing their kids are home safe. In addition, if your teens give you a kiss on the cheek, you can smell anything that is on their breath such as pot, cigarettes, alcohol that could alert you to high-risk behaviors early. Parents cannot phase out the good-night kiss when kids are 12 years old only to reinstate it when the kids are 16, so retain that good-night kiss from their childhood!

*The healthiest source of information about sexuality for kids is the family. Optimally, these conversations about sexuality have been ongoing with your kids ever since they were young. However, it is never too late, even if you have teenagers. Whereas kids and teens can learn about the facts and biology of sexuality from school programs, parents and other adults in their lives play a significant role in conveying values about love, sex and relationships.*

# Chapter 16

# Bisexuality and School Culture: School as a Prime Site for Bi-Intervention

*John P. Elia*

*Bisexuality has been a neglected topic in U.S. schools. This is not entirely surprising given bisexuality's marginal positionality in U.S. society. Before exploring how, and to what degree, bisexuality gets treated in schools, this article sets the larger context by beginning with a brief description and analysis of societal attitudes about bisexuality in general. Then, an examination of the status of bisexuality in schools with particular foci on the curricular (e.g., the sexuality education and general curriculum) and extracurricular (e.g., Gay-Straight Alliances) components is undertaken. Finally, reasons are offered about why bisexuality should be genuinely and fully included in sexuality education and other courses across the curriculum and in extracurricular settings. The main arguments advanced are that there has been widespread binegativity in U.S. society that not only has been harmful to bisexuals, but also has reified and reproduced binary, dichotomous thinking about sexual and gender matters, rendering bisexuality invisible in most circumstances in schools. Another critical point is that though schools are well positioned to eradicate binegativity and use teaching about bisexuality as a way of doing positive cultural work surrounding sexuality and gender, major school reform—including structural changes to the curricular and extracurricular aspects of schooling—needs to occur.*

*KEYWORDS binary, binegativity, biphobia, bisexuality, curricular interventions, extracurricular interventions, Gay-Straight Alliances (GSAs), gender and sexual hierarchies, heteronormativity, invisibility, LGBisexualTQ youth, queer, school culture*

Thanks and gratitude are in order for Dr. Mickey Eliason and Dr. Gust Yep. who are dear friends and colleagues and whose sharp intellect and dogged commitment to gender and sexual justice have forced me—in the very best sense of the term—to think more deeply about various interventions needed to create a more just, equitable and nonviolent world for sexual and gender 'minorities.' My own thinking and academic work have profited enormously from the influence they have had on me as coauthors, and as academic comrades in general.

Address correspondence to Dr. John P. Elia, Department of Health Education, HSS Bldg. 326. San Francisco State University, 1600 Holloway Avenue, San Francisco, CA 94132-4161, USA. E-mail: jpelia@sfsu.edu

*Previously published in the Journal of Bisexuality

> Youth culture is permeated by nuance, especially with regard to sexuality. Sexual behavior and sexual orientation flow within various gender expressions and changing definitions of what is gay, bisexual, straight. If pushed they might agree to vague terms such as "queer" or "not straight." (Savin-Williams, 2005, p. 209)

> Bisexuality unsettles certainties: straight, gay, lesbian. It has affinities with all of these, and is delimited by none. It is, then, an identity that is also not an identity, a sign of the certainty of ambiguity, the stability of instability, and a category that defies and defeats categorization. (Garber, 1995, p. 70)

> Bisexual youth say they have not gained knowledge about bisexuality at school but on their own. In their opinion the sexual education at school seems to reinforce traditional division of homo- and heterosexuality and of masculinity and femininity. (Kangasvuo, 2003, p. 210)

Bisexuality has been an acknowledged phenomenon by sex researchers for more than a century. It has enjoyed some attention by anthropologists, biologists, classicists, historians, psychologists and sociologists among other academics. Writing about bisexuality's presence throughout the early history of the Western world, Eva Canterella (2002), a classicist at the University of Milan, documented the pervasiveness of bisexual behavior in the ancient Western world. Despite these studies and the fairly recent integration of bisexuality in models of sexual identity development, in many ways—and in most instances—bisexuality has enjoyed little more than a nod by U.S. society. In general, bisexuality continues to be given short shrift as a legitimate sexual identity by scholars in lesbian, gay, bisexual, transgender (LGBT) studies and sexuality studies more broadly, as well as by LGBT social/political organizations. This is reflected in schools in terms of the curricular and extracurricular activities. In this article I provide a brief treatment of general societal attitudes about bisexuality. Then I turn to an exploration of how the broader societal views of bisexuality are reflected in school culture, and finally I turn to ways in which schools can be more inclusive of bisexuality as a form of attraction, sexual identity and/or sexual behavior.

## Broad Societal Views About Bisexuality

Although bisexuality is a concept familiar to most, it is curious why it is not more 'on the map' in terms of being thoroughly integrated in scholarly and general discourses. For the most part, bisexuality has not been fully recognized as a genuine and valid sexual identity and sexual lifestyle. There are multiple reasons why bisexuality is not viewed as a fully legitimate, even believable, sexual and social identity and lifestyle. Steven Angelides (2001) puts it best by asserting

> Doubts about bisexuality are not new. Variously characterized within dominant discourses of sexuality as, among other things, a form of infantilism or immaturity, a transitional phase, a self-delusion or state of confusion, a personal or political cop out, a panacea, a superficial fashion trend... even a lie..., the category of bisexuality for over a century has been persistently refused the title of legitimate sexual identity. (p. 1)

Besides the reasons indicated above, there is still a considerable level of heteronormativity at work, and bisexuals continue to be admonished because they are not heterosexuals

(Queen, 1996). The story is even more complicated. Our society tends to be monosexist (see Israel & Mohr, 2004) in that most individuals believe that sexual identity and sexual behavior should be (perhaps, may be only) centered on either same-sex or so-called opposite sex. It constitutes an 'either/or' proposition. Often it is difficult for most individuals to believe and accept that it is possible for individuals—adolescents and adults—to genuinely have a stable sexual identity that includes sexual attraction/contact and/or romantic feelings for both members of the same sex and the other sex.

Bisexuality, in theory and practice, in many ways defies the monosexist model which, in part, has generated prejudice against bisexuals on a number of fronts and has permeated social life in the United States. *Binegativity,* a term that refers to a number of negative attitudes about bisexuality and bisexuals (see, e.g., Eliason, 2001), captures much of the prejudice and resulting violence perpetrated against bisexuals from not only heterosexually identified folks, but also from gay/lesbian identified individuals. As Alexander and Yescavage (2003) pointed out, although there are some members of the gay and lesbian 'community' who accept bisexuals as part of the queer clan, "others, however, question whether bisexuals and the transgendered really 'belong' to the gay and lesbian community" (p. 3). A shared sexual minority status offers little acceptance of bisexuals by many gays and lesbians. Then, there are those in the 'straight community' who write bisexuals off as queers who best belong in the 'gay and lesbian community.' Binegative beliefs and attitudes are widespread and play out in various ways. Some manifestations of binegativity are expressed in the following commonly held beliefs:

- Bisexuality is farce and has no basis in reality, namely, bisexual people are nonexistent (Angel, 2008; Human Rights Campaign, 2010).
- Bisexual people face less discrimination than gays and lesbians (Angel, 2008).
- Bisexuals are in a transitional state from hetero land to homo land (Burleson, 2005).
- Bisexual people are really gay or lesbian but don't have the courage to come out (Eliason, 1997).
- Bisexual males are vectors of disease (primarily HIV/AIDS) and spread sexually transmitted diseases to the straight community (Burleson, 2005; Eliason, 1997).
- Bisexual people are incapable of being monogamous (Eliason, 1997; Human Rights Campaign, 2010).
- Bisexual people are confused and cannot make up their minds (Human Rights Campaign, 2010).
- Bisexuals are confused about their identity (Eliason, 1997).
- Bisexuals conveniently use their bi-identity to enjoy heterosexual privilege (Burleson, 2005).

The list above is hardly exhaustive. These binegative beliefs (sometimes referred to as *biphobia*) and attitudes are widely cited in the literature (for additional examples, see Burleson, 2005; Eliason, 1997; Eliason, 2001; Fox, 1996; Garber, 1995; Israel & Mohr, 2004; Kangasvuo, 2003; Kaplan, 1995). It goes without saying that binegativity has had, and continues to have, a deleterious impact on bisexuals. Schools, as an integral institution of U.S. society, have been inhospitable and downright negative to sexual minority youth (including bisexuals) in a few significant ways.

# Bisexuality and School Culture

Schools are a microcosm of what transpires in the broader societal context. Schools have been hostile to sexual minority youth, including bisexuals, as evidenced by the results of a recent nation-wide empirical study. Specifically regarding bisexuality, there has been an absence and even silence in the school curriculum and in other aspects of schooling. Mistreatment of sexual minority youth in schools by other school-aged individuals, in addition to the curricular and extracurricular silence about bisexuality, is negative forces confronting bisexual youth. First, let's turn to the compelling yet haunting results from a major study, and then an examination of the curriculum concerning bisexuality is in order. An influential and widely cited study involving 1,732 respondents (students) regarding school climate issues and LG*Bisexual*TQ youth was published by the Harris Interactive and the Gay, Lesbian, and Straight Education Network (GLSEN) in 2005. In sum, it revealed that schools in the United States remain dangerous places for sexual minority youth. For instance, 89% of respondents reported hearing the often-uttered derogatory comment "that's so gay." Nearly 20% of the respondents heard homophobic comments, and seldom did school personnel who overheard such comments intervene in any way. Sixty-four percent of the respondents reported being verbally harassed. Thirteen percent were physically harassed, and 18% were physically assaulted. Many students were not out at school, and scores of others did not feel comfortable being themselves at school (Harris & GLSEN, 2005).

Although GLSEN has done a considerable amount of important work to bring more social justice to schools throughout the United States since becoming a national organization in 1995, including conducting a nationwide school climate survey, the survey results make little distinction about how school climate affects specific subsets of sexual minority youths. School climate results were not offered specifically for bisexuality. In other words, there is no information presented about how bisexually identified students (or those who indicate that they are neither straight nor gay/lesbian—increasingly, many youth refuse to be labeled at all) experience school climate regarding their bisexuality. For purposes of visibility and to aid in making targeted, specific interventions in schools for bisexual students, it would be valuable for future surveys to include questions specifically about bisexuality, however broadly defined, to assist school teachers, nurses, counselors, security personnel, administrators, community members, students and parents to be able to target interventions to counter and address the insidious binegativity, biphobia that undoubtedly continues to exists in school culture due to sexual and gender hierarchies, which stress heteronormativity with all of its attendant proscriptions.[1] As the curriculum is the bedrock of the school experience, it is important to examine how bisexuality has been treated in this realm of schooling.

## *Curricular Obliteration*

Heteronormativity is promoted, reified and reproduced in schools. Therefore, it comes as no surprise that schools have largely neglected sexual minority issues, especially bisexuality, in the curriculum and in extracurricular programs. In terms of the curriculum, generally issues related to queer youth in schools fall within multiculturalism and the sexuality education curricula. There is a scarcity of information specifically about whether bisexuality is part of the curriculum. An examination of the multicultural education curricula, however, reveals that "the majority do not address the concern of queer youth within the official curriculum. These missing discourses tell queer youth that they are not worthy of inclusion, that they are and ought to remain invisible" (Loutzenheiser & MacIntosh, 2004, p. 155). This sort of curricular neglect is also true for school-based sexuality education.

## Sexuality Education

Historically, sexuality education has been extraordinarily heterosexist even to the extent of passing and enacting federal legislation in support of abstinence-only-until-marriage, which sends a strong message that sexual contact is reserved for heterosexually married individuals. The Adolescent Family Life Act (AFLA) was passed in 1982, and the most recent legislation was the Title V portion of the Social Security Act, which was passed in 1996. The content of both of these federally based approaches to sexuality education involved restricting discussions and lessons about sexuality to heterosexuality. In most instances coverage of bisexuality and homosexuality was strictly prohibited. In fact, all content in textbooks, workbooks, lessons and lectures reflected the ideas that there were benefits to physical, social and emotional health from postponing sexual activity until (heterosexually) married, and that sexual behavior outside of marriage would likely have negative health outcomes. What results is that

> Students leave the classroom with an understanding that heterosexuality is more revered and is simply better than other sexual identities [and behaviors] and lifestyles. Discussions about bisexuality and homosexuality rarely occur. . . . Essentially, this approach conveys the message that bisexuals, gays, and lesbians are not 'fully sexual human beings' and that their sexuality is downright wrong. (Elia, 2005, p. 51)

This unwaivering heterocentric focus has been a prominent feature of school-based sexuality education since its inception in the early 20th century (Elia, 2009). Sexual and gendered others/minorities are systematically erased and have been for about a century. Again, it should be noted that the term *bisexuality* is rarely if ever uttered. Even when opposition is leveled against abstinence-only-until-marriage sexuality education, often the 'umbrella terms' such as LGBT or queer are identified as groups opposing such measures. Bisexuality gets 'lost in the shuffle.' This is highly problematic and serves to keep bisexuality deeply buried in the closet.

Another issue from which bisexuals and bisexuality have suffered in general and specifically concerning school-based sexuality education is what I have come to call the 'plight of the alphabet soup approach to inclusion.' Anyone who is even remotely familiar with the literature has seen the LGBT moniker, which has expanded over the years to include LG*Bisexual*TQQI (lesbian, gay, bisexual, transgender, queer, questioning, and intersex). For all intents and purposes, it is an empty *B*. It has been a placeholder for bisexuality/bisexuals in the string of letters that are reserved for sexual and gendered others. Loutzenheiser and MacIntosh (2004) indicated that "it seems as if gay and lesbian issues (but not necessarily queer, bi- or transgendered) are appearing everywhere" (p. 151). Although it would be incorrect for me to assert that there has been no work done along bisexual lines as far as school-based sexuality education is concerned, bisexuality is still grossly underrepresented in the literature. For instance, while doing the research for this article, I found a plethora of scholarly articles on LG*Bisexual*TQ youth, but only very few dealing specifically with bisexual youth, and even fewer focusing on bisexuality and school-based sexuality education. Bisexuality and bisexuals only receive a paucity of treatment.

Perhaps the most prominent institutional proponent of broad-based, comprehensive school-based sexuality education in the United States is the Sexuality Information Education Council of the United States (SIECUS). In 2004 it produced the third edition of the *Guidelines for Comprehensive Sexuality Education: Kindergarten through 12th Grade,* which offers developmentally appropriate information about a number of aspects of sexuality along the lines of the biological, ethical, sociocultural, psychological and spiritual aspects of sexuality. Whereas bisexuality is mentioned along with gay and lesbian identities and behavior as valid and acceptable, the guidelines are vague when it comes to bisexuality. For example, bisexuality is not clearly defined, and there are no concrete suggestions about how to approach bisexuality in the classroom in terms of readings, lessons, classroom activities or assignments. Although well intentioned, SIECUS falls into the all-too-common practice of invoking 'bisexuality' without offering substantive suggestions about how to provide comprehensive educational experiences for those students receiving sexuality education. Again, we are faced with the 'empty *B*.'

Beyond the concern that SIECUS glosses over bisexuality is how sexual identities are characterized in the guidelines. They are portrayed as fixed. The terms *bisexuality, bisexual, gay, lesbian,* and *homosexuality* are mentioned as essentialized and unchanging. Offering a critique of the *SIECUS Guidelines,* Elia and Eliason (2010b) noted, "How about the growing number of youth who identify as queer or blur the lines between gay, lesbian, and bisexual and heterosexual sexualities? And, where are gender queer youth in the guidelines?" (p. 34). Additionally, the guidelines tend to 'collapse' all of the sexuality identities together and perpetuate the notion that all sexual minorities—LGBT—get lumped together by highlighting the similarities shared by LGBT people. For example, the guidelines state that "gay men, lesbians, bisexuals are alike in most ways" (for a detailed critique of the *SIECUS Guidelines*, see, e.g., Elia & Eliason, 2010b). It is concerning that SIECUS uses the rhetoric of lumping all sexual identities together as this obscures palpable individual differences. It is critical that bisexuality, for example, stand on its own (i.e., be split apart from other sexual identities, behaviors, etc.). Such lumping together (e.g., LGBTQ) serves to make bisexuality invisible in sexuality education, if the lesson even goes so far as addressing 'sexual minority' issues. What results is systematic erasure, which is a form of violence and neglect. Given the number of youth who identify as bisexual, queer, gender queer or who refuse to claim any sexual identity (see Savin-Williams, 2005), it is incredibly important to mark bisexuality specifically and deal with it substantively in the sexuality education curriculum.

Typically, U.S. school-based sexuality education has virtually ignored the fuzzy, blurry gender and sexual world. Therefore, it is important that we move to question critically and dismantle the binary paradigm and way of thinking. In her article on the problematic aspects of binary thinking, Rebecca Kaplan (1995) noted, "[b]inary thinking is a constraining mode of thought, which divides the world into two discrete boxes. This highly pervasive form of thought leads to the erasure of bisexuality" (p. 267). There is perhaps no more pernicious way to symbolically and materially harm a group of people than to systematically erase their existence. Bisexuals as individuals and bisexuality as a sexual identity have paid a tremendous price due to societal erasure. The cultural hegemony of heteronormativity has been "the quintessential force creating, sustaining, and perpetuating the erasure, marginalization, disempowerment, and oppression of sexual others" (Yep, 2003, p. 18). Erasure of the bisexuality has, indeed, been closely associated with, if not the main cause of, marginalization, disempowerment and oppression of bisexuals. Yep (2003) also called attention to the discursive, physical and symbolic violence that sexual others routinely face due to hegemonic sexual and gender hierarchies. Bisexuals certainly have continued to endure such violence and at every level. Sexuality education in schools could potentially play a significant role in mitigating, if not eliminating altogether, the erasure and ensuing violence from which bisexual people and their allies have suffered.

## Bisexuality Beyond the Curriculum

The most commonly documented form of violence against sexual and gender minority youth focuses on bullying in schools. There is a tremendous amount of literature on bullying of sexual minority youth. School-based sexuality education has been mostly silent about bisexuality and has colluded in its erasure, nevertheless students who are either out as bisexual or queer, or who are perceived to be gay, lesbian, questioning or gender nonconforming are targeted by other students and are often subjected to verbal and physical assaults. The results of the Harris Interactive and GLSEN (2005) school climate survey, mentioned earlier, shows this quite clearly. Put in even more stark terms, "[o]ver 1.6 million public school students are bullied because of either actual or perceived sexual orientation" (Morillas & Gibbons, 2010). Equally alarming is that much of the time adults who witness bullying and violent behavior—verbal or physical—tolerate it (Weiler, 2003). This violence needs to be combated and not tolerated.

Sexuality education based on democracy, nonviolence, and antioppression, in part, can be instrumental in stemming the tide of taunting and bullying. As just one example of an intervention, the philosophy and practice that have emerged from school safe zone programs could be infused in the sexuality education curriculum. The basic tenets of safe zone programs are to create a safe, supportive and welcoming environment for sexual and gender minority students. Integral to the safe zone programs are allies—students, teachers, administrators, and other school personnel—who provide support. The principles of safe zone programs should be infused throughout the curriculum and permeate school culture—curricular and extracurricular, including social events. Safe zone programs should not be viewed, however, as a panacea to combat biphobia, homophobia or sexual prejudice in general. Although they are helpful, they have limitations (Ngo, 2003). Along with infusing safe zone practices in the sexuality education curriculum, there needs to be concerted efforts to reform the sexuality education curriculum to reflect and respect sexual and gender diversity. There is no substitute for deep and meaningful curricular efforts—in sexuality education and across the curriculum—that enlighten the school community about bisexuality and lessen binegativity. Beyond using curricular interventions to ameliorate such violence, an examination of Gay-Straight Alliances (GSAs) and how bisexuality is treated in this arena is in order.

On the extracurricular level, perhaps the most prominent organization that predominantly serves gay and lesbian youth in schools is the GLSEN, which is the parent organization for GSAs that serve youth. No one can deny that GSAs have not only brought gay visibility to scores of schools across the United States, but also have offered support and safety to sexual minority students. It is widely known that, in part, GLSEN's chief purpose is to be support-ive of all sexual minority students. However, I am concerned that in GLSEN's name we see the binary being reproduced. The words *gay, lesbian* and *straight* appear in the title of the organization (to be read as Gay/Lesbian [homosexual] ‹———› Straight [heterosexual]), but nowhere are the terms *bisexual* or *queer, transgender* or *questioning* in the title of this organi-zation. By virtue of the title of the organization—GLSEN—there is a binary set up, and as a result there is at the very least the perception of exclusion. GSA represents another example. The same could be said about the groups Parents and Friends of Lesbians and Gays (PFLAG), Children of Gays and Lesbians Everywhere (COLAGE), and similar organizations. These or-ganizations have done a tremendous service, but how can we make them even better in terms of casting a broader net to include a variety of sexually and gender non-normative students, including those who resist being gender or sexually labeled? There are many youth who resist such labels (Savin-Williams, 2005).

## Conceptualizations of Bisexual Youth: Some Complexities and Realities of Bisexuality

A critical aspect that has been missing in schools—and in a lot of scholarship, for that matter—is an earnest treatment of intersectional forces that shape individuals' experience particularly re-garding oppression and privilege. As a matter of fact, this is an issue in the curriculum and in GSAs. Additionally, this is an important factor for school nurses and counselors, for example, to understand and consider when working with bisexual youth. For instance, it is critical to know that not all bisexuals experience the world in the same way. An upper middle-class, able-bodied White bisexual young man is likely to have different experiences than a working-class Latino bisexual male. Even though they both self-identify as bisexual, their worldviews will likely be different given not only issues of socioeconomic class, social location, race and so on, but also how they experienced privilege and/or oppression. Similarly, an upper-class African American bisexual young woman would experience the world differently than a working-class Asian American, or White young bisexual woman. It is critical that various vectors (e.g., race, class, sexuality, gender, ability, etc.) be marked and that a conscious effort to begin to undo oppression, invisibility, injustices, inequities of not only bisexual youth, but of other vulnerable populations across the sexual and gender continua.

A good place to begin such efforts would be to interrogate Whiteness in school culture. Writ-ing about the problematic aspects of White privilege, Kevin Kumashiro (2001) asserted, ". . . we insist that white-privilege is invisible, unspoken, and normalized in U.S. society" (pp. 3–4). It is important to mark and disrupt the status quo of Whiteness when teaching about bisexuality or otherwise working with bisexual youth in schools. This is important in general, but perhaps even more pressing when working in urban school settings with diverse populations. GSAs and similar extracurricular support groups for sexual minority youth face specific challenges particularly in serving students of color, and/or non-native English speakers; issues of racial segregation and the 'normalization of Whiteness' are barriers to serving students who could otherwise benefit from participating in such school-based organizations (McCready, 2003). Continuing to sound the alarm about sexual minority youth of color, Blackburn and McCready (2009) declared "we are concerned about how GSAs, in particular, seem to be inadequate for LGBTQ youth of color" (p. 227). While working toward making bisexuality more visible and inclusive, it is imperative that we do so very consciously and carefully so as to not reproduce the kind of racism, classism, sexism and sexual prejudice that continues—however unwittingly—to be part of schooling in the United States. Chun and Singh (this issue) provide a tool for conceptualizing various aspects of experience and identity for bisexual youth of color.

Another far-reaching critical issue is the lens through which we view bisexual youth, namely, as individuals who need to be protected from themselves and others, as individuals on the precipice of doom, or contrarily as hearty, creative, resilient young people with a vigor for sexual openness. This is debated in the literature. What it centers on is yet another binary of resilience (protective factors) versus risk factors. Stephen Russell (2005) noted that historically research and programmatic concerns focused on individual risk factors, which was based on a genuine concern for the welfare of sexual minority youth. It is a philosophically contested issue, about which researchers, teachers, school administrators, parents and youth argue. An exemplar on the resilience side of the debate is Savin-Williams (2005) who believes that many sexual minority youth are self-assured and able to handle the vicissitudes of their lives as LG*Bisexual*TQ youth. He went on to say "[w]ithout minimizing the experiences of those in distress, I wanted to suggest that there is another side to being young and gay, Not all such adolescents were suicidal. I wanted to argue against a problem-centered' approach and for a perspective that celebrates the promise and diversity of gay teens" (p. 62). Talburt (2004) argued along similar lines in favor of a more resiliency approach, adding that what adults view as risky behavior might well be interpreted in a positive light as imaginative and workable by others. She also claimed that sexual minority youths' needs are no more transparent than their heterosexual counterparts. Other researchers are quick to be concerned with such issues as school failure, homelessness, substance abuse, discrimination, suicidality and other risks (see Blackburn & McCready, 2009; Mufioz-Plaza, Quinn, & Rounds, 2002; Von Wormer & McKinney, 2003). A plethora of research studies highlight the risk factors associated with being a sexual minority (LG*Bisexual*TQI) youth. In fact, the majority of the commentaries and scholarly writings focus more on risk factors than on resiliency (protective factors). Interestingly and somewhat predictable, however, in keeping with the dearth of specific information on bisexual youth, the vast majority of the work conducted in this area lumps all of the youth (LG*Bisexual*TQQI) together.[2]

Returning to the issue about whether researchers and those working with sexual minority youth should follow the resiliency (protective factor) model or the risk factor paradigm, I think we should stay completely away from the either/or proposition. Following one approach or the other is not only contraindicated, but downright dangerous. As Russell (2005) noted, historically there has been much focus on the risk factors of sexual minority youth. Currently there is research being conducted blending the risk factor and resiliency approaches. A cursory examination of the current landscape of such research reveals that there is a continuum ranging from those on the one side who are staunch advocates of the risk factor approach and in between there are those who, to lesser and greater degrees, blend the two approaches, and on the other side of the continuum are those who focus their research on resilience/protective factors. It is critical that anyone doing work in this area, academic or otherwise, should work with the tensions that are produced from both models. The truth is that many of these youth are sophisticated, savvy, ingenious and solid problem solvers, and at the same time we continue to confront the reality that heteronormativity still reigns supreme and LG*Bisexual*TQ people in general face enormous sexual prejudice, hostility, and shabby treatment in general. Specifically regarding bisexual youth, they often have to confront negativity directed at them from several fronts, including the 'gay and lesbian and straight communities' for reasons mentioned earlier. The bottom line is that those working in the area of bisexuality should not stay stuck in the 'ain't it awful' mode, which would keep bisexuality lodged in the victimology, pathological framework, and at the same time it is also important to not approach bisexuality entirely from the strengths-based perspective (absent of a real-world acknowledgment of the far-reaching biphobia), which would not be based in the reality that there is, indeed, ubiquitous binegativity. Logically, an amalgamation of the two approaches is the best way to proceed (Mufioz-Plaza et al., 2002).

## School As A Prime Site For Bi-Intervention

Schooling is perhaps the single most significant institutional experience that youth from age 5 to 17 years share in common. According to the U.S. Department of Education's Institute of Education Statistics, in 2007 approximately 86% of school-aged youth attended public schools, 11% attended private schools and about 3% were homeschooled (U.S. Department of Education, 2007). The main point is that given such a high percentage of youth attend school, it stands to reason that schools are necessarily well positioned to intervene in terms of creating an atmosphere in which bisexual students—and all sexual minority youth, for that matter—are safe, secure and productive. Private elementary and secondary schools are not in the public trust per se and have their own policies and procedures. They certainly operate more independently than public schools. Although administrators, teachers and parents can be encouraged to be more kind and inclusive to LG*Bisexual*TQ students in these private school settings, there is no real leverage to hold them accountable; these schools are not subject to much public accountability and scrutiny. And, though public schools are in the public's trust, it is clear from the literature that they have a long way to come in terms of being safe spaces for LG*Bisexual*TQ youth. Despite the fact that public schools do not have a particularly good track record of being safe and productive sites for LG*Bisexual*TQ young people, it is awesome to think about the magnitude of positive change these schools could potentially make toward not only the eradication of binegativity—and sexual and gender prejudice (i.e., biphobia, homophobia and transphobia) in general—but also to effect positive social change regarding bisexuality. Achieving such a change toward more bifriendly schools would require that structural changes (reform) be made at the curricular and extracurricular levels.

## Curricular Interventions

The study of bisexuality should not be ghettoized in one particular aspect of the curriculum. As mentioned earlier, one logical place for teaching about bisexuality in the curriculum is in sexuality education, but bisexuality ought to be taught across the curriculum in a sustained way. Heteronormativity runs so deeply in the curriculum (e.g., in lectures, readings, discussions, textbooks, assignments, films, etc.) that often LG*Bisexual*TQ issues are given little if any attention at all. In fact, not only are LG*Bisexual*TQ students viewed as the other and coverage of sexual minority issues often reduced to one-time lessons, but also school books containing LG*Bisexual*TQ content have been banned in the United States and Canada (Loutzenheiser & MacIntosh, 2004). Although the lack of LG*Bisexual*TQ instruction in general subjects is somewhat understandable given the history of U.S. schooling (although wholly unacceptable), one would think that at least a fair amount of LG*Bisexual*TQ education occurs in sexuality education. However, by and large this is not the case. In fact, very little is covered, especially due to the focus on abstinence-only-until-marriage approach, which has constituted the vast majority of school-based sexuality education for the past 15 years since the abstinence-only federal legislation was passed (Elia & Eliason, 2010a, b). The bottom line is that there is very little systematic LG*Bisexual*TQ instruction happening. It is mind boggling that heteronormativity has continued to dominate the overt and hidden curricula. It is irresponsible for U.S. public schools to deny the existence of their sexual and gender minority youth. Writing about the importance of adopting a democratic approach to schooling, Ian MacGillivray (2000) observed,

> In line with the ideals of a liberal democracy, schools should not advocate certain lifestyles, whether religious fundamentalist or homosexual, but they should provide information on both in a nonthreatening and tolerant atmosphere. This requires that the curriculum and practices of the school reflect all of the sexual orientations and gender identities its students represent. (p. 319)

For this sort of approach to be implemented a concerted and sustained effort—including, but not limited to political work at the local, statewide, and federal levels—needs to occur.

A commitment and an investment need to be made regarding full curricular inclusion of LG*Bisexual*TQ issues and individuals. This translates to strong policies, and a commitment on the part of a school community, including all stakeholders. Parental engagement is a critical for such an effort to be successful. There needs to be an infrastructure in place, and schools can no longer afford to rely on 'permissive' or 'cool' teachers to raise issues about sexual and gender diversity. There needs to be a comprehensive approach to ensuring that these issues are taught across the curriculum. For such an enterprise to be successful, a number of aspects need to be put in place and institutionalized. One important and overarching task is to develop and implement school district policies that specify nondiscrimination and inclusion of sexually and gender diverse students and employees (e.g., administrators, coaches, counselors, nurses, librarians, front-office staff members, security personnel, teachers and other staff members).[3] Such policies should be based on democratic and nondiscriminatory values and should include all aspects of school culture from athletics, classroom instruction, performing arts, to extracurricular activities (e.g., school clubs and organizations, including their social events, need to be explicitly open to all students; Weiler, 2003). It is critical that such policies are threaded through every aspect of schooling. As part of the implementation process, school personnel need to be supported in making such a critical change in school culture. A specific example of this, for instance, is to offer regularly scheduled in-service workshops for teachers to learn innovative and effective ways of how to create curricula and gain classroom management awareness from democratic, multicultural and intersectional perspectives. All school personnel—from the principal to the custodial staff—should learn how to (and be expected to) intervene when sexual prejudice manifests itself as verbal taunts and harassment are directed at bisexual and other sexual minority students.

Another important facet of inclusion concerns teacher education (involving future teachers who are enrolled in credential programs). From the perspective of teacher education programs, it is time that professors of teacher education (and student teacher supervisors) equip future teachers with skills to teach about LG*Bisexual*TQ issues from democratic, multicultural and intersectional perspectives. To date this is a subject that remains 'under the radar screen' with the exception of occasional and intermittent coverage of sexual minority issues in multicultural aspects of teacher preparation course-work. Given that *sexual minority* is generally code for gay and lesbian, it is critical that bisexuality be marked and discussed in a thoughtful and thorough way so as to not only avoid commonly-held misconceptions (leading to binegativity) about bisexuality, but also treat bisexuality in a positive manner.

Once in the classroom, teachers need to pay keen attention to the adoption of textbooks and other reading materials and create class activities and assignments that genuinely reflect LG*Bisexual*TQ life. Examples of readings from literature include Petronius' *Satyricon,* Sappho's love poetry, Shakespeare's sonnets numbers 20 and 42, Marlowe's poem *Hero and Leander*, Lord Byron's poetry, Oscar Wilde's *Picture of Dorian Gray*, E. M. Forster's *Maurice,* Radclyffe Hall's *The Well of Loneliness*, D. H. Lawrence's novels, Evelyn Waugh's *Brideshead*, James Baldwin's *Giovanni's Room* and *Another Country,* French novelist Colette's works, Margie Percy's *Woman on the Edge of Time*, Alice Walker's *The Color Purple* and Norman Mailer's *Ancient Evenings.* Although not all of these works portray bisexuality in a positive light, they nevertheless include bisexual themes and can be used as 'teachable moments' to explore the realm of bisexuality and potentially combat binegativity through discussions, written assignments and other class activities (for even more detailed information on examples of bisexual literature listed above, see Hall, 2002) The above-mentioned readings constitute examples that would generally be well suited for courses in American and English literature. It is also important to integrate and infuse instruction about LG*Bisexual*TQ issues, concepts and individuals throughout as many classes and subjects as possible beyond literature and sexuality education courses and ensure sustained, in-depth coverage throughout the entire semester or school year. It is vital to infuse LG*Bisexual*TQ content thoroughly rather than use a superficial additive approach in which content gets piled on top of a fundamentally flawed curriculum.

To support curricular innovations regarding bisexuality and other sexual minority content, it is important that school libraries contain substantial collections of LG*Bisexual*TQ books, periodicals and academic and community resources for any student or staff member who wishes to read about, explore or do research on LG*Bisexual*TQ issues; it is critical that the library contain such materials. Librarians need to make an extra effort to obtain as many bisexual books as possible given that bisexuality has gotten glossed over in teen literature, for example. In fact, Bjorkman (2010) noted that, "only eight out of the 200+ titles... have bisexual characters or themes. Until recently, the in-betweens hovered on the fringe of the literary rainbow world. For instance the Lambda Literary Award only began recognizing bisexual lit in 2006, though the award started in 1988" (para. 1). This underscores the importance of having a knowledgeable, committed and bifriendly librarian.

It is equally important to avoid adultist assumptions about the needs and interests of bisexual students and their fellow sexual and gender minority peers: allow them to co-create the curriculum and assist in the governance of school matters. Create an atmosphere in which these youth feel empowered and comfortable articulating their educational and social wants and needs. Getting LG*Bisexual*TQ youth genuinely engaged in school would increase their visibility and make their school experience rewarding and productive.

Real-life engagement with the larger community (including theatrical performances with LG*Bisexual*TQ themes, community-based organizations/social service agencies that serve sexual and gender minority individuals and families, guest speakers, etc.) would be a worthwhile endeavor. This translates to developing relationships with community-based LG*Bisexual*TQ youth organizations such as the Lavender Youth Recreation and Information Center [LYRIC], which is based in San Francisco. There are a number of such organizations nation-wide.

On the extracurricular front, organizations that are specifically supportive of LG*Bisexual*TQ students (e.g., GLSEN's GSAs, except with a more inclusive title and mission statement—it is critical that bisexual and transgender aspects are highly visible, and a special focus ought to be placed on being deliberately inclusive of students of color, non-native English speakers, people with disabilities and others who have been historically excluded in addition to their LG*Bisexual*TQ status/identity) need to have a strong presence in schools. Extracurricular programming is important in schools, and as already mentioned, GLSEN's GSAs have been a mainstay for a plethora or sexual minority youth across the United States. In fact, they have been the most prominently featured organizations within schools that expressly support LG*Bisexual*TQ youth and their allies. Although the spirit and intentions of GSAs are spot on, there is some fine tuning to be done to ensure inclusivity—and eliminate the binary—even if only to retitle GSA to signal a more comprehensive and an all-encompassing approach to supporting all sexual and gender minority students. Additionally, McCready (2003) sounded the alarm about the possible lack of inclusivity for urban youth or color and non-native English speakers in GSAs and similar extracurricular organizations. There are cosmetic and structural issues with GLSEN's GSAs that need overhauling.

Despite the concerns one might have about GSAs, the truth is that over a relatively short time span literally hundreds of GSAs are estimated to be instituted in schools across the country (Griffin & Ouellett, 2002). There is every indication that this proliferation of GSAs will continue into the foreseeable future. Besides the concerns I raised earlier about GSAs, another disconcerting factor is that GSAs have functioned more or less to correct and/or pick up the slack of the school. Pat Griffin and Matthew Ouellett (2002) pointed out that "GSAs are only part of the bigger picture. . . . Without change throughout a school's organizational setting, the gains of one year may be lost when GSA members graduate or club advisors retire, change schools, or move on to other work" (p. 2). U.S. schools have been inhospitable to LG*Bisexual*TQ youth since the inception of schooling. School culture, including curricular and extracurricular programs, needs to be reformed to be truly inclusive. Just as the additive approach to covering LG*Bisexual*TQ content in classrooms is inappropriate, it is wholeheartedly misguided to have GSAs or similar organizations operating in schools in which the daily functions of schools are in many ways working against the ultimate mission of GSAs, namely, to make schools safe spaces for LG*Bisexual*TQ youth and their allies. On the whole, schools have functioned antithetically to GSAs. Schools and their extracurricular counterparts need to work in harmony toward inclusivity, and specifically to foster and ensure social and sexual justice in schools.

The time has come to include bisexual content throughout the school curriculum at the elementary and secondary levels. Of course, it goes without saying that it is important to teach about LG*Bisexual*TQ issues in an age-appropriate manner, as a teacher would teach any subject. One example of an age-appropriate activity for elementary school students is to show *It's Still Elementary*, a follow-up documentary film on the original *It's Elementary*, which portrays elementary and secondary schoolteachers teaching lessons about sexual minority people and issues. This could produce a plethora of teachable moments. Another idea would be to include reading children's literature with LG*Bisexual*TQ themes. It would also serve teachers and administrators well to read and discuss William J. Letts and James T. Sears' (1999) *Queering Elementary Education: Advancing the Dialogue about Sexualities and Schooling*. This would serve to educate school personnel about the theoretical underpinnings and practical reasons for including such an emphasis in elementary schools. Introducing such controversial content into the curriculum would likely create uneasiness among many parents. To maximize understanding and support and minimize negative fallout, it is critical to engage parents in the educational process. It is important for teachers and principals to contextualize the importance of such educational interventions to parents, and to stress that ultimately LG*Bisexual*TQ inclusion in the curriculum demonstrates a commitment to democratic, antioppressive schooling in which respect is given to all. The same principles apply when integrating such matters into the secondary school curriculum. Although it is not easy work, it is truly needed. Besides the curricular aspect of school, it is critical that schools complement their academic programs with extracurricular programming (particularly at the secondary school level) in support of LG*Bisexual*TQ students and their allies.

# Conclusions

Schools remain the most hopeful site of correcting the destructive forces of societal sexual and gender prejudice. In the scope of sexual and gender minorities, it is safe to say that bisexuality has been the most invisible inside and outside of the curriculum (Kangasvuo, 2003).[4] This is alarming given the number of youth who defy labels and those who are questioning their sexual identities (see Hollander, 2000; Savin-Williams, 2005). And, many more declare that they are bisexual or queer. It is critical that bisexuality become much more visible in the curriculum and in extracurricular programming. It is, however, not simply a matter of visibility. It is the quality of visibility that remains of paramount importance. The manifestations of binegativity have included, but not limited to, giving bisexuals 'bad press' as fence-sitting, duplicitous, untrustworthy and confused individuals. What would be more positive and empowering is to portray bisexuals as cultural workers, who potentially have much to teach us about the malleability of sexuality. That is, teaching about bisexuality becomes an intervention in terms of not only combating the binary and rigid thinking that has dominated Western thought about sexuality and gender, but also affording us a genuine opportunity to examine the complexities and potentialities of gender and sexuality as well. It is much like trans folks being cultural workers in terms of demonstrating the flexibility of gender constructions and variations of gender presentations and performances. We have a wonderful opportunity ahead of us to begin to undo the widespread binegativity and use teaching about bisexuality in schools as a vehicle to liberate us from constraining and negative views about sexuality. It is a worthwhile cultural and educational project, and schools are a prime locale to engage in such meaningful and fruitful work.

## NOTES

1. See, for example, Rubin (1993). It offers a critical analysis of the system of sexual hierarchy and the politics of sexuality.

2. For a thorough description and analysis of the risk factor versus resiliency debate, see Fisher (2009).

3. For an explanation about the importance implementing statewide and local policies, see Griffin and Ouellett (2002). This essay provides a thoughtful and detailed account of the importance of policies to institutionalize safe schools for LGBisexualTQ individuals.

4. Although Kangasvuo's (2003) essay focuses on bisexuality in schools in Finland, from everything I have learned implicitly from the literature, there are uncanny similarities in terms of how bisexuality is (not) treated in schooling in Finland and in the United States.

## References

Alexander, J., & Yescavage, K. (2003). Bisexuality and transgenderism: InterSEXions of the others. *Journal of Bisexuality, 3*(3/4), 1–24.

Angel, C. (2008, December 8). *Myths about bisexuality.* Retrieved July 22, 2010, from http://www.mdjunction.com/bisexuality/articles/myths-about-bisexuality

Angelides, S. (2001). *A history of bisexuality.* Chicago: University of Chicago Press.

Bjorkman, L. (2010, April 12). *Connect with Lauren Bjorkman: Bisexuality in teen lit.* Retrieved July 18, 2010, from http://www.authorsnow.com/category/topic/gay-lesbian-bisexual-transgender-glbt/

Blackburn, M. V., & McCready, L. T. (2009). Voices of queer youth in urban schools: Possibilities and limitations. *Theory into Practice, 48,* 222–230.

Burleson, W. E. (2005). *Bi America: Myths, truths, and struggles of an invisible community.* Binghamton, NY: Harrington Park Press.

Cantarella, E. (2002). *Bisexuality in the ancient world* (C. O. Cuilleanain, Trans.). New Haven, CT: Yale University Press.

Chun, K. Y. S., & Singh, A. A. (2010). The bisexual youth of color intersecting identities development model: A contextual approach to understanding multiple marginalization experiences. *Journal of Bisexuality, 10*(4), 426–448.

Elia, J. P. (2005). Comprehensive sex education is the most effective way to protect teen health. In K. Bailey (Ed.), *Sex education* (pp. 19–58). Detroit, MI: Greenhaven Press.

Elia, J. P. (2009). School-based sexuality education: A century of sexual and social control. In E. Schroeder & J. Kuriansky (Eds.), *Sexuality education: Past, present, and future* (vol. 1, pp. 13–57). Westport, CT: Praeger.

Elia, J. P., & Eliason, M. (2010a). Dangerous omissions: Abstinence-only-until-marriage school-based sexuality education and the betrayal of *LGBTQ* youth. *American Journal of Sexuality Education, 5,* 17–35.

Elia, J. P., & Eliason, M. (2010b). Discourses of exclusion: Sexuality education's silencing of sexual others. *Journal of LGBT Youth, 7,* 29–48.

Eliason, M. J. (1997). The prevalence and nature of biphobia in heterosexual undergraduate students. *Archives of Sexual Behavior, 26*(3), 317–326.

Eliason, M. J. (2001). Bi-negativity: The stigma facing bisexual men. *Journal of Bisexuality, 1*(2/3), 137–154.

Fisher, C. M. (2009). Queer youth experiences with abstinence-only-until-marriage sexuality education: "I can't get married so where does that leave me?" *Journal of LGBT Youth, 6*(1), 61–79.

Fox, R. C. (1996). Bisexuality in perspective: A review of theory and research. In B. A. Firestein (Ed.), *Bisexuality: The psychology and politics of an invisible minority* (pp. 3–50). Thousand Oaks, CA: Sage.

Garber, M. (1995). *Vice versa: Bisexuality and the eroticism of everyday life.* New York: Simon & Schuster.

Griffin, P., & Ouellett, M. L. (2002). Going beyond gay-straight alliances to make schools safe for lesbian, gay, bisexual, and transgender students. *Policy Journal of the Institute for Gay and Lesbian Strategic Studies, 6*(1), 1–8.

Hall, D. E. (2002). Bisexual literature. In C. J. Summers (Ed.), *GLBTQ: An encyclopedia of gay, lesbian, bisexual transgender, and queer culture.* Retrieved July 28, 2010, from http://www.glbtq.com/literature/bisex_lit%2C5.html

Harris Interactive, & Gay, Lesbian, and Straight Education Network (GLSEN). (2005). *From teasing to torment: School climate in America.* New York: GLSEN.

Hollander, G. (2000). Questioning youths: Challenges of working with youths forming identities. *School Psychology Review, 29*(2), 173–179.

Human Rights Campaign. (2010). *Myths and realities about bisexuality.* Retrieved July 15, 2010, from http://www.hrc.org/issues/coming_out/3306.htm

Israel, T., & Mohr, J. J. (2004). Attitudes toward bisexual women and men: Current research, future directions. In R. C. Fox (Ed.), *Current research on bisexuality* (pp. 117–134). Binghamton, NY: Harrington Park Press.

Kangasvuo, J. (2003). Sexually dichotomized culture in the lives of bisexual youth in school context. In V. Sunnari, J. Kangasvuo, & M. Heikkinen (Eds.), *Gendered and sexualised violence in educational environments* (2nd ed., pp. 210–224). Oulu, Finland: Oulu University Press.

Kaplan, R. (1995). Your fencing is sitting on me: The hazards of binary thinking. In N. Tucker (Ed.), *Bisexual politics: Theories, queries, & visions* (pp. 267–279). Binghamton, NY: Harrington Park Press.

Kumashiro, K. K. (2001). Queer students of color and antiracist, antiheterosexsist education: Paradoxes of identity and activism. In K. K. Kumashiro (Ed.), *Troubling intersections of race and sexuality: Queer students of color and anti-oppressive education* (pp. 1–25). Lanham, MD: Rowman & Littlefield.

Letts, W. J., & Sears, J. T. (1999). *Queering elementary education: Advancing the dialogue about sexualities and schooling.* Lanham, MD: Rowman & Littlefield.

Loutzenheiser, L. W., & MacIntosh, L. B. (2004). Citizenships, sexualities, and education. *Theory into Practice, 43*(2), 151–158.

MacGillivray, I. K. (2000). Educational equity for gay, lesbian, bisexual, transgendered, and queer/questioning students: The demands of democracy and social justice for America's schools. *Education and Urban Society, 32*(3), 303–323.

McCready, L. T. (2003). Some challenges facing queer youth programs in urban high schools: Racial segregation and de-normalizing whiteness. *Journal of Gay and Lesbian Issues in Education, 1*(3), 37–51.

Morillas, C., & Gibbons, C. (2010). *Strategies for school personnel to support and protect lesbian, gay, bisexual and transgendered students.* Retrieved July 24, 2010, from Georgia State University Center for School Safety, School Climate, and Classroom Management, http://education.gsu.edu/schoolsafety/

Mufioz-Plaza, C., Quinn, S. C., & Rounds, K. A. (2002). Lesbian, gay, bisexual and transgender students: Perceived social support in the high school environment. *High School Journal, 85*(3), 52–63.

Ngo, B. (2003). Citing discourses: Making sense of homophobia and heteronormativity at Dynamic High School. *Equity & Excellence in Education, 36*, 115–124.

Queen, C. (1996). Bisexuality, sexual diversity, and the sex-positive perspective. In B. A. Firestein (Ed.), *Bisexuality: The psychology and politics of an invisible minority* (pp. 103–124). Thousand Oaks, CA: Sage.

Rubin, G. S. (1993). Thinking sex: Notes for a radical theory of sexuality. In H. Abelove, M. Barale, & D. M. Halperin (Eds.), *The lesbian and gay studies reader* (pp. 3–44). New York: Routledge.

Russell, S. T. (2005). Beyond risk: Resilience in the lives of sexual minority youth. *Journal of Gay and Lesbian Issues in Education, 2*(3), 5–18.

Savin-Williams, R. C. (2005). *The new gay teenager.* Cambridge, MA: Harvard University Press.

Sexuality Information Education Council of the United States. (2004). *Guidelines for comprehensive sexuality education: Kindergarten through 12th grade* (3rd ed.). New York: Sexuality Information Education Council of the United States, National Guidelines Task Force.

Talburt, S. (2004). Constructions of LGBT youth: Opening up subject positions. *Theory into Practice, 43*(2), 116–121.

U.S. Department of Education. (2007). *Digest of education statistics.* Retrieved June 18, 2010, from http://nces.ed.gov/programs/digest/d09/tables/dt09_039.asp

Von Wormer, K., & McKinney, R. (2003). What schools can do to help gay/lesbian/bisexual youth: A harm reduction approach. *Adolescence, 38*(151), 409–420.

Weiler, E. M. (2003). Making school safe for sexual minority students. *Principal Leadership, 4*(4), 10–13.

Yep, G. A. (2003). The violence of heteronormativity in communication studies: Notes on injury, healing, and queer world-making. In G. A. Yep, K. E. Lovaas, & J. P. Elia (Eds.), *Queer theory and communication: From disciplining the queers to queering the discipline(s)* (pp. 11–59). Binghamton, NY: Harrington Park Press.

# Section V

# Sexual Behaviors

# Chapter 17

# Conceptual Models of Sexual Activity: Baseball Is Out; Pizza Is In!

*Al Vernacchio, M.S.Ed.*

Everyone has heard or maybe even used the lines before: "Did you score?" "I got to second base last night." "Watch out; I hear he plays for the other team." Baseball language is used to talk about sexual activity from playgrounds in Middle School to dorm rooms in colleges, to break rooms in corporate offices. Even when the actual baseball-related terms are no longer used, many still, nevertheless, use baseball as a conceptual model to organize their thinking about sexual activity. Far from being harmless word play, the expectations about sexual activity that result from using baseball as a conceptual model lead to unfulfilling, restrictive and inequitable sexual experiences and relationships. A new conceptual model for sexual activity, one that sets up expectations for satisfying, healthy, diverse, and equitable expressions of that activity must be found.

Writing in the early 1990s, Deborah Roffman, in her article "The Power of Language: Baseball as a Sexual Metaphor in American Culture", (1991) points out how ". . . insidiously powerful, singularly effective, and very efficient this [baseball] metaphor is as a vehicle for transmitting and transferring to successive generations of young people all that is wrong and unhealthy about American sexual attitudes" (Roffman, 1991, p. 2). Over two decades later, this is still true. With little prompting, students can generate a list of baseball language that relates to sexual activity, and while they may say they rarely use this terminology in their day-to-day conversations, they readily agree that the framework provided by this language informs how they think about sexual activity and, often, how they behave during sexual activity. The baseball model has staying power in our culture, especially because it goes unexamined. Unless its assumptions are challenged, our society will continue to be led blindly around the bases.

The first step in challenging the baseball model is to examine some of the common terminology it presents. When asked, students can easily generate a list like the one below. These are not invented terms, rather ones students have heard or used themselves:

- "pitcher" = the insertive partner in sexual activity
- "catcher" = the receptive/inserted partner in sexual activity
- "first base" = kissing or "making out"
- "second base" = "touching above the waist" / "feeling up the shirt" / fondling a woman's breasts

Reprinted by permission of Alfred Vernacchio.

- "third base" = "touching below the waist" / "petting" / fondling the genitals
- "sloppy second base" = breast stimulation with the mouth
- "sloppy third base" = oral sex
- "score" or "hit a home run" = to have vaginal intercourse
- "strike out" = to fail to get as far in sexual activity as one hoped
- "bench warmer" = a virgin (by choice or inexperience) or anyone not involved in sexual activity (with the implication that they are not "able" or "good enough" to do so)
- "bat" = penis
- "nappy dugout" = a vagina
- "a glove or catcher's mitt" = condom
- "if there's grass on the field, play ball" = if a woman has pubic hair she's old enough for sexual activity
- "switch-hitter" = a bisexual person
- "plays for the other team" = a gay/lesbian person

The meaning of these terms can vary in different communities, especially what constitutes the "bases". At a gathering of sexuality educators, a colleague who works with developmentally delayed adults reported that one of her clients said first base was holding hands, second base was a kiss on the cheek, third base was a kiss on the lips and a home run was marriage. While the meaning of the bases may change, the fact remains that communities continually reference this model. Another thing revealed by these terms, and noted by Roffman in her article, is their inherent sexism. "Second base" applies only to fondling female breasts. No one gets to second by touching a man's breast. These terms further assume that the male is the insertive partner in sexual activity. Men "play the game" and women are the field upon which the game is played (if there's grass on the field, play ball"). No doubt some young women own this language, being proud of their ability to "round the bases" as well as any young man, but women who "play the game" may be labeled "sluts" or "teases", while men are "players". "Bat" describes a man's penis as a powerful tool, while "nappy dugout" suggests a vagina is a place of waiting or a place for the team (of men, of course) to gather. Beyond the sexism inherent in these terms, note also the homophobia and biphobia present. Baseball as a conceptual model for sexual activity speaks only to heterosexuals and defines sexual activity as a male-female dynamic. Those who are not heterosexual are placed on the outside. "Switch hitters" may be versatile, but they are also seen as a bit odd. "Playing for the other team" places gay, lesbian, bisexual, and transgender people not on the "home team" but rather in the place of the "other". Simply thinking about the assumptions conveyed by these terms is enough to see how this model sets up inequitable relationships. This terminology, as damaging as it is, results from an even more damaging overall conception of sexual activity as tied to baseball. Examining not only the terminology, but also the game of baseball itself, shows how this conceptual model sets up sexual activity to be competitive, goal-directed, and restrictive.

Baseball is such a part of the American consciousness that it can be difficult to tease out its elements so that they can be examined. Ask someone to talk about baseball and they are likely to share game highlights, player statistics, declarations of team-based loyalty, or even comments about the business of baseball. To get to the heart of baseball as a conceptual model for sexual activity requires stripping down the game to its essential elements and rules. To do that, imagine aliens come to Earth from another planet and want to know about baseball. They have no prior knowledge at all, so they need the basic concepts around which the game is built. Stripped down to its essential concepts, baseball might look something like this:

1) Baseball requires two opposing teams: The nature of baseball is competitive. Two opposing teams play against each other.

2) Baseball involves a series of offensive and defensive maneuvers: Offensive players try to get farther into the field and then return home. Defensive players try to keep the offensive players off the field or limit their penetration into the field.

3) Baseball has a strict order of play: The bases can only be rounded in a specified order (to do otherwise is to commit an error). Each defensive player has a set position which focuses on a limited part of the field. Offensive players approach the plate in a strict batting order. Baseball is a rule-bound game, and playing it well requires strict observance of those rules. In fact, umpires are employed to make sure that players follow the rules and maintain the integrity of the game. It is the game itself and not the players that are of primary importance in baseball.

4) Baseball has a specific goal to be achieved within a designated length of time; it is a goal-directed activity. The aim is to score more runs than the opposing team in the allotted nine innings and win the game. It's an all-or-nothing proposition; no credit is given for moving part of the way around the bases, and only one team gets to win. The time frame of a baseball game may be lengthened or shortened, but only in the service of achieving the goal of winning the game.

5) Baseball requires specified equipment and a specified skill set: A host of equipment is needed to play a game of baseball. While some improvisation is possible, it is difficult to play the game without the equipment (indeed, in some cases the game ceases to be baseball and becomes "stick ball" or simply "catch"). More importantly, baseball requires a specific skill set. The ability to hit and throw the ball, run the bases, catch, and a whole host of physical and mental attributes are essential for being a "good" player. While people without this skill set can certainly play the game, they might feel inferior on a team with more skilled players, not "make the cut" for a prime team, and certainly not find themselves highly valued. In a competitive game of baseball, un-skilled players might find themselves in the position of "bench warmers" who simply sit on the sidelines and never get to play at all.

6) Baseball is a team sport: It is difficult, if not impossible to play by yourself.

7) Baseball is seasonal: "Real" baseball is played during a specific season. Baseball can be played out of season, but it is not an activity that can easily take place all year round.

With baseball as a conceptual model for sexual activity, one can begin to see how these concepts translate into messages about that activity. When these messages influence, or in more extreme cases control, our approach to sexual activity, the following messages result:

1) Sexual activity is a competitive, oppositional activity: That is, the participants are playing against each other rather than on the same team.

2) Sexual activity involves a series of offensive and defensive maneuvers: one person (usually the male) aggressively tries to move the activity forward while the other person (usually the woman) resists or tries to slow the forward motion.

3) Sexual activity has a strict order: This is perhaps the most damaging message of the baseball construct. The restriction to round the bases in a particular order corresponds to a scripted and often stagnating repertoire for sexual activity where kissing precedes fondling which precedes oral sex which precedes vaginal intercourse to orgasm. This also sets up a hierarchy of behavior where vaginal intercourse has the highest importance and all other sexual activity is somehow less. Stopping sexual activity before engaging in intercourse is tantamount to leaving the game unfinished. This strict, rule-bound order also sets up a system where each player has a specified role that must not be violated. This is seen most obviously when strict gender roles are overlaid on sexual behavior. Myths such as: men are always ready for sex; women are more concerned with relationships than sex; all physical contact between men and women is a precursor to sexual activity; and many others can be viewed in light of the baseball model as playing one's designated position. Just as a center fielder should not wander into the infield, males and females in the baseball model should play their own designated positions and not cross into each other's territory.

4) Sexual activity is goal-directed, with a specific endpoint: Achieving orgasm through vaginal intercourse ("getting to home plate") is the goal of sexual activity in the baseball model. Again the primacy of vaginal intercourse is emphasized at the expense of other activities, even ones that might bring more sexual, emotional, and/or physical satisfaction. Sexual activity is held to a specific endpoint where orgasm and ejaculation for the male is essential. Women's orgasms are welcome but not strictly essential to a "win". Some consider the elusive goal of the simultaneous orgasm an even better "win".

5) Sexual activity is a team sport: It is not a solo activity, thus masturbation is not considered "real" sexual activity and self-exploration as a form of sexual activity doesn't put one "in the game". Another aspect of the team sport concept is sharing stories of one's prowess on the field with other team members ("locker room talk"). Thus, men get to brag about how well they performed, offering a play-by-play for their fans and fellow teammates. Women certainly have done this as well, although when considered to be the field upon which the game is played, this may be more difficult. In either case, when sexual activity becomes a spectator sport intimacy, privacy, and a special bond between the partners may be lost.

6) Sexual activity requires specified equipment and a specified skill set: The message of having proper equipment may be a positive one in this age of safer sex (i.e. having condoms or other methods to prevent sexually transmitted infections and prevent unwanted pregnancy). However, more often this message has negative connotations. The equipment message is often related to body size and shape, especially penis size as men brag about who has a bigger, more powerful "bat". This may lead to body shame and insecurity about one's ability to satisfy their partner if they think their equipment doesn't measure up. Note again the inherent sexism in this, as vaginal size does not enter into this discussion, or does so only as a negative. Women are certainly

not immune to the equipment message as seen in the explosion of cosmetic procedures used to alter a body so that its equipment might be seen as more desirable. Further, believing that a specified skill set is necessary for "proper" sexual activity can lead to further insecurity as people wonder whether they know the "right" way to pleasure their partner. The huge industry of sexual self-help books, videos, and seminars speaks to our collective insecurity around our sexual performance. Another aspect of this message is that once one's skill set or equipment is past its peak one should "get out of the game". Our society's denial of and lack of comfort with sexual activity among seniors, the disabled, those with chronic illnesses or anyone who is not at the top of their game brings an elitism into the realm of sexual activity. It ceases to be something for all and becomes something for only a specific sub-set, those "in shape" enough to play the game well.

7) Sexual activity must have a specified time and place: While some may argue that this is not a bad message, it can restrict sexual activity, making it not for all times and seasons. Pressure is placed on having sex at times when it is "expected", like the prom, the wedding night, when parents are out of town, when alcohol or drugs are present. This makes the decision to become sexually active an externally rather than internally controlled one.

With baseball as the conceptual model for sexual activity, inequitable, scripted, and in many cases unfulfilling sexual experiences result. In looking at these messages, is it any wonder our society is so unhealthy in its approach to sexual activity? When faced with the prospect of not playing the game properly, winding up on a "losing team", or being a "bench warmer", sexual activity becomes a goal-driven and highly stressful activity. Only methods that enhance the pursuit of the all-important orgasm through vaginal intercourse, and only achieved through the "proper" series of events, are valued.

In trying to discover whether one is affected by the baseball model of sexual activity, consider some of the following questions:

1) Do I see sexual activity as goal-directed? Is it all about getting to vaginal intercourse and/or orgasm?

2) Do I prioritize sexual behavior into a hierarchy where vaginal intercourse is more prized than other expressions of sexual activity?

3) Is sexual activity oppositional? Is one party playing offense while the other plays defense? Is it someone's job to push things further? Is someone else charged with slowing the pace?

4) Do I worry about the equipment I bring to "the game"? Do I worry whether I have performed at a certain level of proficiency?

If one's concept of sexual activity, or actual behavior, is burdened by these expectations, perhaps it is because the conceptual model has set us up for a negative sexual experience rather than a positive one. What would be helpful is an alternative conceptual model.

An alternate model should be as universally understood in our culture as baseball. It must be a model based upon something that people usually associate with a positive and satisfying experience. It must also be a model that sets up a series of expectations about sexual activity that lead to a more equitable, less goal-oriented, and more satisfying experience than the baseball model. All of these aspects can be found in a new conceptual model centered on pizza.

While certainly there are some people who do not like pizza, it is a common part of most Americans' diet. Pizza can be part of a celebration, a social gathering, a romantic evening just for two, or a solitary pleasure. It can be an event unto itself or it can be a part of a larger event. It is something familiar; everyone can be well versed in pizza without ever having to memorize a box score. Again, the first step in working with pizza as a conceptual model for sexual activity is to draw out its essential elements. In trying to explain pizza to aliens who have no concept of it, one might make the following points:

1) Pizza is a food used to satisfy hunger; it starts with a desire, is readily available and not bound by any season: Ideally, we have pizza because we *want* to have pizza. A hunger, a craving, sometimes even a need for it is experienced. While pizza may be a default option to the eternal question "What's for dinner?" at its best it is chosen because pizza is the best thing to satisfy the present hunger. And since there is no "season" when pizza becomes available, it can be enjoyed anytime. No matter what the time of year, or what meal, people can have pizza. It is enjoyed for lunch, dinner, snacks, and even breakfast. Finally, one may be hungry for pizza but decide that it's not the right time, place, or situation for it.

2) Pizza offers many choices, so discussion or dialogue is important before ordering: Bring people together to have pizza and a conversation begins. Sometimes it may be very simple, "Should we get our usual?" Other times debate or negotiation is necessary. "Do you like mushrooms?" / "I'd rather have pepperoni." / "No anchovies, please–yuck!" One of the best things about pizza is that it can be ordered to suit the needs and wants of those ordering it, provided enough discussion to ensure everyone involved will be satisfied.

3) Pizza comes in a variety of shapes, sizes, and styles and may be eaten in a variety of ways: While some styles and varieties of pizza may be more popular than others, there is no established hierarchy. A square pizza is just as acceptable as a round one. Pineapple may not be everyone's thing, but it isn't "wrong" to put it on a pizza. Crusts may be thin and crispy or thick and chewy, all based on individual preference. Once the pizza arrives, how it is eaten is again up to individual preferences. Use a knife and fork, fold the slice in half, eat the crust first—it's all based upon what works best for the individual and all methods are equally valid ones, even though there may be a strong preference for one over another. Unlike baseball, there is no specific equipment or skill set needed to enjoy pizza.

4) At its best, pizza is appealing to the senses when it arrives and eating it becomes a total sensory experience: The anticipation of enjoying a freshly made pizza is enhanced by its appeal to our senses. The sight of the steam rising off of the pizza, the smell of fresh ingredients, the warmth of the crust, and the taste of the first bite all contribute to the enjoyment of eating pizza. The senses are engaged, stimulated, and ultimately satisfied.

5) If there is any "goal" to eating pizza, it is simply satisfaction: For some, one piece is more than enough; others can finish a whole pizza at a sitting. There are no rules that

dictate how much one has to eat. In fact, overindulging leads to us feeling bloated rather than satisfied. Each person involved sets their own limit for when they are finished.

6) Eating pizza can be a solo, shared, or group activity: It's easy and quite acceptable to eat pizza by yourself. It's also OK to share it with others. Pizza also removes the spectator aspect of the baseball model. There is no need to brag about one's ability to eat pizza. It is an experience shared by those participating in it; it doesn't need to involve anyone else.

As with the baseball model, translating these ideas about pizza into ideas about sexual activity provide a very different set of expectations for what that activity can be:

1) Sexual activity should spring from desire and not be bound by a set season: The impetus for sexual activity should be desire-ideally for connection, for intimacy, for relationship, and for pleasure. It should not be something entered into out of obligation, or worse coercion. What determines when and how sexual activity takes place is an individual decision based on individual wants, needs, and values. Its occurrence should not be ruled by set seasons, schedules, or times of day. No event or situation (the date, the prom, or even the wedding night) can dictate when sexual activity should take place. Rather, sexual activity may be included or excluded in every situation based on the desire of the participants. Further, a desire for sexual activity does mean it has to occur. Desire can be considered and a decision can be made about whether its fulfillment is appropriate in this particular instance.

2) Sexual activity requires communication and negotiation before any activity takes place: Couples who are able to set parameters, negotiate behavior, and discuss their sexual activity before it takes place will experience greater intimacy, enhanced communication in their relationship, and more enjoyable sexual activity together. They will also limit the chance of negative consequences such as sexually transmitted infections, unwanted pregnancy, or emotional upset that results from different expectations about what sexual activity might mean. Communication and negotiation removes the oppositional component that is so significant in the baseball model. The people involved in the sexual activity negotiate to make it the best experience for the parties involved; it is not a negotiation to see who will ultimately "win", but a way to ensure that everyone's needs are met.

3) Sexual activity contains a wide range of options, all of which are acceptable and equally valid: One of the greatest benefits of the pizza model is the eradication of a hierarchical system of behaviors in sexual activity. Couples select activity based on their individual preferences and goals. Removing the primacy of vaginal intercourse and orgasm gives couples access to many more options for pleasure. It also makes sexual contact valid no matter what the gender or sexual orientation of the participants. Thus, the pizza model is inclusive of lesbian, gay, and bisexual relationships. Further, with no required equipment or skill set, sexual activity becomes truly egalitarian and open to all, regardless of age, ability, body type, or any other factor.

4) At its best, sexual activity should be appealing, enticing, and pleasing to the senses: Sexual activity is a whole body experience. All of the senses should be engaged;

sights, smells, touches, tastes, and sounds all contribute to a satisfying sexual experience. Again there is no hierarchy of senses to be found here and also no primacy given to the genitals. All senses and all parts of the body should be engaged. The more senses that are appealed to, and the more the whole body is involved, the better the experience.

5) The main objective of sexual activity should be satisfaction, not the achievement of some artificial standard of completion: With pleasure and satisfaction as the main foci, couples are free to create sexual activity that involves as many or as few sexual behaviors as they wish. With the measuring stick of mandatory vaginal intercourse and orgasm (and especially the simultaneous orgasm) gone, couples may define for themselves what amount of pleasure makes them feel satisfied and what is considered their own appropriate ending point. This model also allows the couple to have fluctuating end points depending on the situation. Some may choose an encounter that culminates in vaginal intercourse with orgasm at one time and at other times find satisfaction in kissing and fondling each other whether that results in orgasm or not. Sexual activity becomes directed not by a set of external rules but rather by the needs, desires, and decisions of the people engaged in it.

6) Sexual activity can be a solitary or shared experience: Bringing masturbation and sexual self-exploration into the definition of sexual activity allows those for whom partnered sexual activity is unwanted or unavailable to be included. Humans are sexual beings from our birth to our death. Our sexuality does not depend on being in relationship with another person. No one is forced to be a "bench warmer" in the pizza model.

The pizza model frees the concept of sexual activity from the restrictions and external rules imposed by the baseball model. It establishes the primacy of individual desire and the decisions of the participants as the controlling factors in sexual activity. It opens the participants to a wider range of behaviors that can be expressed and allows them to define the parameters of their own sexual activity. It sets up more equitable, flexible, and hopefully fulfilling sexual activity.

Conceptual models are very powerful tools for setting expectations, defining behaviors, and bringing values to light, for, as our model is so shall our behavior be. Attempts at behavior change without addressing the conceptual model behind that behavior has little chance of succeeding. However, with critical examination and alteration to the conceptual model, positive behavior change can be achieved more easily.

American society is awash in unhealthy sexuality. Rate of teenage pregnancy and sexually transmitted infections are high. Sexual assault, sexual harassment, and sexual coercion seem to be epidemic. A huge number of marriages end in divorce, not uncommonly driven by the couple's dissatisfaction with their sex life. While the source of these problems cannot all be attributed to the baseball model of sexual activity, it is true that such a model leads to beliefs about sexual activity and behaviors that contribute to our nation's state of unhealthy sexuality.

Sexuality and sexual activity are forces that can bring out the best in human beings. Sexual activity can help create intimate, constructive, and fulfilling interactions and relationships.

In order for sexual activity to do this, it must be based upon a model that is open, equitable, and respectful of differences. An examination of the conceptual model that drives one's idea of sexual activity can be an important first step in this process.

# Reference

Roffman, Deborah M. (1991) The Power of Language: Baseball as a Sexual Metaphor in American Culture. *SIECUS Report*, *19*(5), 1–6.

# Chapter 18

# Idiosyncrasy and Social Critique: Alternative Interpretations of Atypical Sexual Behaviors

*Paul Rueckhaus*

This chapter intends to expand upon what general human sexuality textbooks discuss in the area of atypical sexuality. I would like to offer a handful of alternative interpretations of sexual behaviors that fall under the labels of atypical, fetishistic, or paraphilic—terms that serve to stigmatize and pathologize a wide range of sexual behaviors and fantasies rather than encourage investigation and understanding of how these behaviors shape our individual and collective sexualities.

The language that we use to characterize sexuality informs how we think about sexual expression. To this end, a conversation about atypical sexuality seems incomplete without a reflection on what it means to be typical, behave in a typical way, or express a sexuality that is "typical." The language of typicality has political, moral and psychological implications. In a political context, to be typical could be interpreted as conformity—abiding by social norms. That is, conducting oneself in such a way that s/he poses little or no threat to the State, its economy or its various social agendas. In a moral context, typicality suggests reverence, righteousness and piety. Simply put: conduct that would not offend or upset God or the Deacon or the congregation. The psychological meaning of typical can have at least two interpretations. One interpretation can refer to statistical norms and averages. That is, falling within a range of experiences, desires and actions that the majority of other individuals in any given sample or projected population fall within. While many scientists may have statistical averages and standard deviations in mind when they use words like typical and atypical, the meaning communicates something entirely different to the public. Through the lens of psychology, typical behavior suggests mental hygiene, rationality, behaving in a way that is balanced, socially acceptable, normal or "okay."

In all respects, the typical label provides assurance that one's behavior is acceptable, not too offensive, not disordered, sick, dysfunctional nor threatening. The typical label also instills internal surveillance and permits social scrutiny. To use a gendered example, in childhood feminine boys or masculine girls often realize that they do not conform to typical gender

---

Reprinted by permission of Paul Rueckhaus.

norms defined by Western culture and tend to self-police mannerisms, tastes and activities that reveal their "atypical" gender attributes. Similarly, the gender binary and socially sanctioned expressions of masculinity and femininity give parents, classmates, teachers and peers the green light to pass judgment, censor or censure gender nonconforming behavior. The social invention of a typical gender expression, thus allows for the ridicule and marginalization of anything outside of the realm of typical.

So, if a seemingly harmless word like typical can signify political conformity, religious piety, and good mental health in the collective imagination, what does it mean to label a dimension of identity (such as sexuality) or a constellation of behaviors atypical? The act of labeling, itself, is an exertion of power by those who have the political, moral and/or intellectual authority to determine and disseminate the values of the institutions they represent (government, church, the scientific community, professional associations, the academy, and so on). Because of this, what appears typical in one social, cultural context can seem alien, absurd and even threatening in another depending upon the social attitudes and political climate of the time and place. So, the very idea of an atypical sexuality is a moving target.

Take for example, *onania* or the "heinous sin of self pollution" or more simply put, masturbation. If we go back to the early 1700s, masturbation was perceived not only as a grave spiritual transgression but a leading risk factor of physical and psychological disorders (and was, itself, seen as a disorder of sorts) (Anonymous, 1724). From jaundice and retarded growth to senility and 'hysteria,' onanism was a convenient and popular culprit to blame for not only social ills but a range of individual physical maladies. Hence, masturbation was paradoxically perceived as a rare, atypical expression of human sexuality, yet paradoxically a potential threat to public health and morality of the masses. Indeed, its seeming atypical-*ness* served spiritual, political *and* psycho-medical agendas. Today, the scientific mainstream considers masturbation acceptable, harmless, normative human sexual behavior in both men and women. In stark contrast to the Onania manifesto of 1724, sexological and health experts went so far as to suggest masturbation can prevent and ameliorate an ambitious range of medical conditions from heart disease to cancer prevention to depression (see Leitzman, et. al., 2004; Levin, 2007 for examples). The discourse on kink, fetish, paraphilias and what is often referred to as "atypical sexuality," even in the "sex-positive" community, has a great deal in common with that of onanism of 300 years ago. The label of "atypical" ascribed to a classification of sexual behaviors and fantasies carries two dangerous implications: A.) that such a thing as typical, healthy or normal sexuality exists (which it doesn't—at least not in any form that is generalizable to large, diverse populations.). And B.) in contrast to the values of *typical* qualities described above, that any behavior deemed fetishistic or paraphilic is potentially psychologically damaging (in addition to being amoral and subversive). As we can see from the Onania example, what was perceived to be pathological, atypical, unhealthy, shameful at one moment in time can morph in the public and scientific imagination into an irreducible and even nurturing component of human experience.

As you consider the descriptions by authors of general texts that provide a treatment of atypical sexual behavior, keep in mind that their discourse reflects a moment in time. What some would call *atypical* today may become mainstream tomorrow, and later may be so ingrained in the collective schema of normative sexual behavior that they are expected to the point that to *not* exhibit the behavior would be seen as abnormal. While your textbook may cite and catalogue an extensive (though not exhaustive) list of "atypical" sexual behaviors—from foot fetishes to zoophilia—there is no scientific or other consensus on *typical* sexual behavior. Indeed, the idea of typicality in sexual behavior resides in the individual and cultural imagination. Some forms of sexual expression are encouraged by the culture (through media, family, religion, policy, etc.) while others are criminalized, marginalized or ignored entirely. However, cultural narratives of sexual normalcy do not take into account the fluid nature of sexuality. That is, the idea of what is typical is only tacitly defined, highly subjective, and subject to change for any individual at any given moment. If the "typically" sexual individual who, until age 30 only engaged in penetrative intercourse, discovered that she was sexually excited by a particular fetish such as, say, removing her partner's body hair, would she still consider herself sexually typical? If the self-described pervert, who perceived himself to be a sexual oddity, discovered that his fantasy of being handcuffed was actually fairly ordinary and even mild on the grand scale of sadomasochistic fantasies, would he suddenly feel less marginal in his sexuality? Typical, atypical, fetishistic or vanilla—our sexuality is fluid and able to take on unexpected qualities at unexpected moments.

Fetishes describe a pattern of "intense and recurrent sexual arousal to non-living objects . . . body parts or body products (p. 357) (Kafka, 2010)." They are vehicles of arousal. However, they are often described in terms of *interfering* with satisfying sexual expression rather than components of sexual satisfaction. As an example of how a popular college text on human sexuality describes in broad terms individuals who engage in paraphilias, Crooks & Bauer (2013), contend, "these people often find it difficult to establish satisfying sexual and intimate relationships with partners. Instead, their sexual expression can assume a solitary, driven, even compulsive quality (p. 489)." Not only do the authors label an impressively wide range of sexual behaviors—from necrophilia to men wearing women's underwear—as atypical, but they recast the behaviors as indicators of a disordered, even potentially dangerous personality type. In this respect, the *atypical* label does not get us any closer to understanding, appreciating, or making sense of various sexual interests that do not involve masturbation, vaginal or anal intercourse, or oral sex. Instead, the label stigmatizes, distances and rarifies behaviors, desires and fantasies that are (collectively if not individually) anything but rare.

## Sexual Idiosyncrasies

Atypicality is typical. We have labeled, pathologized, investigated and stigmatized just about any variation of sexual expression. The atypical label only exacerbates the pathologizing of sexuality. Instead, I suggest that we see the noncoercive (that is consensual or solitary) paraphilias, fetishes, kinks and fantasies described by many sexuality texts not as atypical, but idiosyncratic. (For a wider list of fetishes and parphilias, see appendix A.) An idiosyncrasy is no more than a peculiarity; a unique fascination, ritual, or way of doing something. Many of the fetishes and paraphilias that fall under the rubric of "atypical" are not as much sexual or psychological oddities or pathologies as they are simply unique ways of getting turned on. To be sure, sexual idiosyncrasies may provoke social stigma, public disgust or make finding sexually compatible partners extremely difficult, which may in turn induce feelings of isolation that are psychologically troubling. However, I would argue that the kink, fetish, paraphilia, idiosyncrasy or whichever term seems most appropriate rarely are signs of disordered behavior patterns or personality types.

Any sexual act can be aggressive. Like any sex act, idiosyncratic sexual activities and interests can be exhibited in ways that are violent, coercive and damaging to adults, children, animals, property and the deceased. It is interesting that rapists; corrupt bosses & teachers and other sexually coercive individuals are not pathologized in the way that kinky people (who often go to great lengths to seek and negotiate consent) are. To be sure, rape and harassment are abuses of power as much as they are abuses of bodies, minds and spirits. However, we have cultural narratives that normalize rape and acts of aggression. Attitudes and sentiments like, *Boys will be boys* and *she must have slept her way to the top*, cast dehumanizing acts of sexual violence and coercion in a light that makes these actions expected (even if unfortunate) sexual events that are not out of the range of "normal." However, we do not have such a cultural narrative that is as generous to the coprophile, who eroticizes the sensory experience of being defecated upon. Even though the scat fetishist engages in consensual, mutually pleasurable sexual activities that happen to involve feces, this desire and other fetishes often inspire more confusion and revulsion than violent, dehumanizing affronts such as rape or harassment.

This is not to suggest that kink or fetish play is free of risks or harm. Kinks and fetishes, especially those involving pain, bondage, humiliation, domination, submission, sadism and/or masochism, pose potential physical and psychological risks to practitioners. Consent is what separates a fetish from an abuse, sex from rape and so on. Because of the heightened awareness of the potential for physical and/or psychological harm, coercion and abuse in performing certain kinks, consent is not only a yes/no agreement to participate in a particular sex act, but a way of planning (or scripting) a sexual encounter and negotiating the terms of the encounter—what the kink community refers to as *risk-aware consensual kink* (or RACK) (see Kink Academy, n.d. or Society of Janus, n.d.). RACK is not a legal proceeding or document but a framework (or way of thinking about) for scripting and enacting fetish scenes that serves three key functions:

1. to assure that the desired fetishes, kinks or fantasies are activated (kink),
2. to set explicit limits upon the range and intensity of sexual activities (consensual), and
3. to address and circumvent physical and psychological hazards that may be associated with performing the kink or fetish (risk-aware).

Instead of being seen as deviant, amoral or pathological, the exploration and performance of sexual fetishes can actually be executed in ways that are thoughtful, ethical, compassionate, even diplomatic. In this respect, the sexual scripts at play within a RACK framework provide a degree of security for the individual exploration of sexual desire, fantasy, curiosity and limits. These same sexual scripts, as they are explored between consenting adults, can also illuminate social phenomena beyond the individual, psychological realms through which they are commonly examined.

## *BDSM: Sex on the Dark Side or Scripting Social Critique?*

Whether in masturbation, fantasy or partnered sexual activities, we all engage in some form of sexual scripting. According to Gagnon & Simon (1973), sexual scripting deals with external or interpersonal components that have to do with "the organization of mutually shared conventions that allows two or more actors to participate in a complex act involving mutual dependence (p.20)." That is, sexual activity is so dynamic and complex, contingent upon the cooperation and overlapping desire of at least two people, we must rely on some form of scripting (conscious or unconscious) in order to perform any sexual act at all. Our scripts also deal with internal components such as "the intrapsychic, the motivational elements that produce arousal or at least a commitment to the activity." Consciously or subconsciously we cast roles and imagine or construct scenes around sexual activity. These scripts are also influenced by culture. Our sexual encounters are what some anthropologists would call "symbolically interactionist" (see Mead, 1934; Longmore, 1998), which basically means behaviors that seem private, spontaneous, routine, or even idiosyncratic interact with their social contexts. That is, much of our experiences are scripted and played out not only to meet our own basic needs, desires, and social obligations but to accommodate or express social, cultural and political values that we have internalized in our psyches and externalize through our actions.

Sexual idiosyncrasies under the rubric of bondage/domination, domination/submission, sadism/masochism or BDSM script sexual activity in ways that incorporate pain, power, violence, and submission. Because of this, these sexual scripts often require a great deal of trust, planning and intention on the part of all the players. While not all BDSM practitioners dramatize their sexual behavior in a role-play, almost all BDSM activities exaggerate or toy with power dynamics between participants. Those BDSM activities that do enact role-plays often tap into the fantasies of authoritarian, powerful or even nurturing figures overpowering subjugated or infantile subjects (e.g., master-slave, parent-infant, and dominatrix scenarios) (See appendix B for a broader list of BDSM role-plays.)

The sexual dramas of BDSM role-play depend upon the imagined "extreme psychological imbalances of power" (APA, 2000). In a society plagued with a great deal of real and symbolic violence—the legacy of slavery, the twin epidemics of domestic violence and rape against women (and men), excessive incarceration, child abuse at the hands of trusted authority figures, the violence of poverty (in the midst of wealth), international warfare, and so on—what function do sadomasochistic sexual dramas serve? Psychoanalytic and psychological theories explain sadomasochistic behavior almost entirely in terms of the family or the individual. That is, the fascination came about due to childhood trauma or early experiences with corporal punishment or some childhood experience that hardwired humiliation, pain or some other force to an erotic response. Some theories suggest that sadomasochistic tendencies are the result of hormonal imbalances. Still other theories admit that some fetishes may come about randomly.

Regardless of "where" the tendency comes from, sadomasochism and the scenes that often capture it are, indeed, subversive and transgressive. They dramatize and even critique institutionalized violence and cultural brutality—that is, the violence that surrounds us, which we may or may not be attuned to. To this end, it is not only the naughtiness or psychological darkness, or "ick factor" that makes sadist and masochistic acts taboo, "atypical" or subversive but their recapturing of broader systems of power and subjugation such as capitalism (master/slave play, business suit/dominatrix scenarios, etc.), white supremacy (master/slave and pony play), and patriarchy (over-the-knee spanking, infantilism, puppy play) (See appendix B).

Indeed BDSM play may very well be atypical, but not necessarily for the reasons that it is rare or pathological, but for reasons that it subverts and even *revises* power dynamics intrinsic to the functioning of the State, the Market and the nuclear household. In the social hierarchy, we have little to no say in what role we occupy and how much power we have in our roles. However, in a BDSM role-play, all of the participants are voluntarily assuming the power or powerlessness of their role. (Of course, the subordinate partner actually has more power than the dominant one in any scene as the entire sexual fantasy depends upon his/her compliance or rather desire to be dominated.) In this respect, the scenes do not only recapitulate symbolic violence alive in the culture, but take control over that violence by scripting it, negotiating it, managing it and most importantly *enjoying* it. I would not go so far as to suggest that these scenes have any sort of healing or cathartic quality to them. I am only pointing out that the discomfort or public disapproval often ascribed to BDSM, may not come about *only* because these are abnormal, deviant or pathological sexual scripts—but because they dramatize power and oppression in ways that force us to confront the social violence that is otherwise invisible to us.

# Conclusion

In this chapter, I have proposed alternative interpretations of fetishes, kinks and other examples of sexual idiosyncrasies to the mainstream, normative discourse that can pathologize and marginalize such behaviors. My purpose here was not only to normalize idiosyncratic sexual behavior by renaming it and analyzing the language used to describe such behaviors. My purpose was to encourage open and critical thinking about the purpose sexual eccentricities serve in our collective and individual human experiences. When authors and educators veil any practice in a discourse of normalcy or typicality or use clinical, stigmatizing language to describe that practice, the reader/student is distanced from its implications. This shuts down (rather than opens up) an exploration about why that behavior exists, why someone might enjoy it, and what we can learn from it. To enhance understanding and encourage an open, non-judgmental exploration of idiosyncratic sexual behavior, I propose three key ways that college texts could introduce and discuss sexual kinks and fetishes.

Explore non-clinical, non-stigmatizing terminology to discuss variations in sexual expression. While sexuality educators and texts have challenged dichotomies of gender (male/female) and sexual orientation (gay/straight), the atypical label perpetuates a typical/atypical binary of sexual expression and behavior that doesn't necessarily exist in the real world. I am not suggesting that another author or association adopt the term *idiosyncratic sexual behavior* necessarily. The term is admittedly clumsy and not immediately clear to every reader. But, it is my best attempt at redressing a constellation of terms that unnecessarily marginalize a wide range of human sexual expression. If other authors experimented with similar acts of renaming, perhaps a more enlightened, generous and cogent discourse on this subject would emerge.

Integrate discussions of fetishes, role-play, kink, humiliation, pain, and various sexual expressions throughout an entire text. By dedicating a singular chapter to "atypical sexuality" with little to no discussion in other chapters exacerbates the perception of rarity and oddity.

While it may be appropriate to dedicate a chapter to kink and fetish behaviors, this does not have to be the exclusive territory of any discussion on sexual variations.

Emphasize the function of consent. Too often, academic discussions of kinks and fetishes overlook or only mention the critical roles of risk awareness and consent. While kinks and fetishes are not always in all cases explored and enacted in safe, consensual ways, it is important that students and the public understand that a kink community exists and that within that community standards for ethical, consensual kinky sex play are valued and enforced. Whether we consider ourselves kinky or not, the kink community can teach any one of us a great deal about expressing, negotiating, respecting and enforcing sexual boundaries of all sorts that we might be able to incorporate into various sexual scenarios. The RACK framework transcends the context of kink and BDSM. Indeed, the key functions of expressing sexual desire, negotiating limits and addressing hazards are communication tools for even the least kinky among us to write more empowered, transparent, conscientious and mutually satisfying sexual scripts.

# References

American Psychiatric Association. (2000). *Diagnostic and Statistical Manual of Mental Disorders* (4th ed. Text Rev.). Washington, DC.

Anonymous. (1724). *Onania or the Heinous Sin of Self Pollution and all its frightful consequences in both sexes*. London, UK. Fliz Rumball.

Crooks, R. & Bauer, K. (2014). *Our Sexuality* (12th Ed.). Belmont, CA. Cengage.

Gagnon, J.H & Simon, W. (1973). *Sexual Conduct: The Social Sources of Human Sexuality*. Chicago, IL. Aldine.

Kafka, M.P. (2010). The DSM diagnostic criteria for fetishism. *Archives of Sexual Behavior. 39*(2), 357–362.

Kink Academy. (No Date). *Experts on Consent*. Retrieved April 20, 2013 from http://www.kinkacademy .com/home/?s=consent.

Leitzman, M.F, Platz, E.A, Stampfer, M.J; Willett, W.C; Giovanucci, E. (2004) Ejaculation frequency and subsequent risk of prostate cancer. *JAMA. 291*(13), 1578–1586.

Levin, R.J. (2007). Sexual activity, health and well-being: The beneficial roles of coitus and masturbation. *Sexual and Relationship Therapy. 22*(1), 135–148.

Mead, G.H. (1934). *Mind, Self and Society*. Chicago, I.L. University of Chicago Press.

Longmore, M.A. (1998). Symbolic interactionism and the study of sexuality. *J. of Sex Research. 35*(1). 44–57

Society of Janus. (No Date). *Askjanus' Blog*. Retrieved April 20, 2013 from http://soj.org/blogs/askjanus.

# *Some Examples of Sexual Fetishes by Category*

| Body Parts | Bodily Functions, Fluids & Smells | Foods & Textures | Materials |
|---|---|---|---|
| Feet<br>Ears<br>Noses<br>Body hair . . . virtually any body part | Urophilia (urine)<br>Coprophilia (feces)<br>Sneezing, mucus, saliva, flatulence, semen, blood, etc. | Phallic food (banana, cucumber, etc.)<br>Jell-o, whipped cream, sticky foods, milk, sauces, etc. | Leather<br>Latex<br>Armor<br>Diapers<br>Cuffs/chains |
| **Articles** | **Personas** | **Scenarios** | **Sounds** |
| Shoes<br>Earings<br>Zippers/buttons<br>Business suit<br>Straight jacket<br>Any clothing article | School girl<br>Religious figure<br>Boy/Girl scout<br>Military/camouflage<br>Doctor/dentist/nurse<br>Animals: puppies, ponies, furries | • Voyeurism (watching sexual activity with or without consent)<br>• Exhibitionism (Performing sexual activity for audience with or without consent)<br>• Role-plays: Abduction, rape, interrogation, etc. | Screams<br>Phone calls<br>Laughter (may include tickling)<br>Sneezing<br>Coughing<br>Household appliances |
| **Instruments** | **Weapons & restraints** | **Body Modification/ Decoration** | **Binding & Suspension** |
| Medical equipment<br>Needles<br>Tuning forks (sounding) | Whips firearms<br>Chains rope/noose<br>Talons cuffs | Branding<br>Scarification<br>Piercing (permanent & play) | Meat hooks<br>Rope bondage (kinbaku)<br>Sensory deprivation |

Paul Rueckhaus, MA, MPH, is a lecturer at San Francisco State University in the English and Health Education Departments. He also teaches health science at Skyline Community College. Correspondence may be sent to him at: rueckhausp@smccd.edu

# *Some Examples of BDSM Role-plays and Possible Social Critiques Embedded in Them*

| Roleplay | Activities | Power Systems Critiqued |
|---|---|---|
| **Master/Slave** | **Dom**: Whipping, tying, handcuffing, humiliating. Sensory depravation. Forcing the slave to do household or sexual chores. Punishing and scolding the slave for breaking rules.<br><br>**Sub:** Complies with Dom's orders | Capitalism. (Symbolizes labor and production. Pain must be endured for profit.) Modern and historic forms of slavery. White supremacy. Human trafficking trade (sexual and other labor). |
| **Infantalism** | **Sub:** Diaper wearing. Bottle or breastfeeding, self-defecation . . .<br><br>**Dom:** Feeds, smothers, scolds, spanks, etc. | The nuclear family. Patriarchy (may involve corporal punishment). Symbolizes utter dependence on the maternal/paternal figure. |
| **Puppy play** | **Sub:** acts like a dog. Is collared and sometimes leashed. Eats from a bowl. Obeys orders.<br><br>**Dom:** Praises, punishes, feeds, pets the sub. Permits bathroom use. | The nuclear family & patriarchy (Man's best friend, unwavering loyalty to the patriarch.) |
| **Pony play** | **Sub:** Dresses like a horse. Carries Dom in a carriage. Is directed by dom.<br><br>**Dom:** Whips and controls movements of sub. Regal relaxation while being carriaged. | Slavery. Aristocracy/monarchy (the comfort of the Dom accentuates the humiliation/subjugation of the pony/sub) |

| Dominatrix scenarios | **Dom (always female or MTF):** Beats, humiliates, whips, restrains, slaps, punishes sub.<br><br>**Sub (male or female):** Complies with Dom's orders | Patriarchy and capitalism. Dominatrix scenarios play upon and subvert gender roles. Women have the power to inflict pain and humiliate men. |
| --- | --- | --- |
| **Drill sergeant/soldier Boy scout/scout leader Nun/School girl Doctor/patient Jailer/inmate Etcetera** | **Sub:** Receives demands, beatings, insults according to the negotiated drama.<br><br>**Dom:** Directs, demands, administers pain, humiliation, etc. | All recapture and hyper-dramatize power imbalances sanctioned by institutions. |

# Chapter 19

# *When Sex Becomes a Problem*

*Albert J. Angelo, M.S.Ed*

- A 32 year-old heterosexual woman removes her wedding ring every time she's away from her husband and in the company of attractive men. In the five years of her marriage, she's had sexual affairs with over 15 men.
- A 41 year-old bisexual man spends 18 hours a day at home downloading and viewing internet porn. While doing this, he doesn't eat or shower. Rather than take a break to use the bathroom, he stays by his computer urinating into an empty milk container.
- A 58 year-old heterosexual man visits his wife in the hospital. After the visit, he drives directly to a local massage parlor for a sexualized massage.
- A 27 year-old homosexual man has had anonymous sex with over 3,000 partners. Often, condoms weren't used during penetrative anal sex.

Do these individuals suffer from an addiction to sex? The answer could be yes. The behaviors these individuals exhibit and the negative consequences they experience could be described as problematic sexual behaviors or, according to Dr. Patrick Carnes, as "sex addiction." In his book <u>Don't Call it Love,</u> Dr. Carnes states sex addiction happens when one's sexual behavior becomes unmanageable and causes harm to oneself and/or to others. Debate exists, however, whether sex addiction is a real illness. The American Psychiatric Association (APA) does not recognize sex addiction as a distinct psychological condition. In their text, <u>the Statistical Manual of Mental Disorders, fourth edition</u> (DSM-IV-TR) no reference to sex addiction is given. This omission is confirmed by researcher Dr. John Giugliano (2009) who writes:

> Neither "sexual addiction" nor "addiction" appears in the DSM-IV-TR. Only disorders involving substances are described with related terms such as "dependence," "abuse," and "obsessive-compulsive disorder." (p. 1)

---

Reprinted by permission of Albert J. Angelo.

Dr. Carnes acknowledges this controversy and states:

> We are surrounded by the signs of sex addiction yet still resist its reality. We can accept that people can be sick with alcoholism or can destroy themselves with gambling or food—but not sex. There are some who see the problem clearly but hesitate to call it an addiction. They choose words like "compulsive" or "hypersexual"—yet they have absolutely no problem calling compulsive gambling an addiction. (p. 10)

While disagreement exists as to whether sex addiction is a valid illness, this article will not further the debate but will acknowledge the generally held view that one's sexual behavior can become problematic and harmful to oneself and to others. To establish consistent terminology, "unmanageable sexual behavior" will be used to reference sex addiction, sexual dependency, sexual impulsivity or any similar problems resulting from one's out-of-control sexual actions.

## Assessing Unmanageable Sexual Behavior

For a person concerned about unmanageable sexual behavior, two excellent questions help illuminate if a potential problem exists:

1. Is one's sexual behavior causing serious problems in one's life and/or the lives of others?
2. Is it extremely difficult or even impossible to stop one's sexual behavior even though such behavior is causing harm to oneself and/or to others?

Dr. Carnes suggests the following ten warning signs as indicators when one's sexual behavior could become unmanageable:

1. A pattern of out-of-control behavior
2. Severe consequences due to sexual behavior
3. Inability to stop despite adverse consequences
4. Persistent pursuit of self-destructive or high-risk behaviors
5. Ongoing desire or effort to limit sexual behavior
6. Sexual obsession and fantasy as a primary coping strategy
7. Increasing amounts of sexual experience because the current level of activity is no longer sufficient
8. Severe mood changes around sexual activity
9. Inordinate amounts of time spent in obtaining sex, being sexual, or recovering from sexual experience
10. Neglect of important social, occupational, or recreational activities because of sexual behavior

Another assessment tool comes from the 12-step group of Sex Addicts Anonymous (SAA). Below are SAA's 12 questions each highlighted by a personal vignette from an individual from the San Francisco Bay Area who self-identifies as a sex addict. Each story is uniquely written and unaltered. However, to protect anonymity, each contributor's name has been changed.

**1. Do you keep secrets about your sexual or romantic activities from those important to you? Do you lead a double life?**

Brad, a 40 year-old homosexual man, wrote:

When I was engaging in anonymous sex, I kept my behavior completely separate from all other areas of my life. My instinct to keep my addictive sexual behavior secret was driven by shame, fear and self-hatred. I always had a lie ready to explain to the people in my life where I was, where I was going or where I had been. I felt that my friends, and especially my boyfriend, could never know what I was really doing. It became complicated and stressful to keep track of all my lies, and all the lying also created a distance and isolation which further fueled my addiction.

**2. Have your needs driven you to have sex in places or situations or with people you would not normally choose?**

Marc, a 39 year-old homosexual man, wrote:

I would regularly have sex with people that would typically repulse me. I have gone into crack dens, the most crime ridden parts of town and had sex in the filthiest rooms imaginable. At the time I was relentless in my pursuit for only sex—no personal interaction, no kissing, nothing remotely intimate. I would have sex with people who were very unattractive, sometimes appeared to be homeless, and were unwashed. I didn't care about whether someone was married and even slept with people who were the partners of friends of mine. It was all about the relentless pursuit of the next conquest. I regularly lied about my HIV and STD status and exposed men to HIV and STD's. I accepted money from men that were old and physically not attractive to me. I did all of this while being in love with the man of my dreams, living the life I had always hoped I could have. I had a great, well paying job, lived in a beautiful home, yet felt the overwhelming compulsion to lay down with anyone who wanted to have me—for free or for money.

**3. Do you find yourself looking for sexually arousing articles or scenes in newspapers, magazines, or other media?**

Douglas, a 36 year-old homosexual man wrote:

I would spend numerous hours a day viewing Internet porn. I would search various x-rated websites, collect thousands of images of men having sex with other men and women, and view the pictures and videos not only at home but at work. My two biggest fears were losing my job, because I also used my work computer to collect and view porn, and losing my partner due to my activities.

Yet, despite the risk to my job and to my relationship, I couldn't stop. I would promise myself I wouldn't use my work computer for searching and viewing porn but I repeatedly broke my promise. I would also tell myself I wouldn't search for porn for more than one hour a day or wouldn't view any of it when my partner was home but again I couldn't stop. Thankfully, from therapy and 12-step recovery work, I have no sexually explicit images saved on my computer, and I have been able to abstain from viewing porn for more than two years.

**4. Do you find that romantic or sexual fantasies interfere with your relationships or are preventing you from facing problems?**

Sam, a 63 year-old heterosexual man, wrote:

I am a heterosexual male over sixty. As long as I can remember, I have had compulsive sexual fantasies usually when masturbating. Masturbation and the fantasies associated with it do interfere with my relationship. They reduce my sexual drive for several days and then I'm not interested in being sexual with my partner. I have found that, even though I now have a wonderful relationship with my partner, my fantasies usually involve women from my past who were strictly sex objects, with whom I had no relationship.

Jennifer, a 31 year-old heterosexual woman, wrote:

I fantasize all the time, even in 12-step meetings. It keeps me from being present. When I am anxious, I can't even sleep, because I am consumed by fantasy. The fantasies bring me momentary pleasure, as if my body does not know that the fantasy isn't reality, but fantasizing keeps me disconnected from my partner and from others. I am always imagining life, or sex, with a man other than my husband. It is distracting and I feel shame about it. From being in Sex Addicts Anonymous (SAA), I have been sober from acting out for over a year, but the fantasizing persists. I recently began telling my partner when I am fantasizing. He is a sex addict too, and this rigorous honesty seems to bring us closer. When I admit to fantasizing, it stops much more quickly. I have also employed the "three second rule," where I only allow myself to run with the fantasy for three seconds.

**5. Do you frequently want to get away from a sex partner after having sex? Do you frequently feel remorse, shame, or guilt after a sexual encounter?**

Alonzo, a 50 year-old homosexual man, wrote:

As my addiction progressed, I became progressively less interested in dating or romance. Eventually, I was putting no time or energy into either. My M.O. became to seek sex when I wanted it, and to avoid any entanglements afterward. On rare occasions, I would become romantically and/or sexually obsessed by a sex partner, but for the most part, after sex, I couldn't get away from them fast enough. Also, after years of strictly adhering to safer sex guidelines, I began to engage in unsafe behavior with increasing frequency. If I wasn't particularly attracted to someone, I would demand from them degrading and often unsafe behavior. I'd find this momentarily exciting, but when the sex was over I would be filled with shame and guilt for putting them at risk coupled with feeling contempt for them for being self-destructive. If I found someone particularly attractive, I would often be the receptive partner in unsafe behavior. When the sex was over, I'd feel crazed with regret and fear about my behavior. Either type of encounter would leave me avoiding sex for months afterwards because I couldn't trust myself to have appropriate and safe boundaries around my sexual behavior. Inevitably though, after enough time had passed, I'd be back at it and the cycle would repeat again and again.

6. **Do you feel shame about your body or your sexuality, such that you avoid touching your body or engaging in sexual relationships? Do you fear that you have no sexual feelings, that you are asexual?**

Anita, a 28 year-old homosexual woman, wrote:

Being a woman, being gay, and being an incest survivor, I internalized a lot of harmful ideas about sexuality. As a girl, I am not "supposed" to want sex at all, let alone sex with another woman; culturally, this is considered shameful. As an incest survivor, my earliest experience of sexuality was as a mode of violence. I feared that having a sex drive meant I was a perpetrator myself, so I learned to shut down this part of myself for long periods of time. When I did periodically act on sexual desires, I felt I had to hide it. I thought of my sexuality as something dangerous, a problem. I tried different strategies to hide it, contain it, limit it, or kill it altogether. Escaping into fantasy seemed a "safe" release sometimes. In no way did I understand sex as a means for emotional and spiritual intimacy. In fact, experiencing my sexuality as a dangerous problem set me up to compulsively avoid both intimacy and reality. It also left me vulnerable to dangerous and problematic sexual behaviors, as I had the expectation that all sexuality would by definition be characterized in this way.

7. **Does each new relationship continue to have the same destructive patterns which prompted you to leave the last relationship?**

Bill, a 51 year-old heterosexual man, wrote:

I have had three marriages and one other serious relationship. It wasn't until I jeopardized the third marriage that I began to see that there was a common, destructive pattern to my life. In fact that pattern became progressively worse over the years. Specifically, I craved acknowledgement and attention from women, whether they were my wife or someone else. In some perverse regard, even negative attention, such as my wife's anger upon discovery of an extramarital affair, was rewarding to my craving for attention.

My ego was clearly an important factor in all this behavior. Passage of time would allow it to do one of two things, usually in some weird combination. On the one hand I would "forget" how painful and destructive my adultery was to me and the people around me, including our children. At the same time, my ego would lead me to believe that this time would be different. That is, I had learned from my past mistakes that led to the discovery of that adultery, and I wouldn't make them again. Of course, I was wrong on both these counts.

This is particularly dismaying because I am in a profession that looks at and puts a lot of faith in historical data, and then tries to create new models for the future. Unfortunately, I couldn't adapt my professional predisposition to my personal life.

8. **Is it taking more variety and frequency of sexual and romantic activities than previously to bring the same levels of excitement and relief?**

Drew, a 42 year-old homosexual man, wrote:

Before the age of 40, I had been sexual with over 3,000 men. I've engaged in all kinds of sexual behaviors (safe and unsafe) in all kinds of places including parks, beaches, bath houses, in the back of retail stores, and many times in the steam room at the local gym. In the beginning, "vanilla" sex was hot, but over time more intense sex was needed to get me off. To have an orgasm, I needed more men, in more physically and legally risky ways, with more degrading and humiliating acts. I remember one day hunting online for hours for a man to come over to my house for sex. Finally, a man came over and we were sexual but it wasn't "hot" enough for me. When the guy left, I immediately went back online looking for another sex partner. I remember thinking: "How many guys does it take before I find it hot enough to have an orgasm?" Why isn't one enough?

9. **Have you ever been arrested or are you in danger of being arrested because of your practices of voyeurism, exhibitionism, prostitution, sex with minors, indecent phone calls, etc.?**

Henry, a 70 year-old homosexual man, wrote:

In the decade of my 30s, I was arrested 5 or 6 times. I cannot remember how many times because it was so upsetting and humiliating, but not enough for me to be able to stop the behaviors. Sometimes it had to do with my alcoholism, but always it had to do with my sex addiction. It was voyeurism in public bathrooms and having sex in public places. Once I was charged with filthy language and resistance. My lawyer recommended that I plead guilty to the resistance charge so that the filthy language charge would be dropped since filthy language was a sex offense.

After I moved to San Francisco, I continued to be a voyeur in public bathrooms and also picked up hustlers for which I could have been arrested. To help me to stay sober, I keep a memory of being handcuffed face down in a dirty alley with the police saying unkind and nasty things about me and the young man I was with. It is a relief to not be doing these behaviors in sobriety.

10. **Does your pursuit of sex or romantic relationships interfere with your spiritual beliefs or development?**

Craig, a 49 year-old heterosexual man, wrote:

Before entering recovery for addictive sexual behavior, pursuit of sex whether tactile or visual always came first. Not only did it block any hope for spiritual development, I had zero interest in such development and had only scorn for things spiritual. I was living a "catch-as-catch-can" life. I lived for the sexual high. I had friends and jobs and family relations but all that was carried out half-heartedly in between binges.

Now in recovery and free from my destructive sexual behaviors for several years, I sometimes indulge in behaviors that are linked to addictive sex, although not the behaviors that brought unmanageability to my life before recovery: things like sneaky and obsessive staring at women, or rather, at parts of their body and clothing. This, along with unhealthy sexual fantasy, represents the sexual aspects that interfere with my quality of life now and nearly always cut me off from a sense of myself, my goals, and my ability to live life free from sexually compulsive behavior. I just can't have both: I can't have my addiction AND spiritual peace. What has changed in recovery is recognizing when I am indulging and then making a conscious choice to desist. I now can come right back to my spiritual foundation and I don't have to spend hours wallowing in self-disappointment.

**11. Do your sexual activities include the risk, threat, or reality of disease, pregnancy, coercion, or violence?**

Donna, a 44 year-old homosexual woman, wrote:

My sexual activities have included all those things. I have had gonorrhea, chlamydia, genital warts, hepatitis A, hepatitis B, yeast infections, bladder infections, and a couple more things I can't remember at the moment. I still have my exposure to hepatitis C, which will always show up in my blood tests as well as herpes I and II. While turning tricks with men I didn't know, I got raped several times, beaten bloody once, almost killed twice, and coerced into having sex beyond my comfort zone an uncountable number of times.

**12. Has your sexual or romantic behavior ever left you feeling hopeless, alienated from others, or suicidal?**

Robert, a 42 year-old heterosexual man, wrote:

Most of my relationships have the same pattern:

1. I begin believing having an attractive girlfriend will make me feel good about myself and make others envy me.
2. I get to know someone new and start flirting with her. It's all exciting and I feel high in the beginning.
3. As soon as I know I have her affection and things get more serious, I become self-conscious and I feel insecure. I fear my girlfriend will leave me for someone better and I view how often we have sex as an indication of the strength of our relationship. This, however, makes me jealous of other men and my personality changes. I become jealous, anxious, uneasy, and obsessive.
4. Fearing that I could get hurt from feeling rejected by my girlfriend for wanting someone else, I break off the relationship usually by acting cold towards her, and cheating with other women.
5. We break up and then I feel despair and hopeless.
6. Then the pattern starts over again with a new woman.

# Treatment Options for Unmanageable Sexual Behavior

A major obstacle in the treatment of unmanageable sexual behavior is the difficulty and controversy in diagnosis. As Giugliano (2009) writes:

> Without clear clinical criteria and definitions, making a definitive diagnosis of a client experiencing sexual dependence is difficult if not impossible. (p. 2)

With this controversy, therapeutic options are generally limited to models adopted for the treatment of substance abuse. Such treatments may include group therapy, anti-depressant and anti-anxiety medications, cognitive behavioral techniques, and 12-step programs (Giugliano, 2009). Dr. Carnes created a comprehensive recovery program detailed in his book Don't Call it Love. His treatment approach recommends therapeutic support, adoption of healthy cognitive and behavioral techniques, participation in 12-step recovery programs, and developing healthy sexuality behaviors while abstaining from those self-identified as harmful. Whatever the treatment modality, breaking the secrecy from unmanageable sexual behavior and seeking support begins the path to recovery and ends a life of shame, isolation, and despair.

## For More Information

More information about help with unmanageable sexual behavior can be found from the following organizations:

1. Sex Addicts Anonymous: http://saa-recovery.org/
2. The Meadows Addiction Treatment Center: http://www.themeadows.org/
3. Pine Grove Behavioral Health & Addiction Services: http://www.pinegrovetreatment.com/patrick-carnes.html

Albert Angelo has worked in the field of health and human sexuality education for over 25 years. He earned a bachelor's degree in Psychology in 1988 from Shippensburg University and immediately began working with disadvantaged youth in the Philadelphia area helping them learn important health and wellness information and acquire valuable life skills. In 1993, after earning a Master's degree in Human Sexuality Education from the University of Pennsylvania, he accepted positions as a health educator and part-time lecturer at San Francisco State University and, most recently, at CSU San Bernardino. In addition to teaching, he has published two college text books in 2000 and 2005. Albert currently lives in Palm Springs, California.

## References

Carnes, P. J. (1991) *Don't Call it Love: Recovery from Sexual Addiction*. Bantam Books.

Giugliano, J. (2009) Describing and Treating Out-of-Control Sexual Behavior. *Focus: A Guide to AIDS Research and Counseling*, 24(1), 1–2.

Sex Addicts Anonymous. (2009). *Are You a Sex Addict: Self-Assessment* from http://saa-recovery.org/IsSAAForYou/SelfAssessment/

# Chapter 20

# Sex Offenders: Myths and Facts

*Catherine Piliero-Surbeck, Ph.D.*

## Myths

There are many myths in our society about sexual offenders and the crimes they commit. Lack of accurate information, stereotypes of sex offenders and victims, and media portrayal of sex crimes contribute to these myths. Some commonly held misperceptions about sex offenses are that:

- they occur as a result of an uncontrollable sexual urge, or due to severe mental disorders;
- sex offenders can be recognized by the way they look. For example, they are men in trenchcoats who loiter in public bathrooms and schoolyards, or they are men considered too unattractive to find a consenting sexual partner;
- gay men pose a special risk to children because they are prone to molesting boys;
- most sex offenses occur in dark, isolated places against women walking alone;
- men with "mental deficiencies," such as mental retardation, are more prone to sexual aggression than "normal" men;
- sex offenders are men and their victims are women or girls; and
- rape is not an act of sex but of violence.

Contrary to these beliefs, sex offenders are not usually "crazed" or psychotic attackers who are driven by uncontrollable sexual urges. Nor are individuals with mental retardation or "mental deficiencies" more prone to commit sex offenses than those without mental handicaps. In fact, these groups, the mentally retarded and mentally ill, are more likely to be *victims* of sexual abuse, rather than perpetrators. Regarding gender, more sex offenders are male than female, but women do commit acts of sexual aggression, and are increasingly being recognized in the courts as sex offenders. This writer has worked with women who have molested children, raped adolescents and committed incest. In terms of the gender of victims, it is important to recognize that both males and females are sexually abused. The sexual abuse of males is not uncommon, and males are most at risk for sexual abuse during their late childhood and early adolescent years. Some experts in the field of sexual abuse consider boys to be at almost equal risk as girls. In a 1994 study of sex offenders conducted by this writer, it was found that almost half (47%) of the victims abused by the offenders in the study were

Reprinted by permission of Catherine Piliero-Surbeck.

male. This is consistent with a recent survey conducted by this writer of the victim gender patterns of child molesters. This survey found nearly equal rates of sexual abuse against male and female children.

# Facts

Sex offenders can be persons of either gender. They can come from lower, middle or upper social classes. They can have advanced education and work in elite, respected professions, or they can be poorly educated and work in blue-collar jobs. They are not more likely to be homosexual than heterosexual. A homosexual sexual orientation is not considered a "risk factor" for sexual aggression, and is not associated with a proclivity to molest or rape. Far more sex offenders are heterosexual than homosexual. Even men who molest boys are not necessarily homosexual, as they may be married to women or have girlfriends. Sex offenders cannot be identified on thee basis gender, educational level, physical appearance, social class or sexual orientation. They are not typically "sex maniacs" who have no control over their sexual urges.

Sex offenders *are* people who have the ability to be aroused and gratified by sexual activities that are against the law, and which usually pose some type of harm to others. These acts include child molestation, rape, indecent exposure, voyeurism or "peeping," frotteurism (rubbing of the genitals against someone's private parts in a crowded place), incest, sexual contact with animals, obscene telephone calls, necrophilia (sexual contact with corpses), and stalking. It is a misnomer to call rape (or other acts of sexual aggression) an act of violence, and not an act of sex. By their very nature, sex offenses are sexual acts. Rapists and other sex offenders commit their assault by abusing the sexual body parts of their victims, and it is often associated with sexual arousal and gratification for the offender. Many use the memories of the sexual offense as the basis of fantasies to which they masturbate and ejaculate afterward. This is not to minimize the violent nature of sexual abuse, or the roles of anger, violence and aggression. Emotions of anger, hatred, rage, and aggression often underlie sex offenses and contribute to the acting out of sexual abuse. In fact, physical aggression, poorly managed anger and impulsive expressions of anger can be risk factors for sexual offense. Anger management problems and misdirected rage are common traits among sex offenders. Many were sexually abused (at least 60%) prior to becoming perpetrators. Even more have histories of physical abuse and neglect. Their feelings about their own abuse are often unresolved and displaced onto others through sexual aggression. There are also issues of control, power and domination that contribute to sexual aggression. Many sex offenders derive a sense of ego strength and self-esteem by being able to control and dominate their victims. However, it is a fallacy that sex offenses are not sexual acts. To minimize the sexual aspects of these crimes is to ignore a crucial area that requires close attention in therapy, that is, the role of sexual fantasies and arousal response patterns. One of the characteristics shared by most sex offenders is that *they are sexually aroused and often gratified by their acts of sexual abuse.* If the acts were not sexually arousing and gratifying, they would not be as likely to be repeated. Another common trait shared by most sex offenders is that they are prone to repeat their crimes without special intervention and supervision. Most sex offenses are the products of cycles that involve a build-up of negative emotion and sexual arousal. There are also phases in the cycle called "cruising" (going out to locate a victim) and "grooming" (preparing the victim for assault, the so-called "buttering up phase" when the victim's trust is obtained and they are lured into situations conductive to abuse). Acting out the sexual assault is another phase of the cycle. And the final cycle, or the "post-assault" phase, consists of all the behaviors, fantasies and thoughts the offender has after the act of sexual abuse. Often, masturbation to fantasies of the assault takes place in the post-assault phase. These cycles are likely to repeat themselves, and in some cases, they become compulsive and habitual, unless intervention occurs.

The early part of this paper highlighted the commonly believed myths about sex offenders and who sex offenders *are not*. The following list highlights some facts about sex offenders, the common characteristics that many share, and who *they are:*

- Most sex offenders begin their cycles of assault during adolescence, sometimes even earlier.
- Most sex offenders have been physically, sexually or emotionally abused prior to becoming perpetrators.
- Some sex offenders are sexually aroused by the pain and suffering they cause to their victims, so called sadistic offenders. Others are aroused in spite of it.
- Most victims of sexual offense know the offender. Most offenses take place in the home of either the victim or the perpetrator.
- Adolescent sex offenders are most likely to commit acts of sexual abuse during babysitting situations.
- Fire-setting, animal cruelty, truancy, pre-mature use of pornography and physical aggression are common behavior problems among adolescent sex offenders.
- Sex offenders are more commonly diagnosed with character disorders or personality disorders, rather than with severe mental disorders.
- Many sex offenders aggressively deny their offenses when caught and are prone to blame their victims or other external sources for their problems.
- Fear, control and power are often used as weapons by sex offenders to manipulate or coerce their victims.
- Psychopathic sex offenders, exhibit impulsive, opportunistic habits. They take pride in tricking, conning and manipulating their victims to get what they want. They have a belief system of "entitlement." They show no signs of conscience. They are indifferent to the harm they cause. And they may use their interpersonal relationships, their jobs, or their status to gain access to potential victims.

# Treatment

The treatment approaches most often endorsed in the research literature are cognitive-behavioral and social skills-based. Specific techniques include relapse prevention training, covert sensitization, victim empathy training and arousal re-conditioning. *Relapse prevention* teaches offenders self-control skills for managing sexual urges. It also teaches about the cycles of sexual assault and the triggers for re-offense. Offenders learn to avoid high-risk situations to reduce the chance for relapse. *Covert sensitization* is a treatment intervention that has three goals. It teaches offenders to recognize the antecedent factors that can lead to assault; it teaches offenders to pair natural negative consequences with the assault and with deviant sexual fantasies; and it teaches offenders appropriate outlets for the feelings that can lead to assault. *Victim empathy* training challenges the cognitive distortions, rape myths and defense mechanisms sex offenders use to justify their behavior and minimize the impact of the assault on their victims. It teaches them about the psychological and sexual harm that victims experience after assault. It teaches offenders to assume full responsibility for their actions, and fosters empathy for those they have harmed. It is considered one of the most important aspects of sex offender therapy. *Arousal re-conditioning* addresses the role of sexual fantasies and deviant sexual response patterns. Through the use of masturbation exercises, it teaches offenders to associate sexual pleasure with healthy sexual fantasies of age-appropriate consensual sex, and negative consequences with fantasies of deviant sex.

Sex education and social skills training are also part of treatment. Medication may be used when deviant sexual urges are compulsive and resistant to psychotherapy along. Certain anti-depressants, such as Prozac, have been used with some success in controlling deviant obsessive-compulsive sexual behaviors. Libido-reducing drugs, such as Depo-Provera, have been used with greater success, and work by reducing the level of testosterone (the sex drive hormone) in the blood.

Sex offender therapy is best provided in group settings. Group treatment is considered more effective than individual therapy. Confrontation by the peer group, and also the support of the peer group, is highly effective in resolving the denial that most offenders present with in the early stages of therapy. The intensive phase of treatment can be expected to last an average of 18 months, but sex offenders often require ongoing therapeutic maintenance after they complete treatment. There is no cure for sexual offending. A reasonable expectation is that sex offenders will learn the self-control skills necessary for relapse prevention, but they are not considered cured, even after completing treatment successfully. It is important that sex offenders have access to treatment, either in prison if they are incarcerated, or in the community if they are probationed or paroled. Those who are highly motivated to rehabilitate themselves, who are fully accountable for their offenses, and who have the support of families and treatment resources, will have the best prognosis for rehabilitation and successful adjustment in the community.

# Section VI

# Sexuality and Society

# Chapter 21

# Sex and the Internet: An Overview

*By Deb K. Levine, BSW, MA*

## Introduction

It's hard to believe, but it was only about 15 years ago that the Internet went mainstream (1996) and changed the way people accessed explicit materials, learned about sex and sexuality, and normalized their sexual experiences. Before that, we had to rely on word-of-mouth, X-rated magazines, embarrassed classroom teachers and parents, and chatty friends.

The Internet takes many forms: email, chat rooms, forums, listservs, Q&As, website content (text and images) and social media. Each has its place in regards to our sex lives, sexuality and sexual health. Early adopters of the Internet—fetish communities, gay and bisexual men, and heterosexual men–were the first to use it as a medium to explore sexuality. This had some inherent benefits as well as risks and challenges. Benefits included freedom of expression and the ability to virtually meet new people with shared interests. Risks and challenges included, for some, the widening of their "real life" sexual networks and with it, transmission of HIV and other STDs; addictions and compulsions and infidelities.

Despite it all, the Internet is here to stay. It has a role in our ever-changing sexual culture by making available sexual materials; affording privacy and perceived anonymity for sexual exploration; and the technology to prohibit developmentally inappropriate access for children and teens. The Internet has also been used as a tool for promoting sexual health and positive messages by social service, public health, and other professionals.

## Objectives

1. To identify the role the Internet can play to enhance sexuality and sexual understanding.
2. To demonstrate an understanding of how online sexual materials have affected the sexuality of early adopters (fetish communities, gay/bisexual men, heterosexual men).
3. To explain how the Internet can be a useful tool to health and social service professionals in their work.
4. To describe the role of the Internet in our present and future sexual culture, mores, and norms.

## Role of the Internet to Enhance Sexuality and Sexual Understanding

Being behind a screen, whether it's a computer, laptop, or mobile phone, offers a sense of anonymity that allows people to access their vulnerabilities. Our culture is still squeamish about sex and sexuality, considering them sensitive, personal issues. The Internet offers a space where people can safely explore their sexual interests, find like-minded communities, and learn about their bodies, fantasies and desires.

Whenever there is new technology out there, the first thing people do is get involved with sexual content. Whether it was filmmaking, video, Internet or camera phones, before corporations knew what to do with it, people were out there sharing sexual materials. As gay men were early adopters of the Internet, they were one of the first communities to recognize its power and potential around sex and sexuality. They learned chat; chat rooms were a great place to hookup with other gay men locally looking for sex. They set up amateur file sharing sites for adult pictures, and used online sites like Gay.com to do everything from finding gay-friendly vacation spots to advocating for more research on HIV/AIDS.

Academic researchers started studying online gay hookup culture to determine if the Internet posed an environment for more risky behaviors than in pre-Internet times. The jury is still out, although most scientific articles have concluded that the Internet is not the cause of risky sexual behaviors; simply one more mechanism whereby people who are going to have unsafe sex can meet up. See: *AIDSCare:* Special Issue on the Internet and STD/HIV Prevention. 2004.

Many people who have felt disenfranchised by their sexual interests or disenfranchised because of their age, disability or gender, now find community online. Witness GimpGirl, for people with mental and physical disabilities, the wealth of BDSM sites, including SF's very own Kink.com, or the adult baby community. Web communities provide people with legal ways to explore their fetishes and sexual interests, in a safe environment without shame or embarrassment. In the case of people interested in BDSM, there are guides for safe play, including Gloria Brame's sites, as well as Columbia University student group—Converso Unum. There are sites for tall women who like short men; for people over 65 who are still sexually active, and for trans folks to meet other people who are trans and their supporters.

## Sex Education and Teens

Ninety-three percent of teenagers are online. American youth ages 8–18 average 44.5 hours per week in front of a screen (Kaiser Family Foundation 2010). Thirty-one percent of teenagers have searched online for information on a health topic that's hard to talk about (drugs, sex, etc.). Seventy-five percent of teens have their own mobile phones, with no significant differences by race or ethnicity. Fifty-four percent of teens text daily (Lenhart 2010a). In fact, text messaging has become so much a part of teenagers' lives that 87% of those who text said they sleep with, or next to, their phone (with the power on).

U.S. youth of color are much more likely to use advanced telephone functions than other American teens (Lenhart et al. 2010a). In addition to mobile phone use, nearly three quarters (73%) of online teens use social networking sites, like Facebook and MySpace. Teens from lower-income families (a family income of less than $30,000 annually) are more likely to use online social networks than teens from wealthier households, with more than 80% of teens from less well- off households using social networks (Lenhart et al. 2010b). In terms of health, technology is not an end for young people, but a means to accelerate information provision, widen social networks, and sharpen the questions a young person might ask when they do access health services (Fox 2009).

There are many sites online that operate outside of the school system to provide comprehensive sex education, information and advice to youth and young adults. Ranging from Sex, Etc. to Scarleteen, to Planned Parenthood dot org, they each have their own strengths and weaknesses. However, many teens do not know about these sites, so when they do have a sex question, they simply head to Google and search. Most times these sites are not first in the list of search results, because of a lack of knowledge by sex educators about search engine optimization and how teens search online. In some schools, these sex education sites are censored, and in other situations, outside of institutions, paying sites are pushed to the top of the list. These days, there is a movement afoot to engage more philanthropists and corporate social giving in "learning outside the classroom," or sex education online. In order to do this effectively, we need to be able to put corporate marketing practices to work so that when a young person searches to find out the best ways to have sex or what to do if the condom broke, solid, relevant information comes to the top of the search engine results.

According to ISIS' 2011 white paper, TechSex USA: Youth Sexual and Reproductive Health in the Digital Age, today's teens take a multimedia approach to learning about sex–pop culture and reality TV have a huge influence, along with the Internet, social media, friends, family and trusted brands. For the paper, we surveyed 1500 youth who visit popular online gaming sites, and conducted focus groups with youth in Oakland, CA and Chicago, IL. Everyone we spoke to knew "16 and Pregnant". While much maligned by parents and educators across the country, what you probably don't know is that there is a curriculum guide for the show to use in classrooms and after school programs, giving a relevant teaching aid to adults who need conversation starters around sex. You can access the curriculum guide at The National Campaign to Prevent Teen and Unplanned Pregnancies website.

## Effect of the Internet and Sex Workers

There has been much debate over whether the Internet has transformed sex work positively or negatively. Witness Craigslist and the lawsuit that claims they are responsible for people posting disingenuous ads. Sex workers, on the other hand, say the Internet has freed them from pimps, paid them more money, and helped empower them to take charge of their business. The criminal justice system says that a new way has arisen for pimps and johns to take advantage of their cadre of prostitutes, especially those who are underage. They are seeing a lot of minors in Juvenile Court who claim their pimps posted ads on Craigslist and other sites "on their behalf."

Tips for sex worker safety online exist, and small cooperatives where workers watch out for each other help keep the dangerous activity to a minimum. West Coast Cooperative for Sex Worker Professionals arose from Vancouver Health Department, where despite the fact that sex work is still illegal, they are much more liberal and tolerant in society. The health department even hosts programs and provides HIV and STI testing services for members. This is another group for sex workers based out of New York City called Red Umbrella. They host salons and events where sex workers can express themselves artistically, reducing shame about the profession and encouraging camaraderie and support.

This topic is not covered without mention of Craigslist. We all use it to find apartments or roommates, gigs, and meet-ups. As far as sex goes, though, it's totally controversial. The terms of service for Craiglist say users are not allowed to post ads to meet people for money, but there are many code words, etc. that people in the know use to advertise paid services, illegal drugs and risky sexual activities. Craiglist takes no responsibility for ads posted on their site, as they are community-driven and they are simply providing the platform for the community. Quite a few years ago, ISIS (www.isis-inc.org) got together with the San Francisco Department of Public Health and started a safer sex forum on Craigslist. The staff at Craigslist thought it was so important to have this forum that they made it national (it started as just Bay Area) and they still promote it from all their Personal Ads pages today.

## STI/HIV prevention

In 1999, a man came into San Francisco City Clinic and was diagnosed with syphilis. He had had sex with many men but didn't know their names, although they were all members of the same SF-based AOL chat room. Health officials went into the chat room and alerted chatters that someone in their group had been diagnosed with syphilis and told them about free and low cost testing services in the City. Nine cases were diagnosed related to the index case. Today, 12 years later, the Centers for Disease Control and the National Institutes of Health have federal programs dedicated to using the Internet, mobile and social media for HIV and STI prevention.

There have been numerous peer-reviewed articles published about the feasibility, acceptability and effectiveness of using various forms of new media and technology for sexual health, including rigorous literature reviews, particularly in the HIV prevention field (Cole-Lewis and Kershaw 2010; Fjeldsoe et al. 2009; Noar et al. 2009; Swendeman and Rotheram-Borus 2010). Individual studies have looked at the key elements of technology-based interventions, such as reach, especially to underserved populations; ability to provide standardized information; ability to customize and tailor; interactivity; privacy; autonomy; portability; and cost-effectiveness (Bull 2010; Gold et al. 2011; Tortolero et al. 2009). Recently, there was a study in the Journal of Preventive Medicine (Bull, Levine, Santelli, et al. 2012) about an HIV prevention study conducted on Facebook with young adults (age 18–24) of color across the U.S. The study found positive short-term results from an 8-week multimedia content driven Facebook page called Just/Us. A play on a private space for Just Us and the idea of sexual health as a social Just/Us issue, the Facebook page has over 1,500 friends engaged in discussions of positive sexuality and relationships. www.facebook.com/justusISIS.

In terms of mobile interventions, recent reviews concluded that short message service (SMS) can be used successfully to promote short-term behavior change for a variety of health behaviors, including sexual and reproductive health (Lim et al. 2008, 2011). While these studies are important to establish effectiveness and efficacy, unfortunately, many of them employed a "laboratory-setting", making them difficult for others to scale and replicate outside of an academic research setting. Qualitative and descriptive work has been published on the use of cell phones and new media for prevention of HIV/sexually transmitted infections (STIs) and unplanned pregnancies (Gilbert et al. 2008; Levine et al. 2008). There is also a growing literature documenting the promise of new media for sexual health (AIDS.gov 2008; The National Campaign 2007; Weldon 2009). This research suggests that mobile phones and other new technologies have considerable promise and potential for the field.

## Sex and Gaming

Online games can be used as study guides or learning supplements to promote safer behaviors, and to teach collaboration, critical thinking, and deductive skills. Online video games offer rich, interactive environments that motivate learning, in some cases in groups of young people from around the world (massively multiplayer online games). The Pew Internet and American Life Project (Lenhart et al. 2008) found that 99% of boys and 94% of girls play games on a console, computer, portable gaming device, or cell phone. Among teens who play daily, 65% are boys, 35% are girls.

> Example: RePlay: Finding Zoe
>
> RePlay: Finding Zoe is an online video game that seeks to promote healthy relationships and challenge the acceptance of violence and unhealthy relationships in young people's lives. The game centers on a group of kids searching for their friend Zoe, who is believed to be in an abusive relationship. Players discover Zoe's diary, in which she chronicles her boyfriend's transformation from "perfect" to controlling, suspicious, and abusive. While seeking clues to her whereabouts and gathering friends to show Zoe they care, players are faced with multiple choices in response to rumors and gossip. Players are also asked to take a multiple choice survey about their own relationships. The game was created by Take Action Games and Metropolitan Action Committee on Violence Against Women and Children (Ontario; http://www.metrac.org/replay/index.html).

## Sex advice and counseling

This business has yet to take off. Many online sites have cropped up offering licensed professionals for sex therapy, counseling and advice. Some are free and operate like advice columns, like Savage Love. Others are providing services for a fee (payable by credit card online). It's hard to know what you actually are going to get for your money, and it seems like most users try to get as much as they can before/without paying.

That said, there is still one of the original sex advice columns online, Columbia University's Go Ask Alice. Started after a talk in residence hall where a difficult question was asked about Ecstasy, Prozac and erections, Go Ask Alice remains a medically accurate, conversational advice column about sexual health, sexuality, sexual activity and relationships. www.goaskalice.columbia.edu

## *Conclusion*

The Internet is here to stay, and so is sex. Whether it's Instagram, Tumblr or the next new thing, rest assured, you will also be able to find amateur sexual content, explore diverse sexualities and sexual experiences, and find communities of people who like the same things you do. And at its heart, it will always be controversial—and not just Craigslist. People today complain about sexting, censorship, and there's still uproar over access to pornography online. We figure as long as people are talking about sex, it's a good thing, and can help advance our culture to a more open, positive view of sexuality and sexuality communication throughout the lifespan.

Deb Levine, BSW, MA is a health educator, who began her career at Columbia University with the creation of Go Ask Alice. She has gone on to found ISIS (Internet Sexuality Information Services, Inc.), a non-profit organization based in Oakland, CA whose mission is to use technology and media for sexual and reproductive health and the development of healthy relationships. She was a 2009 Pop!Tech Social Innovations fellow, and a member of the 9 Women to Watch by Elle magazine in 2011. Her work has been celebrated by the White House, the U.S. Department of Health and Human Services, and the National Institute of Medicine.

# References

AIDS.gov. (2008). Why New Media and HIV? Available from: http://www.aids.gov/using-new-media/basics/why-new-media-and-hiv/. Accessed on: 5 Dec 2010 579

Bull, S. (2010). Technology-based health promotion (pp. 1–10). Thousand Oaks: Sage Publications.

Cole-Lewis, H., & Kershaw, T. (2010). Text messaging as a tool for behavior change in disease prevention and management. Epidemiologic Reviews. doi:10.1093/epirev/mxq004.

Fjeldsoe, B., Marshall, A., & Miller, Y. (2009). Behavior change interventions delivered by mobile telephone short-message service. American Journal of Preventive Medicine, 36, 165–173.

Fox, S. (2009). The social life of health information. Pew Center for Internet & American Life at the Pew Research Center. Available from: http://pewinternet.org/Reports/2009/8-The-Social-Life-of- Health-Information.aspx

Gilbert, P., Ciccarone, D., Gansky, S., et al. (2008). Interactive "Video Doctor" counseling reduces drug and sexual risk behaviors among HIV-positive patients in diverse outpatient settings. PLoS ONE, 3(4), 1–10.

Gold, J., Lim,M.,Hocking, J., et al. (2011). Determining the impact of text messaging for sexual health promotion to young people. Sexually Transmitted Diseases. doi:10.1097/OLQ.0b013e3181f68d7b.

Kaiser Family Foundation (2010). Generation M2: Media in the Lives of 8- to 18-Year-Olds. Available from: http://www.kff.org/entmedia/8010.cfm. Accessed on: 16 June 2010.

Lenhart, A., Kahne, J., Middaugh, E., Rankin Magill, A., Evans, C., Vitak, J. (2008). Teens, video games, and civics: teens' gamingexperiences are diverse and include significant social interaction and civic engagement. The Pew Internet & American Life Project at the Pew Research Center. Available from: http://www. pewinternet.org/Reports/2008/Teens-Video-Games-and-Civics. aspx . Accessed on: 16 June 2010.

Lenhart, A., Ling, R., Campbell, S., Purcell, K. (2010a). Teens andmobile phones. Available from http://www.pewinternet.org/Reports/2010/Teens-and-Mobile-Phones.aspx. Accessed on: 4 July 2010.

Lenhart, A., Purcell, K., Smith, A., Zickuhr, K. (2010b). Social media and young adults. Available from: http://www.pewinternet.org/Reports/2010/Social-Media-and-Young-Adults.aspx. Accessed on: 16 June 2010.

Levine, D. (2009). SMS for health: A how to guide. In B. J. Fogg & R. Adler (Eds.), Texting4Health. Palo Alto: Stanford University.

Levine, D., McCright, J., Dobkin, L., et al. (2008). SEXINFO: a sexual health text messaging service for San Francisco youth. American Journal of Public Health, 98(3), 393–395.

Lim, M., Hocking, J., Hellard, M., et al. (2008). SMS STI: a review of the uses of mobile phone text messaging in sexual health. International Journal of STD & AIDS, 19, 287–290.

Lim, M., Hocking, J., Aitken, C., et al. (2011). A randomised controlled trial of text and email messaging for sexual health promotion to young people. Journal of Epidemiology and Community Health (in press).

Nielsen Company. (2009). How teens use media: a Nielsen report on the myths and realities of teen media trends. Available from: http://blog.nielsen.com/nielsenwire/reports/nielsen_howteensuse-media_june09.pdf. Accessed on: 22 September 2009.

Noar, S., Black, H., & Pierce, L. (2009). Efficacy of computer technology-based HIV prevention interventions: a meta-analysis. AIDS, 23(1), 107–115.

Swendeman, D., & Rotheram-Borus, M. J. (2010). Innovation in sexually transmitted disease and HIV prevention: internet and Sex Res Soc Policy.

# Chapter 22

# Sex Work: A Contemporary Introduction to the World's Oldest Trade

*Carol Queen, Ed.D.*

## Introduction

"Sex work" is a term that serves a dual purpose. First, it allows us to consider the provision of sexual services or entertainment in terms of economic exchange, not in terms of sexual or legal deviance. "Sex work" is now a preferred term for referring to prostitution, for example, because it emphasizes that prostitution is in fact a form of work, a prostitute one category of laborer.

Second, providing erotic goods or entertainment or sexual service is work not done only by prostitutes, and so the term "sex worker" also lets us consider a wider range of types of work within what is often called the "sex industry" or "sex trade." Besides prostitutes, the sex industry employs people as peep show workers and strippers; porn models and performers; professional dominants and other S/M practitioners; phone and computer sex "operators"; writers, editors, and publishers of pornography; adult industry distributors and retail sales workers; and in diverse other capacities. In fact, I will argue that a case can be made for using the term "sex worker" to describe anyone who works primarily with sex, including in a research or educational capacity, although this use of the term is not very common.

It should be noted that reference to the "sex industry" does not mean that all elements of it are connected. They are not. Nor are all sex workers employed by someone else. Many are self-employed or small-business owners. There exists no overseeing corporation that ties the disparate elements of the sex industry together, although some businesses that run sex shops, publishing ventures, video production and distribution, etc., are sizeable, and the industry as a whole is big business.

Prostitution is often termed "the oldest profession." There is no doubt that discussing it (and related professions) is of interest in virtually all eras. Even where they are socially stigmatized, prostitutes elicit fascination because they supposedly have access to great sexual knowledge and hidden information. Most early written pornography used prostitutes as main characters, because whores were seen as the only real female representatives of explicit, active

---

Reprinted by permission of Carol Queen.

sexuality. But looking at sex work today sheds light on more than a culture's sexual secrets. It also provides a window on the sexual attitudes of a society and on its gender issues.

This discussion of sex work is intended to serve as a wide-ranging overview, including some history, a look at the diversity within contemporary sex work, and more. It is focused especially on the US, but does not exclude information from other parts of the world. Topics covered will include feminism and gender politics, criminalization, research, and the sex workers' rights movement. However, it *is* an overview, and interested readers are urged to explore the topic more thoroughly than is possible here.

My approach owes a great deal to the contemporary sex workers' movements, especially the academic/research arm of these movements. They are attempting to describe and analyze working conditions and other related issues from an insider's point of view, something that has rarely been done in the past.

# Research

Some of the earliest modern social science research focused on prostitutes (and the possibility that they might spread sexually transmitted diseases). Since then, research about sex workers has fallen into many categories. It can be done from various points of view: historical, anthropological, psychological, sociological, criminological, epidemiological, and more. Archaeology has even gotten into the act, excavating ancient brothels in Pompeii and elsewhere.

Particularly as "hands-on" research goes—participant observation and survey research, in particular—academics who wish to study sex workers can face an extreme version of the problems confronting all researchers who wish to gain knowledge about taboo or little-understood topics from human subjects. As with the subjects of any research on sex or illegal behavior, many sex workers will not easily trust a researcher. They may answer questions incompletely or incorrectly, tell the researcher what they think s/he wants to hear, or refuse to participate in the research at all. Finding study subjects in the first place can be challenging. It is next to impossible to do a random sample on a secretive subgroup, so most survey research on sex workers uses convenience or snowball samples, less generalizable than other forms of research. Sample size may also be too small to be really useful.

This problem is worse when the research is being done on prostitutes and others whose work is criminalized. Still, other sex workers share some of the stigma attached to prostitutes and may be equally hesitant to stand up and be counted, much less questioned in depth.

Additionally, much general sex research does not even ask sex workers to stand up and be counted, so any opportunity such research may offer to query a general population about sex work experience goes unexploited. Research that asks about frequency and variety of sex practices usually includes nothing that would allow the researcher to identify and analyze the responses of sex workers.

Bias can enter into a research project from many directions. Convenience sampling, as I have noted, is not considered highly generalizable to large populations, although if done well it can usefully describe a particular subgroup. Substantial bias and misinformation enter such a sample when the researcher makes the mistake of assuming the sample s/he got adequately describes the population as a whole. For example, many studies on prostitution conducted by sociologists rely on populations that are incarcerated. Similarly, much research is done simply by applying the federal government's own crime statistics; this, too, counts only those who have been arrested. Prostitutes who work the streets are much more likely to be arrested and convicted than those who work indoors as escorts or "on call," so prison studies disproportionately include streetwalkers. Furthermore, however street workers are more likely than other prostitutes to be poor, of color, less educated, and drug-using—so prison and crime statistics-based studies disproportionately describe the "average" prostitute (a creature no researcher has adequately described) as drug-addicted and downtrodden.

Researcher often includes built-in biases. Some researchers approach sex workers with fascination others with distaste. Pre-existing, unexamined attitudes about prostitution, pornography, and sexual entertainment can taint a study and make its conclusions open to debate, but for too long such debate was rare in academics. That tendency is changing today partly because more current and former sex workers have spoken up to debunk the bias inherent in much so-called research.

An interesting source of bias in most contemporary research on sex work is a form of gender bias: We are much more likely to think of sex workers (especially prostitutes) as female than male, even though men work in the sex industry in virtually every capacity women do. Potentially interesting comparisons between female and male sex workers are made. Sex workers are often described generically, as it were, as female, since the culture tends to see provision of sexual service as part of the "normal" female role, not the male's. The experiences of male sex workers are hence more hidden and less examined, and it is harder to differentiate male and female experiences.

There is also substantial class bias in research, as noted in the discussion of prison studies, above. Researchers may expect to find sex workers who come from the underclass and fail to look very hard for exceptions to the "rule"—or when they find such exceptions they may assume they are anomalies and not listen to the alternative information they may offer. Conversely, researchers may find educated and articulate sex workers and look no further. Either bias misrepresents the real diversity among sex workers.

In short, although there is a lot of research that looks at sex workers, much of it is not very useful outside the context of the specific group profiled in each particular study. Beware of researchers who generalize their findings to all prostitutes, all porn performers, etc.

# History

"The oldest profession" has been practiced in one form or another in a great many epochs and cultures. There is even recent evidence that sexual favors traded for valuable exchange (food, nesting materials, etc.) may be practiced in the animal kingdom. Considering historical sources or sites (such as archaeological digs) for information about the sex trade in other times and cultures is made difficult by several things. Historical sources may be just as tainted by bias as contemporary researchers' work. Information about a vanished culture can be simply incomplete or speculative. A real gender bias exists in most historical information—much more has been written about female than male prostitutes. Some cultures are relatively open about sex, while others maintain a high level of privacy in sex and gender relations.

Perhaps most interestingly (not to mention confusingly), since female prostitutes get the most scrutiny, historians' interpretation of the role of sex workers in any given culture is affected by the role of women within that culture—particularly as relates to sexuality. In cultures in which women have a high degree of sexual freedom and autonomy, prostitution may take very different form than it does in societies that seek to control women's sexual expression and outlets. When the larger question of gender roles is not addressed, the picture painted of prostitution can be rather misleading.

Prostitution is intimately related to the history of pornography, at least in the West. The word pornography translates as "writings of or about whores," and as we have seen, prostitutes became fixtures in pornographic writings because they were openly sexual when other women of the times were not supposed to be.

History gives us glimpses of times and cultures in which prostitution was not as marginalized and demonized as it is today. Sacred prostitution may have been practiced in some pre-Christian Middle Eastern cultures: in these goddess-worshipping societies, priestesses made themselves available for sex with the men of the community, who paid them for the privilege of having this encounter with the divine. Funds raised this way went into temple coffers. It is thought that this practice is the reason the Bible rails against the "Whore of Babylon." Some prostitutes today feel that they are re-creating this form of prostitution and may term themselves Quadesha or sacred whores. In some cases they may attract clients who appreciate their spiritual approach, but in most cases the spiritual importance of this identity helps support the sex worker herself, allowing her a stronger self-image in a society that does not value her or her work.

More historical material is available on prostitutes who worked with the wealthy and titled than on those who provided sexual service to the lower classes, just as there is more documentation of every kind about the lives of the powerful. Hetaerae in ancient Greece, courtesans in Middle Ages Europe, and geisha in imperial Japan led very different lives from other women, often being among the most well-educated and cultured women of their societies. Prostitutes were sometimes the only independent women in cultures that restricted women's freedom and required male oversight of their lives.

There is an exception to the historical blackout of common prostitutes. It is generally recognized that at times of social change, especially wars and migrations, prostitutes emerge to provide sexual service to men who are single and separated from their wives. This occurred in Europe's great period of urbanization, in America's Western migrations, and it is commonly associated with military encampments and troop movements. We typically do not know much about the individual prostitutes who made their living under these conditions, but we often know something about how they lived, how their businesses worked, and who their customers were. Much historical documentation is available about certain red-light districts, such as Storyville in New Orleans, which were a recognized part of their communities for many decades.

Developments in technology have historically impacted the sex industry, in two main ways. The first has to do with the way new technologies can change an entire society's economic circumstances, as implied above: Europe's great migrations were set in motion by the Industrial Revolution, and urbanization changed traditional communities and provided the opportunity for the growth of red-light districts and an expanded economic niche for prostitutes. The second involves the way certain new technologies can be used by the sex industry itself: this list of specific technologies is long and involves contraceptive methods, prophylactics, photography, film, video, telecommunications, and computers. Totally new inventions can be exploited for sexual purposes and may involve the development of entirely new branches of the sex industry; pornographic movies would not exist without motion picture and/or vide technology, for example.

# Different Jobs Within the Sex Industry

As noted above, sex workers come in many diverse subtypes. Though "sex worker" is often used as a synonym for "prostitute," many other types of erotic or sexualized labor can also be described as sex work, and most of the workers doing other jobs in the sex industry do not understand themselves as prostitutes of any kind. Of course, it often happens that an individual does several jobs in the sex industry; a porn star may pose for photos as well as doing videos and may also do live shows and strip or even turn tricks. But there are definite lines between different kinds of work, and they are not always crossed. This section will briefly explore the various types of work sex workers do.

## *Prostitution*

Prostitutes may be male, female, or transgendered. They may work the streets of an urban red-light district, linger at truck stops, gather in massage parlors or brothels, or work discreetly in their own or their clients' homes. The fee they receive for the sexual service they provide may range from just a few dollars to several hundred dollars or more. Because their work is illegal in most parts of the US (and in many other parts of the world), prostitutes do not often speak for themselves, and so many stereotypes abound about their work, lives, habits, and histories. Some of these stereotypes are essentially true for some prostitutes. But no stereotype adequately describes the "average" prostitute, because there is such great diversity among these sex workers that no one type could be called average.

Common stereotypes include: Prostitutes are drug-addicted; they are repulsed by sex with strangers but are forced to it by economic necessity or inescapable pimps; they can't do any other sort of work; they are young; they are female; they are more likely to have sexually transmitted diseases than non-prostitutes; they have been sexually abused.

Many of these elements are more commonly seen in the lives and experiences of street workers than among prostitutes in general. Street workers' experience can definitely be harsh, and many are well served by leaving prostitution, when and if they can find other economic alternatives. But the majority of prostitutes probably do not work the street. In fact, researcher Priscilla Alexander has estimated that only about 10% of prostitutes in America are street-based. Far more are employed in brothels and massage parlors or by escort services, while still others work independently. The latter, often called "call girls" (men will often be called "escorts" or "models"), advertise in the classifieds or work with a madam or other individual who helps procure clients.

Because independents work in a less-organized and obvious fashion, they are less likely to risk arrest, and so they are harder for researchers to locate and study. In between well-publicized busts of madams whose rings of call girls service wealthy or famous men (think Heidi Fleiss or "the Mayflower madam," Sydney Biddle Barrows), the general public does not see call girls in their midst, because they don't hang out on street corners wearing skimpy outfits. Rather, they blend in, and one of the many qualities they offer their clients is discretion.

Class background and education level help determine the future of a prostitute, and this distinction underlies the great diversity among prostitutes. As we have seen, this has been as true historically as it is today. While it would be incorrect to say that poor, undereducated women and men always end up on the streets while individuals with a more privileged class and educational background end up working solo or with an escort service or a madam, this split exists more often than not. Some street prostitutes say they prefer the flexibility and freedom of such work, but most are probably there because their life choices are circumscribed. Conversely, many escorts are better-educated and often do have more choices; often people gravitate to this level of the sex industry because they like the money, the freedom, and the fact that, at rates of $200 per hour or more, they have to work relatively little to make ends meet. Many prostitutes save to buy businesses, go to school, or devote time to art, activism, or other interests. These people are more likely to think of themselves as professionals and to view customers not as johns but "clients;" they may start prostitution when they are older, and they often rely on regular clients (contradicting another common stereotype, that prostitutes have sex with "strangers").

Prostitutes are sometimes termed "sexual slaves" who "sell their bodies" for money. But in fact they are not "selling" anything except their time and their skills, just as anyone does who labors for a wage, and they typically are not enslaved by their clients, even for an hour at a time. It is commonly supposed that a prostitute will do, or has to do, anything a client wants her or him to do, but this is not the case. Most prostitutes have clear limits about what they will and will not do for money, and they negotiate with clients about issues like safe sex, specific or intimate practices like anal sex or kissing, time availability, and more.

It is true that some prostitutes are forced (by dire circumstances, or by another person) to turn tricks. It's difficult to say what number do not practice prostitution of their own free will, but it is clear that not all prostitutes with pimps are forced into sex work. (And not all prostitutes work with pimps; probably a minority does.) Pimps are, if anything, more subject to stereotype (often race-based) than prostitutes. In the US, the stereotypical pimp is a black man who has "stable" of female prostitutes who work for him, turning tricks and bringing him all or most of their money. He may control them through sweet talk, violence, drugs, or all three, but (still stereotypically speaking) he calls all the shots.

In fact, the legal definition of pimping has to do with receiving money from a prostitute, meaning that anyone who is supported by, or even simply residing with, a prostitute could be charged with pimping, as long as the prostitute was covering household expenses. Prostitutes' spouses or lovers are often charged with pimping; it can happen whether or not they are involved with the prostitutes' business. In many places it is a more serious charge than committing an act of prostitution, because it is assumed—sometimes correctly, other times not—that the pimp is the person in charge. (Many prostitutes argue that this is an inherently sexist assumption—someone else, probably a man, *must* be in control.)

Street prostitutes may work with a pimp for safety: someone to keep an eye on possibly violent clients, watch out for vice officers, and hold the day's take to guard against theft. Often, though not always, the pimp is the prostitute's spouse or lover. However, many street workers do not work with a pimp. Instead they work solo or develop a network of other prostitutes so they can watch each other's back.

A related role is that of "madam." A madam works, depending on the context, as an employer or manager (as in a brothel), or as a referring agent, putting prostitutes in touch with clients. Often the madam is a former prostitute who has moved into this management or agenting role. For the work s/he does, the madam or agent is paid a cut of the prostitute's fee. This legally makes her or him a pimp, and other laws may be used against a madam too, including pandering and keeping a bawdy or disorderly houses.

The issue of international trafficking will be addressed below.

## *Peep Show Work and Stripping*

From the exotic dancers of the nineteenth century whose work evolved into tease-oriented burlesque to present-day strippers who "show pink" and leave nothing to the imagination, the sex industry has made a place for artistes whose work is too bawdy for the prevailing standard of the times. Live shows range from stripping, with at least some focus on dance and movement, to shows featuring masturbation and live sex acts. These are now mostly centered in adult theaters and strip clubs in or near urban areas, although strip clubs (also known as "titty bars," "gentlemen's clubs," or by other names) are on the rise in the US and can sometimes be found outside of cities. While most such places feature female performers only, there are clubs featuring only male performers too, either oriented toward female audiences—like the famous Chippendales dance troupe—or toward male ones.

Depending on the location of the club and the laws and zoning of the area in which it operates, full nudity and even explicit sex may be the norm; in other places erotic dancing is available, but dancers must cover genitals and sometimes breasts, and explicit behavior is illegal. Strip clubs usually feature a stage with a surrounding audience, and in many of these venues an attraction beyond the stage show is called lap dancing, in which a scantily clad performer sits on an audience member's lap and wiggles to stimulate him (or, more rarely, her). Table dancing, wall dancing, and couch dancing are all variants.

In some countries live heterosexual sex shows can be viewed. These are not common in the US, whose clubs feature male and female masturbation as well as lesbian (or "girl-girl") sex shows when live sex is featured at all. Nevada brothels may feature heterosexual shows as well as girl-girl acts. Peep shows often feature porn video booths as well as booths allowing a view of dancers or performers on a stage. Sometimes one-on-one talk and masturbation shows are available.

## *Porn Models and Performers*

Pornography is available in various forms: written, photographic, film, or video. It is published in magazines and books as well as online. In most cases visual porn involves models and performers, some of whom are well known to their fans and appear in dozens of photo layouts and movies; others are amateurs who may appear just a few times or only once. Successful porn performers tend to be sexually exhibitionistic, and many see themselves as actors. Some viewers might disagree—porn is almost never very highbrow—but many performers prefer working on more elaborate productions because it reinforces their sense of themselves *as* performers.

All the personnel involved in a nude photo shoot or a porn movie can also be described as sex workers, at least when such work is their primary way of making a living.

## Professional Dominants

Professional dominants (a.k.a. "pro doms") are usually self-employed or work in a loose affiliation of other dominants; occasionally they work for a "house," which is owned by someone else, and they pay part of their fee to the house in much the same way that a prostitute who works in a brothel contributes a percentage of her fee to the madam. Pro doms are not prostitutes, however; they work with clients who want sadomasochistic or dominant/submissive scenes. They do not have sex with their clients (at least, not the way most of us think of sex). In session they may do widely varying activities, depending on their interest and expertise and the desires of the client. Some of these include: bondage; whipping; cross-dressing; psychodramatic erotic roleplay; piercing; and "slave training," in which the paying submissive is trained to serve the dominant as s/he specifies.

Males as well as females work as pro doms, with either male or (more rarely) female customers. The women tend to be more high profile, with publications such as *Dominants' Directory International* devoted to showcasing them in their fetish garb. Female doms may also be known as mistresses, dommes, or dominas, while males are usually known as masters. In some cases pro doms may employ or work with professional submissives, so that they can accommodate a client who wants to be the dominant partner in a session.

Professional dominance is a highly specialized type of sex work, requiring substantial specialized knowledge. In spite of this, it usually pays a little less than escort work, probably because it is not as illegal as prostitution. Few, if any, locales specify S/M and D/S practices in laws and ordinance. However, pro doms are sometimes charged with operating a disorderly house, and even with prostitution, especially when authorities do not clearly know the difference between professional domination and prostitution.

## Phone and Computer Sex

In both phone sex and live computer sex a person makes her/himself available to customers for erotic talk. In the case of computer sex, a camera often allows the customer to see the sex worker live. In this case the computer becomes a virtual peep show. In the case of phone sex, though, the worker's only salient qualities are voice and imagination. Customers often call with specific fantasies they want to talk through, though others let the phone fantasy worker take the lead; customers often also request a phone partner of a particular body type, hair color, or ethnicity, and phone sex workers are adept at portraying themselves as blonde or African American, brunette or lesbian, depending on the desire of the customer. Both phone sex and computer sex workers may work either from home or from a group "office" where several people can take calls at once. Both types of erotic entertainment may cost the customer a fair amount of money; but often the worker gets only a fraction of it.

## Porn Writers

A sex industry job that requires no fancy clothing and little human contact, writing may cover the range from porn movie scripts to *Penthouse* letters, literary short stories to smutty paperbacks. It usually does not pay a great deal, so successful porn writers are the ones who can produce fast, especially if they can write a variety of scenarios and from various erotic points of view. It is not unusual to find erotic writers working for heterosexual and gay porn magazines simultaneously. A really professional writer may be prepared to tailor her or his work to the venue at hand.

## Adult Industry Distribution and Retail

The sex industry obviously includes people who directly provide sexual services and entertainment, but it also encompasses people whose job it is to get sexual products into the hands of those who want to use them. From video and sex toy importers and distributors to sales staff in retail sex emporia, sex workers in distribution and retail are hidden behind a veil of commerce. These may be mom and pop businesses or sizeable corporations. Many cities now have erotica shops that cater to and/or are owned by women. The largest of these have catalogs and ship to all parts of the globe. Many of these businesses operate on the Web, too; whether a retail staffer sees her/his customers or simply downloads their e-mail, they remain sex workers.

These businesses, large and small, differ from other retail businesses, which are not at risk for obscenity prosecutions, as some retail sex businesses are. Moreover, the legal definition of obscenity is vague and undefined enough that many distributors and retail staff have a hard time protecting themselves. Many sex workers in the retail and distribution side of the industry have been charged with crimes.

## Surrogate Partners

Surrogate partners, also known as sex surrogates, may do all the things that prostitutes typically do, but they do not do them for the erotic entertainment of the client, but rather to teach him or her sexual skills and assist in the client's therapy. Surrogates almost always work in conjunction with, and by the referral of, sex therapists, which helps protect them against prostitution charges. Surrogate therapy was pioneered by sex researchers and therapists William Masters and Virginia Johnson, who felt people would benefit better from sex therapy if they had a partner with whom to go through a series of experiential exercises, many of which are explicit. A client will work with a surrogate partner for a prearranged number of sessions, and the client's therapist may recommend further work after the basic program is done.

## Sex Educators and Therapists

Many people's idea of sex work stops with surrogate partners. But a case can be made that anyone who works primarily with sex is a sex worker, and that definition would clearly include therapists, educators, and other academics, whose professional focus is about sexuality and sexual health. Surrogates often describe the difference between their work and a prostitute's by saying, "Going to a prostitute is like going to a restaurant. Seeing a surrogate is like going to cooking school." Therapists and sex educators are also instructors in that school.

## Porn Crusaders and Vice Officers

People who earn their living by focusing on sex may be neither restaurateurs nor cooking school instructors; they may be trying to shut the restaurant down. Seeing vice cops and prosecutors as sex workers may be stretching the definition to the breaking point, but it bears noting that these people, too, make a living from society's focus on, and contradictory feelings about, sex—and some of them are as closely focused as any copy editor on a porn magazine.

Using this definition, while not one all sex workers (and certainly not all vice officers) will concur with, allows us to look at sex work from a neutral distance, one unclouded by the moral assumptions that underlie so much discussion about the sex industry.

# Clients and Customers

Sex workers' clients and customers have little in common with one another—except the majority of them are male, whether they prefer their sexual entertainment from women or from other men. They tend to be able to compartmentalize the sexual entertainment or services they purchase, since many are married or partnered and tend to keep their dealings with the sex industry private as far as their spouses or partners are concerned. In many cases, these customers say they have sexual interests they can't share with their primary partners. This is particularly true of the clients of pro doms, clients who want to explore variant sex practices with prostitutes, and male, heterosexually partnered clients of male prostitutes.

In other cases, clients want very ordinary sexual experiences, but they want these experiences with a variety of partners, without emotional entanglements, or according to a specific schedule their partner does not wish to accommodate. A stereotyped view of clients presents them as unable to find partners because they are unattractive or otherwise unsuitable, but in fact, while certainly some men who patronize the sex industry are not likely to find partners elsewhere, most *are* partnered, and they use the sex industry as an outlet or entertainment source separate from the life they share with their partner or spouse.

Clients are stigmatized just as prostitutes are, and many tend to keep their involvement with the sex industry to themselves. Hence it is difficult to say what percentage of men patronize prostitutes, strip clubs, and other sex industry venues, or take advantage of the more private entertainments of adult video rental, phone sex, and sex on the Internet. However, it is clear that the sex industry is established and in many places thriving, that it exists on a global scale, and that in most cultures today there is either a tolerance for the sex industry or at least a "boys will be boys" attitude about men who patronize it.

Countering this, though, is a newer trend that attempts to further criminalize men who patronize prostitutes. Many jurisdictions in the US have adopted tougher laws in recent years, and the trend may be going global. Sweden passed such a law recently in the name of protecting prostitutes, many of whom say they would prefer not to be protected from engaging in their livelihood.

Though the majority of clients and customers are men, some change is occurring today; women are increasingly becoming consumers of pornography, which has changed somewhat in an effort to attract more women and couples. (This change is not seen across the board, but many videographers and publishers have seen the writing on the wall and are purposely making porn for women to enjoy.) Other sex industry venues are seeing more women customers, too: sex toys stores that cater to women, like San Francisco's Good Vibrations and Boston's Grand Opening!, can be found in several cities; many traditionally male-oriented places have cleaned up and tried to make themselves more women-friendly; more women are venturing into strip clubs as patrons. Although the industry as a whole has not embraced this change (nor, for that matter, have the majority of women), there are signs that it may continue and transform at least some corners of the business into welcoming female patrons.

Women who do *not* patronize the sex industry today sometimes say they would if they had more money, and indeed, there still is a pay differential between women and men that may allow men more disposable income to spend on erotic entertainment. Many women also view sex industry venues as dangerous places and avoid them for safety reasons. This complex (and sometimes real) association between sex and sex-related venues and danger is clearly a stumbling block for women who might otherwise explore sexual interests outside of relationships. Also a factor is the lack of visible female sex industry patronage. Men can explore the sex industry and justify it by saying that other men are doing the same; far fewer women are blazing the trial for other women. (When they do venture in, however, the erotic entertainers at strip clubs and peep shows are often very happy to see them.)

# Laws Affecting Sex Workers

Prostitution is illegal everywhere in the US except in certain counties in Nevada. Prostitution-related offenses range from actual acts of prostitution—exchanging sex for money—to soliciting for prostitution, frequenting or maintaining a house of prostitution (also called "bawdy house" or "disorderly house" laws, giving a clue as to their archaic origins), and pimping or pandering. Prostitution is regulated, if not illegal, in most places in the world. In many places, including the Nevada brothels, a prostitute must obtain a license to legally practice the trade. In these locations certain areas are usually set aside as red-light districts, and the state attempts to confine prostitution to these areas. In some British Commonwealth countries, the act of prostitution is not illegal, but many of the surrounding activities are: "communicating for the purposes of prostitution" is a crime, for example.

In the US prostitution-related offenses may vary by state and municipality. Offenses may be misdemeanors or felonies, depending on the offense and the place in which it is committed. Prostitutes who work when they have HIV are sometimes guilty of a more serious offense, even if they limit their sexual contact with customers to a hand job. And as we have seen, in many venues there are also laws against customers: johns may be ticketed, have their cars impounded, or be arrested.

Laws meant to control prostitution can also affect pro doms (especially disorderly house laws, which are usually written so broadly that anything from a brothel to a swing club to a crack house to a loud after-hours party might fall under them). They could theoretically be applied to sex surrogates, as well, although such prosecutions rarely happen.

Laws and ordinances may control or criminalize what goes on in a peep show or strip club, especially as regards full nudity, contact with customers, and live sex acts. Zoning laws are also routinely used to keep such businesses in certain parts of town. Any sort of adult industry venue may be subject to these zoning regulations, including erotica shops.

Obscenity law is the other sort of law that is most relevant to sex industry workers. Laws against obscene behavior can affect erotic performers (as, we should note, can local laws regulating *any* sexual behavior: in a state with a sodomy law that includes lesbian sex in the definition of sodomy, a live lesbian act would invoke that statutes as well as any public indecency, lewd and lascivious, or obscene behavior laws on the books).

Obscenity statutes are most often used in the US today to regulate certain kinds of pornography, although in the past they were regularly used to regulate sexually explicit literature as well, or even literature that is not especially explicit but is considered socially harmful for its era, as in the prosecution of Radclyffe Hall's lesbian novel *The Well of Loneliness* in the late 1920s. In fact, much of the "smut" hunted down by morals crusader Anthony Comstock (after whom the Comstock Act, regulating sending obscene material through the US mail, was named) would be considered sex education or literature today.

Statutes may be interpreted to cover pornography performance, as in a movie or video; but most at risk are the distributors and sellers of the material. Since obscenity law typically cites "community standards," conservative areas host obscenity trials far more frequently than liberal urban areas. After the Meese Commission on Pornography was held in the 1980s, more federal prosecutions of pornography were done, always held in areas with conservative populations.

# International Issues

The sex industry is global, but it takes different forms depending on the cultural context of each region, country, and locale. For instance, in Senegal there is no local word for "prostitute"—instead, the women who exchange sex for money in that culture are known as "women who go out." (Women there are typically overseen by husbands, fathers, or brothers, so women who go by themselves to conduct their own business apparently need no further definition.) Certain cultures place much more judgment on prostitution and other types of sex work than others do.

Partly because of the opprobrium sex workers, especially prostitutes, may face at home, many go elsewhere to work. Border crossings like this happen all over the world. Some travel to another country within their region, others emigrate to the other side of the globe, and some merely go to the next town, but the phenomenon is often made more complex by xenophobia in the host country. Still, it is in many places more acceptable to spend time doing sex work elsewhere than to do it at home.

An extreme form of this phenomenon is known as trafficking. This is most often seen when people from an impoverished area or Third World country come to an urban, usually First World area to do prostitution, exotic dancing, or other form of sex work. Since this form of immigration is extremely costly, a broker will often help the person make the trip—paying for travel expenses, living expenses in the arrival country, and often papers and visas—and the immigrant must pay the broker back, sometimes at extremely inflated rates. This is known as "debt bondage," and it is not done only in the context of sex industry jobs. Resident aliens in many kinds of jobs (mostly menial) have been relocated by these brokers.

Trafficking is often represented as a nonconsensual situation in which women are kidnapped or duped into going to another country to work, only to find themselves in the power of the broker or the broker's associates. In fact, while this does happen, it is frequently the case that the trafficked individual wants to immigrate, knows s/he will be doing sex work, and has even done it before. Still, a life that amounts to indentured slavery in the arrival country, often to pay back tens of thousands of dollars, is abusive no matter what. Trafficking is a big business, and it is being organized against around the world. To the trafficked individual, however, it may not seem entirely positive to be released from a brothel only to face deportation. This is usually the fate of these illegal residents, since the visas provided by the trafficker are often faked.

Prostitutes are not deported only because their papers are not in order. Globally, the HIV/AIDS epidemic has been hard on prostitutes. Many sex workers, especially in the West, have been scapegoated as AIDS carriers even though a prostitute is more likely to practice safe sex than a non-sex worker. In poorer cultures, though, information and prophylactics are not so readily available, and it is the most disadvantaged sex workers who have thus borne the brunt of the epidemic—and of blame for it. However, even in enclaves of disadvantaged prostitutes, education and organizing has helped empower sex workers and save lives. Grant money has become available through governments and NGOs, and it has been used in literacy campaigns, economic development projects that aim to make prostitutes self-sufficient in other trades, safe sex education projects, and more. Such organizing has occurred in Thailand, India, Brazil, Mexico, and many other Third World countries, as well as in Australia, the US and Canada, and several European countries.

The strategies and needs of sex workers in developed countries may be very different from those in developing nations. Several global organizations work with prostitutes and other sex workers, but the best approach seems to involve regional focus and local autonomy.

# Sex Workers as Abuse Victims/Survivors

Among the most prominent recent stereotypes about sex workers is that a very high percentage have been sexually abused. The underlying suggestion seems to be that non-abused adults would not choose to provide erotic entertainment or services unless something had predisposed them to do so, and those who advance the abuse theory clearly cannot imagine someone doing sex work of his or her own accord. In fact, some sex workers *do* recognize such a connection in their own personal histories, but many more do not. Studies that suggest an extremely high percentage of sex workers were abused mostly fall prey to the research problems described above. Until good research is available, this will likely remain an open question, but sex worker advocates remind us to think of all the people with histories of abuse who do *not* become sex workers—clearly a cause-and-effect relationship is not present, at least in most cases.

# Feminism and Sex Work

Modern feminism has had an extremely mixed and often difficult relationship with sex work. The contemporary sex workers' rights movement (about which more below) derived great inspiration from the women's movement of the 60s and 70s. Many sex workers are staunch feminists, and many more *would* identify as feminists if mainstream feminism were not so openly hostile to the sex industry. Virtually any sex worker could give a critique of the sex trade; nobody thinks it is perfect and without worker abuses; but sex workers and sex worker advocates often get rather defensive about mainstream feminism's seemingly total discomfort with (and their harsh judgments about) the facts of sex workers' lives.

Feminists have been among the most vociferous anti-pornography and prostitution crusaders since the 1970s. By the end of that decade "the sex wars" were in full swing. Feminists developed strong (if not rigid) positions against porn, prostitution, S/M, and other sexual activities with which most mainstream feminists were uncomfortable. These positions seemed to be grounded in ideas about sexuality, female autonomy, and gender that seemed anything but feminist to women who disagreed with their moralistic tone, and a substantial split within feminism resulted. The tendency that made theorist Gayle Rubin call feminism as "system of sexual judgment" left some women feeling judged, and many felt this judgment was unfair and unduly conservative. "Sex-positive feminism" emerged to allow women (and others) to continue to identify with feminism's larger goals of equal treatment and an end to misogyny, while allowing more room for feminists to lead the kind of sexual lives they preferred. Sex-positive feminists argue that if feminism means that a woman owns her own body, the things she can choose to do with it should not be unduly restricted.

In fact, mainstream feminism is not monolithic, and feminists' attitudes about the sex industry are gradually being affected by the increasing numbers of sex workers (especially feminist ones) who are speaking up and telling their own stories. Sex workers have made many trips to national NOW (National Organization for Women) conferences to lobby and communicate with that organization, and the result is that the discourse among feminists now leaves more space (and support) for sex workers and their advocates. It remains an uneasy relationship, because both feminism and sex work are diverse, opinions multifaceted and strongly held. But progress is slowly being made.

## *Sex Worker Rights Organizing*

This progress would probably not be happening without the unified voices of the sex work advocacy movement. This movement is global, though in many countries talking to feminists takes a far back seat to priorities like human rights abuse issues, standard of living issues, and health education and support. Still, international whores' congresses are held a couple of times a decade, and organizers are united in a loose network of affiliation that spans the world.

COYOTE (Call Off Your Old Tired Ethics) was started in the early 70s in San Francisco by Margo St. James. It created a standard for US (and other western) organizations: a strong emphasis on advocacy and support for sex workers, plus a high public profile designed to raise consciousness and dispel stereotypes. Organizations inspired by COYOTE include COYOTE

Los Angeles, Prostitutes of New York (PONY), Hooking Is Real Employment (HIRE, in Atlanta), and Willing Women Workers (WWW, in Minneapolis/St. Paul). In the San Francisco area other spin-offs included CalPEP (the California Prostitutes' Education Project), which focuses on AIDS and safe sex education and was founded by Gloria Lockett; BASWAN, the Bay Area Sex Worker's Action Network, helmed by Carol Leigh (a.k.a. performer Scarlot Harlot, who coined the term "sex work"); the Exotic Dancer's Alliance, which formed to organize strippers to fight workplace abuses in strip clubs; and the Cyprian Guild, which organizes for support, advocacy, and to promote professionalism among prostitutes.

Another wing of the prostitutes' rights movement originated in England with the socialist-feminist Wages for Housework movement. A radical anti-poverty organizing effort, it soon added prostitutes' rights to its list of issues. It supported sex workers' strikes in France and Britain in the 1970s and 1980s, and inspired organizers in the US as well. It is known as the English Collective of Prostitutes in Britain and US-Pros, or the US Prostitutes' Collective, in the US.

A big issue in the US sex workers' rights movement is the legalization of prostitution. Really the question is whether to support some form of legalization, as Nevada has, vs. decriminalization. At issue is whether prostitutes should be licensed by the state or whether laws against consensual prostitution and related offenses should simply be removed from the books. At this writing one state in Australia has completely decriminalized prostitution, and while decriminalization is generally preferred by sex worker activists, it is recognized that in the often-moralistic US, that goal might be difficult to achieve. Certainly legalization is supported by many who feel the state needs to monitor prostitution for health reasons; those who disagree feel prostitutes' attitude of "My body's my business" will be sufficient to ensure safe sex. An issue in some other parts of the globe (notably Europe) is probably far in the future for the US prostitutes' movement, namely state pensions, health care, and other worker benefits.

However, a step in that direction may be occurring in the US with a recent emphasis on occupational health and safety issues among sex workers. This emphasis goes fa beyond safe sex and AIDS education and includes all kinds of health issues relevant to sex workers: how to find a physician one can trust, stress management, substance abuse issues, OSHA violations in workplaces, and much more. The first health clinic for sex workers, the St. James Infirmary, has just opened in San Francisco as of this writing. This health focus is the brainchild of Priscilla Alexander, a sex worker advocate who spent several years working with the World Health Organization.

In the strip club industry a wave of organizing has occurred to protest policies that allow the clubs to hire dancers as independent contractors. They are paid no wages or benefits, and often have to pay the house for the privilege of being booked. Arguing that this practice is illegal, the EDA, individual dancers, and other organizations have brought lawsuits and instituted organizing efforts in various clubs. Union organizing has even been attempted in some clubs, successfully at San Francisco's Lusty Lady Theatre. The union-busting firm hired by the club's management was completely unprepared to deal with articulate, college-educated, union-savvy workers, rather than the unclothed bimbos they had been expecting. The Lusty Lady victory was not only a union victory, but also a blow against perhaps the commonest sex worker stereotype, that of the bimbo: the dumb female without other life choices.

In addition to the occasional Whores' Congresses, mentioned above (which are now commonly held in conjunction with International AIDS Conferences), and International Conference on Prostitution was held in 1997 in conjunction with University of California at Northridge (followed by a similar conference on pornography in 1998) and attended by sex workers, sex work advocates, and academics. This gathering could not have come together without Whorenet, an Internet news group that connects activist sex workers all over the world.

Finally, an interesting new organization has emerged that puts a new spin on sex work organizing. Helmed by Norma Jean Almodovar (head of COYOTE L.A. and author of *Cop to Call Girl*), the International Sex Work Foundation for Art, Culture, and Education (IWS-FACE, pronounced ice-face) is working to buy the historic Dumas brothel in Butte, Montana to use as a museum, cultural center, and research institute.

## Conclusion

As noted above, the topic of sex work is enormous, and this discussion has really only provided an introduction to a series of issues that deserve much more attention. A list of selected readings is included below for readers who would like more information and a more nuanced discussion of issues briefly addressed here.

The sex work movement is not monolithic by any means, and many sex workers claim no affiliation with it. A prostitute in Calcutta and an adult video distribution clerk in Los Angeles don't have much in common—except that they are both, in separate ways and cultural contexts, laboring to provide for someone else's erotic entertainment, and in certain ways both are at risk because of it. Since the desire for such entertainment seems to persist over time and across many cultures, the trade that has developed to cater to it (or control it) brings these and other disparate people somehow together.

Because sex and the economy are both basic facts of human existence, though developed very differently in different cultures and epochs, sex work and the many issues that devolve from it are to some degree universal. Because sex is rarely a neutral fact of cultural life, but is embedded in a nexus of kinship and relationship structures, taboo, religious prohibition, and state control, examining the particulars of any culture's sex industry opens multiple windows of enquiry into that culture's core issues. It is hoped that this abbreviated tour of sex work-related issues opens such windows of enquiry for the reader.

# Recommended Readings

There are many books on prostitution, in particular, not listed here because they are out of print and/or are based in not particularly useful, often stereotypical, views of the sex industry. Of these, the ones dealing with history are probably most worthwhile for contemporary scholars and those interested in sex work-related issues.

The list below should not be viewed as a comprehensive bibliography on the subject, but a place for the interested reader to start developing a deeper grasp of the issues.

Alexander, Priscilla and Frederique Delacoste, ed. *Sex Work: Writings By Women in the Sex Industry.* San Francisco: Cleis Press, (1987) 1998.

Bell, Laurie, ed. *Good Girls/Bad Girls: Feminists and Sex Trade Workers Face to Face.* Seattle: Seal Press, 1987.

Bell, Shannon. *Reading, Writing, and Re-Writing the Prostitute Body.* Bloomington: Indiana University Press, 1994.

Chapkis, Wendy. *Live Sex Acts: Women Performing Erotic Labor.* New York: Routledge, 1997.

Doezema, Jo and Kamala Kempadoo, eds. *Global Sex Work.* New York: Routledge, 1998.

French, Dolores and Linda Lee. *Working: My Life as a Prostitute.* New York: E.P. Dutton, 1988.

Keefe, Tim. *Some of My Best Friends Are Naked.* San Francisco: Barbary Coast Press, 1993.

Nagle, Jill, ed. *Whores and Other Feminists.* New York: Routledge, 1997. Pheterson, Gail. A Vindication of the Rights of Whores. Seattle: Seal Press, 1989.

_____ *The Prostitution Prism.* Amsterdam: Amsterdam University Press, 1996.

Queen, Carol. *Real Live Nude Girl: Chronicles of Sex-Positive Culture.* Can Francisco: Cleis Press, 1997.

Roberts, Nickie. *Whores In History: Prostitution in Western Society.* London: Grafton (HarperCollins), 1992.

Stubbs, Kenneth Ray, ed. *Women of the Light: The New Sexual Healers.* Larkspur, CA: Secret Garden, 1997.

Sycamore, Matt Bernstein, ed. *Tricks and Treats: Sex Workers Write About Their Clients.* Binghamton, NY: The Haworth Press, 1999.

Vance, Carole, ed. *Pleasure and Danger: Exploring Female Sexuality.* Boston: Routledge and Kegan Paul, 1984.

# Chapter 23

# *Complexities of Discussing the Erotic Lives of People with Disabilities*

*Sandy O'Neill, Ph.D. (cand.)*

## Introduction

Many current textbooks on human sexuality include short sections discussing the matter of sexuality and people with disabilities. In preparing to write this article I reviewed several of them specifically from what I'll refer to as a disability rights perspective. Not surprisingly, I found some textbooks better than others. Yet, as a disabled person, I came away from this research troubled not so much by these specific visible sections discussing people with disabilities having sexual lives but by both our presences and our absences in many other places throughout these books.

For instance, few photographs or other illustrations include people with disabilities in any section except those specifically discussing this subject. One unfortunate exception is a text that in a section on problems encountered in pregnancy discusses chromosomal "abnormalities" as part of a list including toxemia, RH incompatibility, etc. A small photo of a boy with Down's Syndrome is included in a column of definitions of terms such as toxemia and eclampsia. The child's picture is unintentionally captioned in a manner that suggests he is a syndrome![1] Other introductory texts produce similar jarring juxtapositions in attempting to analyze this relationship of disability and sexuality.

The absence of a specific disability rights framework shows up particularly in accounts of the history of sexology. Disabled people are not generally mentioned. Yet, the fact of disability along with racist, ethnocentric views were central to the development of eugenics, which had an influential role in developing this and other social 'science' disciplines.

This short article obviously cannot take up each issue in depth. Rather, I would invite the reader to think of some of the issues that arise in societal conceptions of disability/illness particularly as they pertain to the topic of sexuality. Posing the following questions from an anthropological standpoint conscious of cultural issues of power, oppression and liberation

---

Reprinted by permission of Sandy O'Neill.

[1]Carroll, Janell L. and Wolpe, Paul Root, Sexuality and Gender in Society, Harper Collins College Publishers, 1996, p. 391–94.

begins to get more clarity about the complex nature of intertwining sexology studies with a disability rights/disability studies perspective. Figuratively stepping back to situate larger questions of the role of disability in society in general places those specifically dealing with sexuality in a different, more differentiated conceptual framework.

These questions to be discussed include:

- What is a disability?
- How can we define people with disabilities?
- What is a disability studies/disability rights perspective?
- What types of societal conceptions and/or misconceptions about and expectations of people with disabilities might shape our ideas about them/us?
- Are people with disabilities culturally perceived as being asexual (non and/or under interested in sex) or in being over-sexed?
- Which stereotypes about disabled people affect views on their/our sexuality?
- What is it that mandates including discussions of disability issues in human sexuality texts and courses?
- How does including people with disabilities in thinking about sex change notions of sexuality and the erotic?
- A final section points the interested reader toward some literature mentioned throughout this article.

To avoid disappointments, I'll note here that readers who are seeking information on the how-tos of sex with people with a variety of disabilities will not find that information here. It can be gathered in a number of places in libraries, sex research programs, or from sexual therapists and most clearly from people with disabilities themselves. This article starts from a conception that people with disabilities are sexual beings despite societal prejudices and misgivings that have had the effect of making a specific discourse on disability and sex necessary.

# Defining Disability

Defining disability moves into contested territory from several angles. Who defines who is disabled  What does it mean to identify as such when some groups particularly from Deaf communities who are commonly thought of as disabled reject that definition of themselves? Those working for disability rights haven't always been and won't always be as clear as might be desired about these definitions either. Often terms such as able-bodyism are used not to define disability per se but to define the prejudices often expressed toward us. However, this terminology usually excludes those with mental or emotional disabilities from the group being considered. (This, of course, depends quite a bit on one's understanding of both the causation of these conditions and beliefs about defining the body and body/mind connections. See further reading for more material on this.)

I think it is most wise to see or define disability as a permeable category with self-definition as the major criterion, more so than in other social/political identity questions. Self-definition of disability can change depending on people's location in other cultural points as well. For example, a Japanese man who is a friend of mine is color blind and an artist. In Japan, he found his color-blindness to be a disability whereas here he doesn't. Another example is a Nicaraguan friend who is unable to have children; she considers this a disability.

In life, people with some conditions may move in and out of being and/or identifying as disabled. Or people may become disabled for a lengthy time but return to "normal" status. There is a great deal of variation among this category ranging from people who are born with disabilities to those (the majority) who acquire them later. Differences also show up in distinctions between observable or noticeable disabilities and non-noticeable ones, between physical and emotional and/or developmental differences.

It's sometimes useful to break disability down to types such as physical disabilities, including mobility impairments, hearing, sight, etc, and chronic diseases. Also, there are learning disabilities, developmental disabilities and emotional disabilities. Additionally, I include those with substance abuse addictions as members of the disabled population. Not everyone discussing disability does so. The government agencies involved in defining who is and isn't eligible for various benefits often define disability quite narrowly as many people with disabilities can attest to.

To make things even more complex, here in the United States, we are immersed in a culture geared toward diagnosing and thereby medicalizing an increasing number of problems. For example, there has been a huge increase in diagnosing attention deficit disorders in children and all types of addiction in teenagers and young adults over the past 15 to 20 years. The wide penetration of a psychologized viewpoint of human behavior can be seen in the broad usage of terms like "road-rage" and the analysis of this and other phenomena as particularized forms of stress reactions. Guests on popular TV talk shows confidently attribute problems in their lives to a lack of self-esteem on their part.

This section in looking at ways to define disability and who is disabled is meant only to give an indication of some of the ways in which these classifications are made and, more important, to begin to get a grasp of the wide variety of people signified when discussing disability issues. Unfortunately, the complexities of defining disabilities are too often used as a rationale to dismiss questions of disability and ableism as a critical area of discourse.

# Ableism and Disability Rights

The emergence of a disability rights movement and the concomitant creation of disability studies are important to understand in continuing to ask how we define the questions of disability identity. I think the clearest summation of the diverse viewpoints being put forward from these perspectives is that disability rights/studies rejects the medical definition of disability and posits that disability is not an individual medical or psychological problem. Rather, disability is defined as a social problem, which is created and institutionalized by social attitudes and prejudices.

It is of some interest to note that the creation of disability studies curricula in some university departments is proceeding even while there is a popular conception that passage of laws, especially the Americans with Disabilities Act, have somehow already remedied any disparity in access to goods, services, education, housing, etc. also play into this. Unfortunately, the realities of life for many of us who identify as people with disabilities are still marked by the frustrations of encountering barriers, both physical and attitudinal, in our daily lives. Consider for example the social situation of many young people. Get-togethers of people in their early 20s often take place at bars or cafes. Even if one can get in the door, the percentage of accessible bathrooms is quite low.

On a larger social plane, few people seem to even know the history of genocide of people with disabilities. The murders, sterilizations and other forms of persecution directed at people with disabilities in Nazi Germany during the Third Reich are often omitted from history books. Yet, research shows that the idea of ridding the population of people with disabilities wasn't met with total shock anywhere in the world. In fact, eugenic ideology did not arise in Germany but was largely imported from the United States and England.

The two examples above obviously differ greatly in severity. Yet, this can be the nature of any specific social oppression. In defining and discussing the oppression of people with disabilities in diversity workshops and classes, I am often struck by how quickly comments about our own mortality come to the surface. This is probably a good part of the explanation of some of the fear and hatred expressed toward us. My fears are aroused more by the fact that people don't want to hear about the reality but are keenly interested in the disabilities themselves, which are simply different ways of being than that which is culturally dominant or normalized.

In defining ableism here as the systematic, pervasive, routinized, institutionalized mistreatment of people with disabilities, I am drawing on a model used in work aimed toward "unlearning" oppression that explores the subjective conditions of emancipation and domination and the ways in which social realities construct psychological realities. I've found the effective practice emanating from liberation theory to be a vital and necessary one for many reasons. Too often, in its concentration on the individual, the field of psychology ignores the manner in which societal relations of inequality affect people intrapsychically. Paradoxically, social movements can often dismiss the necessity of addressing subjective aspects of oppression thereby missing part of the problem.

This theory is rooted in a version of Critical Theory.[2] It contextualizes inter and intra psychological phenomenon. As in the disability rights/studies perspectives, power distribution and issues arising from this area seen as socially constructed products of society, while each particularized type of oppression is defined as the systematic, routinized, institutionalized, pervasive mistreatment of the targeted group based on their membership in that group. Oppressing others then is not viewed as innate in anyone. The differences in human beings are not responsible for oppression. Rather, everyone is conditioned to accept particular roles in society in relation to the power dynamics that are in operation at the particular sites or intersections of various cultural and subcultural groupings. This conditioning or socialization is understood as painful for everyone, no matter which side of the equation they are on in any particular grouping. (This is not in any way interpreted as excusing or ameliorating the horrors of oppression but a way to get at the source of prejudices.)

Conditioning to accept imbalances in power arrangements occurs in childhood. In a broader academic sense, it is part and parcel of the inescapable enculturation process of

---

[2]Often referred to as the Frankfurt School and/or Western Marxism. This work is located more precisely as an extension of the work that is known or identified as that of the first-generation Frankfurt school with an openness to both a postmodern variant and a multicultural emphasis.

humanity. Everyone individually and in social groupings resists being oppressed and at least initially resists being oppressors. Yet, the circulation of misinformation about the targeted groups is ever present throughout society, both in dominant culture and in subcultures. The form that the oppression resulting from the misinformation takes is different for those targeted than from those in the dominant group. Internalized oppression is the form that this takes for those in target groups. This is a construct associated with the Frankfurt School and not a pathologizing form as presented in some humanist psychologies.

Delineating hierarchies of oppression is not seen as usually useful in any effort toward liberation. Nor is there a quantifying of pains or oppressions. I wouldn't say that since I'm oppressed as a woman and by being poor and disabled I am not only triply oppressed but am not capable of oppressing anyone else/any other group so I do not need to explore where and how I've not only been exposed to racism, but as a Euro- or white American, I have played a part, even passively and unwillingly in perpetuating racist thinking. Rather, although no one likes being regarded as an oppressor, I am called upon to investigate and oppose racism as an ally. No group can fully gain their liberation while others are oppressed.

There are differences between active right-wing oppression and subtle forms. The subtle forms though can and have led to a passive attitude toward the oppression of others, either by not seeing the oppression or acting to stop it. Individual or specific types of oppressions reinforce each other and are often intertwined.

Oppression that is learned can be unlearned. People can decide either altruistically or in recognition of their own interests to change their views/consciousness and act to stop oppression. The following exercise is one I've developed to get at the specific nature of ableism. In simplified form, it represents the breadth of the oppression. I think most people will find one or another portion of it resonates with some cultural message they have been exposed to.

# Exercise Exploring Ableism

## *People without Disabilities*

Think about whether you've ever thought that:

- you need to be tough on disabled people so they'll learn independence
- disabled are just too needy and dependent
- you'd rather be dead than blind or in a wheelchair
- (told) a disabled person how much you admire him/her because you couldn't deal with their life
- if people w/disabilities took better care of themselves they wouldn't be in this shape
- wished a friend or relative w/terminal or degenerative condition would hurry up and die
- ever chosen not to get close to person because he or she had disabilities
- ever felt really frightened about your body decaying
- been afraid of dying
- been afraid of becoming disabled
- felt confused about whether or not to help a person with disabilities
- felt confused about how to respond to advocates of civil rights for people with disabilities
- lived, worked, played, or prayed in inaccessible (segregated) places?

Think about the following: Where did you learn ableism? How did you resist? How have you been an ally? Think about how your own fears of becoming disabled may determine your relationship to the topic.

### People with Disabilities

Think about whether you've ever:

- heard people call you a cripple
- had teachers or bosses give you a hard time about needing time off or extra time on projects for medical reasons
- lost a job/place in a school/ because of your disabilities
- gotten a lot of unwanted advice about caring for yourself
- felt it was your own fault for getting sick
- felt you had to hide your disability even when it meant more pain or worsening of your condition.
- been refused housing
- felt that you were not really welcome if you make a fuss about having your needs met
- been upset when friends tolerated your being discriminated against
- felt you constantly had to prove how independent you are.

Many more things could have been chosen. There are entire areas of emerging literature focused on the specific nature of ableism and the emergence of disability cultures. A few titles of articles and books dealing with social theories of liberation and oppression, multi-cultural resources are included in the final section. We can now turn to some of the specific intersections of human sexuality and disability studies.

# Nowhere or Everywhere? Too Little or Too Much?

I now will turn back to the questions posed in the introduction, utilizing the framework we are developing to problematize some notions of 'disabled sexuality.' Particularly, we'll briefly explore the question of whether people with disabilities are depicted only as asexual beings or whether there are more complex messages being expressed. By pulling examples both from current popular culture and the more arcane literature of sexual dysfunction, we can, in simple form, begin to pinpoint some of the specific stereotypes about disabled people's sexuality.

When thinking about how disability in general is represented in mainstream culture or even in some alternative or counter-cultural formats, I think the first "common sense" instinct is to conclude that people with disability are generally desexualized by society just as we are absent from the scene more often than we are included. This is true even in product advertisements. Disabled actors are rarely cast in movies or on TV unless the disability is the topic of the show.

One exception to this is the Carrie Weaver character on NBC's ER. Her disability is visible but not explained. Her character defies the sweetness stereotype and goes more in the direction of portraying the opposite stereotype of disabled people as bitter, frustrated individuals as she humorlessly pursues efficiency at the cost of relations with her coworkers. Yet, Carrie is shown at times as insecure, probably due to the fact that she was abandoned by her birth mother for not being "perfect."

Perhaps the most discussed character among disability rights groups over the past couple of years is not a TV character but a new friend of that popular sexual icon, Barbie. Barbie's new friend, Share-A-Smile Becky, fits more easily into the mold of an asexual character than the irascible Doctor Weaver. Becky, you unlike Barbie's numerous other friends, carries the introductory Share a Smile moniker appropriate for images of long-suffering but brave disabled girls, is the school photographer. While the "normal" girls prepare frantically for their big proms and parties, Becky loads another role of film. She won't need any of those revealing clothes the others wear. And, of course, Mattel's first version of Becky's wheelchair wouldn't fit in Barbie's house!

Many depictions of the desexualized disabled come to mind. Yet, people writing from a disability studies/rights perspective have pointed toward the other side of the equation.[3] Rather than only showing our absence, there are countless representations of disability in films. Unfortunately, disability is usually the symbol for tragedy, evil, or dependence with little attention to the disabled characters as full human beings.

Our initial efforts to survey the breadth of those falling into the category of people with disabilities comes back into play here. Many culturally held stereotypes involve people with disabilities as desexualized. Depending on the type of disability, we are discussing how other people with disabilities are viewed as oversexed and indeed dangerous sexual beings.

In the past few years alone, the very popular TV drama, *NYPD Blue* had two episodes focusing on how easily developmentally or emotionally disabled figures can be blamed for sexual assaults or murders of children. Of course, in these dramas, the cops are the ones who understand that it's not the homeless man who killed a child. Sipowitz and Simone again immediately sense that it is not the building supervisor's developmentally disabled son who hurt a young girl. Despite the lack of realism, these accusations of people with disabilities point toward an underlying prejudice about people with these types of disabilities.

Peter Knoepfler, in an article on sexuality and psychiatric disability, discusses the following three ways that psychiatric disabilities and sexuality can be linked:

## Sexual Behavior is the Disability

Mr. A. is a man in his twenties who functions well in most areas of his life. His predominant form of sexual expression is being an exhibitionist. Psychiatry considers this form of sexual expression a psychiatric disability.

## Sexual Behavior is Unrelated to the Disability

Ms. B. Suffers from a severe case of agoraphobia. Sexual behavior in a bedroom does not trigger Ms. B.'s phobia and it is therefore unimpaired.

---

[3]See for further reading, particularly Lennard Davis and Sander Gilman.

## Sexual Behavior is an Integral part of the Disability

Mr. C. is suffering from a severe depression. While depressed, his sexual desire and interest are impaired. When the depression is treated and relieved, his sexual interest is likely to be awakened.[4]

Exploring sexuality literature on the specific topic of developmental disability, brain injuries, and emotional disabilities, reinforces the view that some disabled have dangerous libidinal urges. Therapists and others in helping professions in general pay much more attention to ways to instruct people about where to have sex than to explaining sex safe practices, etc.

The duality of sexual imagery concerning people with disabilities that is being pointed to in this section is quite similar to that discussed by other groups of people who are on the targeted side in various societal power dynamics. Women, for instance, are often sexually stereotyped as either Madonnas or whores. As people with disabilities, we are either long-suffering martyrs to be kept on a pedestal or lazy malingerers taking advantage of others. These dichotomized images put those in the marginalized groups into a classic dual bind situation. There is no way to win since one side or the other of someone's preconceived notions of who we are will come into the picture on some level.

# The Strange Case of Abasiophilia

In an effort to further complicate the ideas one might have on disability and sexual practices, I thought surfing the Web might reveal an interesting facet of the developing discourse. While the following may seem a distraction from the major thrust of the article it serves the purpose of asking us to think even more deeply about the relationships of power in our society and how these are expressed and repressed culturally. This meditation will lead us into the concluding sections on the entangled and sometimes unpleasant history and relationships of those who study sex in its broadest sense and people with disabilities.

Abasiophilia is defined on a Web site devoted to "Legbrace (Caliper) Fascination" as a fascination with physical disability and the orthopedic appliances used in its management. Now, sexology and psychiatry have more exact and complicated definitions of this and characterize a few discrete paraphilias and fetishes. There have been established categories for what are seen as disorders in medical literature for over 100 years. There are indeed people who are sexually excited by leg braces, crutches and casts. Others are sexually attracted to amputees or others with a particular physical difference. Richard Bruno characterized those suffering from this collection of disorders "devotees, pretenders, and wannabes."[5] Yes, like other oppressed groups, people with disabilities apparently have wannabes. I don't propose to offer a full analysis of this phenomenon except to note that the literature that exists on this topic points to people being envious about what they perceive to be the special treatment

---

[4]Knoepfler, Peter T., Sexuality and Psychiatric Disability in Marinelli, The Psychological and Social Impact of Disability, Third ed., Springer Publishing, 1991, p. 211.

[5]Bruno, Richard L. Ph.D., Devotees, Pretenders and Wannabes; Two cases of Fictitious Disability Disorder in Journal of Sexuality and Disability, 1997; 15:243–260.

afforded those of us with disabilities. Case studies reflect that patients believe people with disabilities are admired for their courage and stand out from others in this respect.[6]

The problem I'm posing here is similar to the more widely reported fetishisms and paraphilias of infantilism. The adult babies as they prefer to be called appearing on his TV show even stumped TV host, Jerry Springer. Understanding them was much too difficult for even this ringmaster. I would not want to judge or stigmatize anyone's sexual practices particularly as what is known of fetishes and paraphilias indicates that this is not a conscious choice. The problem I wish to call attention to is twofold.

In the first case, of those attracted to people with particular disabilities and/or attracted to or aroused by disability paraphernalia, the underlying stereotypes about the experience of disability in this society are uninformed. In the second case, my objection after perusing their Web pages is that many of those active in various groups express a longing to not have bladder and bowel control. They express this by referring to those with incontinence problems as the "lucky ones" and even have sites devoted they say to helping young people who must wear protection feel better about themselves, raise their self-esteem and such. This attitude also reflects a real lack of information about the experience of living with a disability in an ableist society. It encourages a romanticized view of disability. (As for helping young people with disabilities feel better about themselves, I would posit that this is better done by having adults with disabilities as role models.)

The other question I want to pose about the phenomena discussed here is a more philosophical one to ponder. What does it say about our cultural values as a whole that (no matter how different they may seem to many of us) these specific attractions to items that symbolize disability or imitation of people with disabilities are classified as a type of mental aberration? Does this say anything about the social ranking accorded people with disabilities or is the classifying itself perhaps a move to protect us (people with disabilities) from people with a now defined type of mental problem?

Obviously many questions could be posed flowing from this particular intersection. While a bit out of the ordinary, this is also a reminder of just how medicalized and psychologized a society we live in. This brings us to the concluding section, which argues for a more thorough treatment of disability issues in social science disciplines, especially sexology. It also points to the potential advantages of a deeper inclusion.

## Moving Forward by Uncovering History

I began this piece by indicating some of the problems I see with omissions of people with disabilities from general introductory textbooks on human sexuality. The problem in reality is broader than this. Our absence is perhaps most noticeable in this field because there are so many intersecting points emanating from disability studies tied not to narrowly defined issues of sex but also those issues of reproduction, health, and medical research. For instance, how much medical research is given over to preventing the birth of disabled people rather than raising that intangible something called quality of life? It's not really so intangible.

---

[6]Ibid.

And too often, when a disabled child is born, decisions are made to withhold medical treatment, as it is euphemistically termed. All treatment including food is sometimes withheld until the child dies. (I don't know how it's humane even if a baby can't be medically saved to allow her/ him to starve). Rarely if ever are parents facing this situation given a chance to talk to people with similar disabilities about what living with disabilities does and does not mean. It's impossible not to sympathize with the anguish of parents faced with these decisions. Yet people with disabilities are written off and parents are often told by experts that their child's future is bleaker than it could be.

These examples indicate only part of the problem. Another aspect, which was alluded to earlier and directly bears on teaching sexuality, concerns the history of sexology itself. When books refer to the work of Havelock Ellis, for instance, and his *Studies in the Psychology of Sex,* it is equally important to discuss his "The Task of Social Hygiene," which is written specifically in support of eugenics ideas. While he was a relatively mild "positive" eugenics advocate, this is a critical area of discourse in understanding the history not just of people with disability but many people of color and poor people in this country who were involuntarily sterilized under these doctrines. A better understanding of these issues can be obtained by including this type of historical analysis. Recent books on the history of eugenics along with many uncovering forgotten bits of disability history of eugenics along with many uncovering forgotten bits of disability history add a more complete picture. For example, the switch to defining norms rather than ideals in statistics is tied to the discourse around many of these questions as studies of demographics and populations took on a "scientized" tone.

In other words, just expanding sections on disability and sexuality, even if this material is more explicit about ableism, is not adequate. A more rounded inclusion of a disability perspective is needed. Invocations of the identity/diversity mantra remain superficial devices that aren't even prosthetic when only used to signify political awareness of oppression without regard for how these realities change the configurations discussed.

There is an emerging cultural creation or at least feelings of solidarity among some disabled cultural groupings that feel new. Better representations of our lives are already flowing from this, yet if these reflections remain isolated and only viewed by people with disability, we will not be the only losers.

The incorporation of disabled experience and history can add much to current discussions on sexuality as a whole. This is most obvious in the very definition of what is sensual and erotic. For example, an expansion of the meaning of sexual enjoyment sometimes including but sometimes bypassing the usual genital areas and discovering other erotic sensations is an obvious part of sexuality for some people with disabilities.

# Conclusion

This paper has attempted to stimulate thinking around the complexities of the topic by touching on areas not always thought through adequately. Those interested in further reading may find some of the following books useful:

Adams, Mark B, 1996, *The Wellborn Science, Eugenics in Germany, France, Brazil and Russia*, Oxford University Press

Davis, Lennard J. 1995. *Enforcing Normalcy, Disability, Deafness, and the Body*, Verso New Left Books, London.

Fine, Michelle and Asch, Adrienne, Eds. 1988. *Women with Disabilities Essays in Psychology, Culture, and Politics*. Temple Univ. Press, Philadelphia

Kevles, Daniel J., 1985, *In the Name of Eugenics: Genetics and the Uses of Human Heredity*, Alfred Knopf Publishing.

Marinelli, Robert P. and Arthur E. Dell Orto, eds. 1997. *The Psychological and Social impact of Disability*, Third ed., Springer Publishing.

Morris, Jenny, 1991. *Pride Against Prejudice*. New Society Publishers.

Paul, Diane, 1998, *The Politics of HEREDITY, Essays on Eugenics, Bio-medicine, and the Nature-Nurture Debate*, SUNY Press.

Porter, Theodore M., 1986. *The Rise of Statistical Thinking, 1820–1900*, Princeton Paperbacks.

Proctor, Robert N. 1988. *Racial Hygiene, Medicine Under the Nazis*. Harvard Univ. Press, Cambridge.

Russell, Marta, 1998. *Beyond Ramps, Disability at the End of the Social Contract*, Common Courage Press, Monroe, Maine.

Shapiro, Joseph P. 1994. *No Pity, People with Disabilities Forging a New Civil Rights Movement*. Times Books.

# Chapter 24

# Sexuality and Spirituality: The Relevance of Eastern Traditions

*Robert T. Francoeur, Ph.D. ACS*

In recent years, the age-old association of sex with Adam and Eve's original sin in the Garden of Eden has lost its meaning as individuals increasingly accept sexual desire and pleasure as a natural good. Social turmoil, technological changes, increasing recognition of personal needs, and a sexual revolution have wreaked havoc with the meaning and relevance of the traditional Judeo-Christian sexual images, icons, and myths of the purpose of sex, monogamy and male primacy over female.

Because cultures draw their life blood from their myths and archetypes, human beings are searching for new myths and archetypes.[1] At the same time, Americans in particular are increasingly fascinated by the more sex-positive images of Eastern sexual philosophies. This article outlines two major Eastern sexual and spiritual traditions, Tantrism and Taoism, within the context of Hinduism and other religions and philosophies. After contrasting these Eastern views with Western values, some practical applications that complement Western sexology are discussed.

## Eastern Sources

Even when the hidden roots of Eastern sexual traditions can be detected, they are found to be far more tangled than the origins of sexual values in Judaism, Christianity, and Islam. Archaeologists have found 8,000-year-old clay images of feminine power and fertility in the pre-Indus settlements on the northwest edge of India. Similar early expressions of a great Goddess who guarantees fertility have been found, with her subordinate male consort, in regions of ancient Egypt, the Aegean, the Danube, Asia Minor, and western Asia. Between 1800 and 1500 BC, waves of migrating Indo-Aryan people moved from eastern Europe, over the mountains, and into the Indus valley of western India. Their worship of a great Goddess intermingled with the fertility religions of pre-Aryan inhabitants they conquered in the Indus River valleys.[2,3,4] Historian Karl Jaspers calls this the pre-Axial period of human consciousness.[6] In this context, Jaspers is using the term Axial to mean turning point.

From *SIECUS* Report, Vol. 20, No. 4 May/April 1992, pp. 1–8. Copyright © 1992 by SIECUS. Reprinted by Permission of Sex Information & Education Council of the U.S.

According to Jaspers and others, this striking transformation in human consciousness occurred in China, India, Persia, the Middle East, and Greece with the advent of Confucius, Lao Tzu, Buddha, Zoroaster, the Jewish prophets, and the pioneering philosophers of Greece. This opened the first Axial period. Everywhere male consciousness and power gained ascendancy over the female principle. In Christianity and Islam, phallic power virtually subdued the power of the female, except for the veneration of Mary, the Virgin Mother of God. After a male God gave man dominion over nature in Eden and ancient Greece gave priority to analysis and objectification, nature became Western man's toy to control and exploit. Although feminine images of sexual power persisted in the East, they were subordinated to the phallocentric male. But unlike the West, Eastern cultures maintained a respect for nature, emphasizing that health and spirituality are only achieved when humanity respects its place in the cosmos and places itself in harmony with nature.[5,6]

# Hinduism

In India, the amalgam of pre-Aryan fertility religions with the emerging dominance of male consciousness produced Hinduism, a generic term for the traditional religion of India. Hinduism encompasses a wide range of seemingly contradictory beliefs, including reincarnation or transmigration of souls, atheism, and a pantheon of gods and goddesses who symbolize the many attributes of an indescribable supreme principle or being. Hinduism embraces both monistic and dualistic beliefs, and contains many popular local deities and cults. Thus it is not a religion in the same sense Westerners use that term to refer to a system of clear beliefs about a personal God and a spiritual world apart from this material world.[7]

The ideal life of a Hindu male embraces a wide spectrum of roles, from the student of religion to the householder who produces a son to carry on ancestral tradition, and from the hermit who tries to achieve indifference to everything in the world he previously found desirable to the homeless wanderer who renounces all earthly ties. Passing through these four stages is the *Way of Knowledge,* an expression that denotes the spiritual path, which leads to spiritual union with the Infinite. Along the Way of Knowledge, a Hindu male can pursue four goals: *kama* (sexual love), *artha* (power and material gain), *dharma* (spiritual duty), and *moksha* (liberation).[2] The first two goals deal with desire, the last two extol duty and renunciation. Typical of Axial thinking, Hindu sacred texts explain the paths of desire only from a male viewpoint, as if desire, pleasure, and power play no role in the lives of women whose primary activities are childrearing and household duties.

This mix of desire and duty in Hinduism allows a strong tradition of sexual abstinence by celibate monks to coexist with an equally strong religious celebration of sexual pleasure in all its forms as a path to the Divine. While sexual abstinence is favored at certain stages, Hindu sexual asceticism complements the celebration of sexual desire and pleasure, unlike Christian sexual asceticism, which is rooted in the need for redemption from original sin. Most Hindus, even the ascetics and monks, view sex as something natural, to be enjoyed in moderation without repression or overindulgence.

Hindu sacred writings, devotional poetry, and annual festivals celebrate married love, the fidelity of women, and the religious power of sexual union. Hindu myths of gods and goddesses are symbolic of spiritual powers and energies within and the daily challenges of life faced by all human beings. While monotheistic Western cultures tend to objectify and personalize their God, Eastern cultures view their mythologies as psychological and metaphysical metaphors that reveal the miraculous and natural wonders of human life and its desires.

Mythology provides a key to Hindu sexual views. *Brahma,* the Creator, *Vishnu,* the Preserver, and *Shiva,* the cosmic dancer of the cycle of destruction and rebirth form the basic triad of gods in the Hindu pantheon. Hindu sexual values are expressed in images and rituals associated with Shiva and his consort, the goddess *Shakti.* Shakti has several images, appearing as *Parvati,* the gracious embodiment of sensuality and sexual delights, as *Durga,* the unapproachable, and as *Kali,* the black wild one, the helpful, awesome goddess of sex's transcendent powers.[2,8] The *lingam,* a stone or wood phallus, represents Shiva and the concentration of sexual energy by asceticism. Triangular stone sculptures of the *yoni* represent Shakti and the vulva. Mystical geometric patterns called *yantras* combine the circular lingam with triangular yoni. Used in meditation, yantras reflect the belief that sexual practices can be a way of balancing the male and female energies of one's body and experiencing cosmic unity. The worship of lingam and yoni, of Shiva and Shakti, are a regular part of public and household rituals. *Kama,* the Hindu god of love, is also believed to be present during all acts of love. He represents love and pleasure, both sensual and aesthetic. His wife, *Rati,* is the embodiment of sensual love.

Hindu scriptures include hundreds of treatises on the art of eroticism, allegedly written by the gods and sages. Only three of these manuals, the *Kama Sutra, Kama Shastra,* and *Ananga Ranga,* have been translated into English. The *Kama Sutra* (second century BC) discusses the spiritual aspects of sexuality, with advice on positions and techniques for increasing the sensual enjoyment of sexual intercourse. The beautifully illustrated *Ananga Ranga* or *The Theater of God* (15th century AD) describes the sexual organs and erogenous areas of men and women, the cycles of erotic passion, and an encyclopedia of lovemaking positions. This spiritual tradition of erotic love appears in temple art depicting *mithuna,* loving couples in sexual embrace. Such sculptures reached their peak in the sensitive, emotionally warm, and intensely spiritual bas-reliefs celebrating all forms of sexual behavior (except adultery and violence) that cover the 1,000-year-old "love-temples" of Khajuraho and Konarak.[9,10]

# Taoist Sexual Traditions

In their quest for spiritual and physical health, including longevity and immortality, the Chinese traditionally turned to Taoism, which originated from the teachings of the sixth century BC philosopher Lao-Tzu.[7] Taoism views nature and spirit as interdependent and mutually sustaining. Tao is "the Way," the "eternally nameless" path followed by the wise, the everchanging rhythmic source of life, and living in harmony with all things. Taoism advocates a life of simplicity, integration, cooperation, and selflessness, and has no formal dogma or church. It does not recommend asceticism or reject natural desires or cravings. It recommends self-cultivation, healthy living, and the fuller enjoyment of both earthly and heavenly joys.[2,11,12] Harmony in one's sexual desires, passions, and joys is a natural and important aspect of health. Sexuality is considered part of nature and is not associated with any kind of sin or moral guilt. In fact, lovers joined in ecstasy can experience a transcendent union with the cosmos.[13]

> "... Eastern cultures maintained a respect for nature, emphasizing that health and spirituality are only achieved when humanity respects its place in the cosmos and places itself in harmony with nature."

Some Taoists have sought the secret of longevity in an alchemical formula. Others have sought longevity by bringing the body and soul into a perfect, harmonious balance,[11,12] or by transforming the male or female essence into the "Elixir of Life."[14]

Taoist sexual traditions emphasize the importance of female satisfaction in all sexual relations. It talks of "a thousand loving thrusts," and the importance of nongenital touch for both the woman and the man.[11] In order to increase the enjoyment of sexual intercourse for both women and men, Taoist exercises help a man gain control over his ejaculation, with simple but sophisticated versions of the Sensate Focus, Stop and Go, and Squeeze Exercises popularized 2,000 years later by Masters and Johnson for treatment of premature ejaculation and inhibited female arousal and orgasm.[11] Taoism teaches that men cannot experience true sexual ecstasy unless they develop the ability to control their ejaculation.

This emphasis on male ejaculation is often misinterpreted. It is not the same as coitus reservatus (withdrawal followed by ejaculation) or the "male continence" practiced by the members of the Oneida Community in the 1800s to prevent unwanted pregnancies. It is not the same as the passive lovemaking of *karezza,* an ancient technique for prolonging sexual intercourse without ejaculation, popularized by Marie Stopes in her 1920s best seller *Married Love.*

Taoism also emphasizes the difference between male orgasm and ejaculation, a distinction rediscovered by modern sexologists. According to Taoism, men deplete their energy when they are driven to ejaculate too frequently. Specific Taoist exercises can enable a man to pleasure his partner and enjoy several "non-explosive" orgasms prior to ejaculation.[13]

The early Taoist traditions recognized the greater capacity of women for sexual pleasure and their vital role in introducing men to the treasures of sexual pleasure and ecstasy. But this mutual, harmonious concern for female and male pleasure did not last. In the Han Dynasty (206–219 BC), male interests began to dominate as Taoist exercises were converted into techniques that focused on men's pleasure, including intercourse with virgins and with numerous women in order to become immortal. Women became the footbound pleasure toys of men in the T'ang Dynasty (618–906 AD). During the Manchu Dynasty (1644–1912 AD), the egalitarian Taoist sexual philosophy practically disappeared in male obsessions.[12,13]

For guidance in the customs and proprieties of society and public life, the Chinese looked to the teachings of Confucius (551–479 BC). Early Confucian thought was quite sex-positive. Only in the last thousand years of imperial rule did Confucianism adopt a negative view of sexuality.

Both Taoism and Confucianism appear to have borrowed the basic idea of two vital energies, Yin and Yang, from earlier Chinese who lived centuries before Confucius and Lao-Tzu. Everything stems from the dynamic interaction of *Yin* and *Yang.*[15]

The polarity of Yin/Yang energies is very different from the body-soul opposition that underlies Western thought. Western thought maintains a very clear split between the body and spirit or soul. In Christian thought, salvation and redemption are achieved by subjugation of the body and its passions to reason and to the spiritual soul. In both Taoism and Confucianism, the vital energies of Yin (earth, dark, receptive, female) and Yang (heaven, light, penetrating, male) are complementary rather than opposing aspects of nature. The challenge of life is to achieve a healthy, dynamic balance between these two energies.[8,12,13]

Since both Yin and Yang coexist in every man and woman, in different proportions, everyone can cultivate, balance, and unite their psychosomatic energies. In sexual play Yin and Yang are aroused and can be channeled from the lower levels to the heart and head. According to some modern interpreters, this can be done in self-pleasuring, and in both heterosexual and homosexual relations.[11,13,16]

Some Taoist masters recommend that a male release his semen according to seasonal changes and infrequently, for example, only two or three times out of ten instances of intercourse, in order to direct and transform the vital life energies. Similarly, women are taught to use proper breathing exercises and meditation as ways of circulating and transforming their Yin energy. The mutual exchange of Yin and Yang essences in intercourse and orgasm is believed to produce perfect harmony, increase vigor, and bring long life.

## Tantric Sexual Traditions

Some suggest that Tantric sexual traditions were derived from ancient Chinese Taoism, or that Taoist sexuality was derived from Tantra.[13,14,17,18] Others believe that the earliest Tantric traditions predate Hinduism, Buddhism, and Taoism and that they were derived from the pre-Aryan religion of Indus Valley natives and religious symbols brought from paleolithic Europe by the Indo-Aryan invaders about 1800 BC.[19] Whatever their origins, Tantric ideas are found in Hindu, Buddhist, Jain, and Taoist writings in Nepal, Tibet, China, Japan, Thailand, and Indonesia.[2,19]

Over the centuries, the ecstatic, and at times orgiastic, cults inspired by Tantric visions of cosmic sexuality were attacked by ascetic Hindus and buddhists, denounced by the invading Muslims, opposed by the British colonial government in India, and outlawed by the Chinese communists.

Tantra is a Sanskrit word meaning thread" or "continuity." Tantra involves active ways of transforming one's perceptions and energies that plunge one back into the roots of personal identity to nakedly experience the truth and reality of oneself and the world. Tantric rituals are kept highly secret, and require severe discipline and every kind of physical, sexual, mental, and moral effort. Instead of recommending abstinence from the pleasures of life as celibate asceticism in other religious traditions do, Tantra cultivates the realization of an ultimate bliss in order to experience awareness of the true nature of reality, beyond all dualistic conceptions. In Philip Rawson's modern wording, Tantra urges its practitioners to "Raise your enjoyment to its highest power and then use it as a spiritual rocket-fuel."[4] The original Tantras use a cryptic "twilight" language difficult to understand. Some modern books on Tantra such as *Sexual Secrets* by Nik Douglas and Penny Slinger are filled with such symbolic terms, while other writers such as Mantak Chia mix traditional with Western terms to more clearly elucidate the meaning of esoteric terminology.[11,17,20]

# Hindu Tantric Doctrine (Shaktism)

In Hinduism, Tantric rituals became associated with the worship of Shakti, Shiva's consort. Hindu Tantra reached its most profound external expression in the "love temples" of northeastern India (700-1100 AD).[7,9,10] Right-handed Shaktism is a refined philosophy that focuses on the benign side of Shakti as the energy of nature and mother-goddess. Left-handed Shaktism focuses on Durga and Kali, the violent side of Shakti, and sweeps one into conventionally forbidden expressions of natural impulses to achieve transcendence. Ritual violation of social taboos against adultery and incest, and coitus for otherwise celibate monks, are an important part of these left-handed Tantric rites.[2,19] In Victor Turner's social dialectics of structure-antistructure, Tantric taboo-breaking (anti-structure) rituals may play a vital role in maintaining the flexibility, dynamism, and creativity of a social structure or culture.[21]

Participants in the *Rite of the Five Essences,* a Tantric love ritual, for instance, use the five forbidden *Ms: madya* (wine), *mansa* (meat), *matsya* (fish), *mudra* (parched grain), and *maithuna* (sexual union) in a kind of holy communion.[2] It includes enhancement of the environment with flowers, incense, music, and candlelight, a period of meditation designed to hasten the ascent of the vital energies of the kundalini (see below), the chanting of a mantra, and the couple's visualization of themselves as an embodiment of Shiva and Shakti, the supreme couple.

# Buddhist Tantric Doctrine

In Buddhism, Tantra refers to a series of teachings delivered to humans by the Buddha. According to Buddhist Tantra, the most effective means of awakening to the true nature of reality is not by intellectual pursuits, but by experiencing the state of voidness and bliss through one's own body and mind. The Buddhist Tantrik controls his/her body and its psychic powers to attain Buddhahood by coming face to face with the elemental forces of the world and transcending the desires aroused by them.

In Tibetan Buddhism, devotion to male and female deities stresses the interaction of external and internal energies.[4] *Yabyum* is the Tibetan term for the mystical experience of oneness and wholeness men and women can achieve through sexual intercourse.[22] In mystical sexual union, the male and female principles are combined in an experience that resolves all dualities and reflects the union of wisdom and compassion. Because all natural forces and the deity are a union of male and female elements, the highest and most harmonious energies are experienced in such unions as the realization of the inherent luminosity and emptiness of all phenomena.[22]

# Tantra and Yoga

The system known as yoga was first mentioned in the Hindu *Upanishads* (eighth-fifth? century BC). Yoga, literally translated from the Sanskrit as "union," means being aware without thinking. It is the silence of the mind that is broken by trying to tell another person what one experienced in a yoga meditation/exercise.

Yoga is a highly evolved technique of meditation and concentration for disciplining mind and body and purifying the senses from their bondage to limiting concepts. Yoga combines physiological and psychological methods, which involve postures, breathing, and in some cases the rhythmical repetition of proper sound-syllables or *mantras* that suppress the conscious movement of the mind in body.[23] When the whole body is disciplined to aid the gradual suspension of consciousness, one can experience a state of pure ecstasy that is without thought or sensation. In this ecstasy, the yoga practitioner may use ritual, devotion, meditation, the intellect, or physical pleasure to find a complete freeing of the true self from the external world and natural causation.[24]

Both early Tantra and Taoism adopted yogic exercises to gain access to the spiritual through physical pleasure and discipline. The central concept in sexual yoga is a physiology that conceives of the body as interconnected by many channels, or *nadis,* that are conduits for energy. Two main channels run along either side of the spinal column, connecting power centers known as *chakras,* which correspond to the Taoist *tan tien,* located between the loins and throat. The third conduit, the *susumna,* runs from its base in the perineal region to the crown chakra. The *kundalini,* named for the goddess Kali, is the powerful but latent energy source that lies coiled like a serpent at the lowest chakra. The kundalini is also believed to represent Shakti, the feminine aspect of the creative force, the serpent power or mystical fire in the subtle body. The aim of sexual yoga is to arouse the kundalini or serpent power and channel it upward.[25] Once aroused, the kundalini can be channeled upward through the seven chakras of the subtle body until it merges with the eternal Shiva to confer freedom and immortality. By redirecting the body's most basic and vital generative energies of semen and ovum to the brain, the yoga practitioner hopes to gain spiritual energy, cosmic consciousness, and salvation, the experience of real self completely freed from earthly bonds and joined with all reality.[24]

In developing the idea of kundalini energy, the Tantriks and Taoists may have adopted earlier Persian ideas, using meditation, breathing control, postures, and finger pressure to prolong sexual intercourse without ejaculation. In the process, they added the goal of transforming and circulating the sexual energy upward in the body and in exchanges with a partner, thereby extending the enjoyment of many orgasms without ejaculation.

Orgasm and ejaculation are two distinct processes and can occur apart or together. William Hartman and Marily Fithian, for instance, report that men are capable of experiencing multiple orgasms as long as they do not ejaculate.[26] While most Tantric teachers urge males to avoid ejaculation at all times, Taoist teachers place more emphasis on gaining control of ejaculation rather than eliminating it altogether.[11,13]

The !Kung of Africa, Sufi mystics, and ancient and contemporary practitioners of yoga, Tantra, and Taoism, have cultivated the awakening of kundalini energy. Descriptions of these experiences bear intriguing similarities to reports of spontaneous experiences of Christian mystics and secular contemporaries. Strange as these reports sound in terms of Western physiology, their consistency and persistence over thousands of years deserve serious attention from Western scientists. There are hints in the preliminary research of neurophysicist and author Itzhak Bentov and psychiatrist Lee Sannella that a serious clinical and experimental investigation of the kundalini experience may reveal important new insights, much as modern medicine has benefited from clinical investigations of acupuncture and Ayurvedic herbal medicine.[27,28]

# Blending East and West

To understand the Tantric and Taoist sexual systems and appreciate their rich messages, one has to go beyond the surface of sexual acts, rituals, and roles to get in touch with the cosmology, philosophy and world view that frame these exercises. One also has to deal with Eastern erotics, the way the Taoists and Tantriks interpret sexual feelings, ideas, fantasies, excitements, and aesthetics—what is beautiful or ugly, luscious or nauseating, dull or titillating.[29] Unfortunately, too many manuals, especially those presenting Tantric sex, are exotic recipe books or tourist brochures for a sexual Shangri-la. Fang-fu Ruan rightly notes that many books on Oriental sexology, while useful, ". . . are limited by either concentrating on a specialized topic or presenting a popular treatment of their subject. Some, by treating sexuality as a domain of pleasure independent of the changing contexts of medicine, religion, family life, reproductive strategies, or social control, effectively reinforce stereotypes of exotic Oriental cultures."[12]

Complicating any effort to evaluate the extent to which Westerners, raised with very different, even opposing world views and erotics, can understand, practice, and incorporate these sexual systems into their daily lives, is the fact that, while some proponents rhapsodize about the potential for ecstatic and cosmic experiences in Tantra and Taoism, very little can be actually known about the subjective experiences of men and women who practice these systems.[11,20]

These ancient traditions celebrate the naturalness of sexual pleasure and the spiritual potential of sexual relations, a view that may fit well with many people's sensitivities and yearnings. They also accept female sexuality and women's unlimited sexual potential, a view that is congenial with contemporary feminist awareness. Contemporary sexuality can be enriched and broadened by a reawakening of the experience of sexuality as integral to whole-person connectedness. It can also benefit from seeing sexual satisfaction as a fluctuating, non-goal-oriented, continuum of responses that includes pleasuring, orgasm, and ecstasy.[30] Can these ancient and yet very modern views be translated into the Western consciousness without being trapped by faddism? Advocates of yoga and acupuncture have succeeded in similar challenges.

In Western religions, spirituality refers to a loving, personal union of a human being with the Creator who has no gender or sex, although we are said to be created in "His image and likeness." In the Bible, sexual pleasure is commonly associated with an original sin—a fall from grace. Sexuality tends to be viewed as antagonistic to spiritual liberation.[31,32] In the words of Joseph Campbell, in the West, "eternity withdraws, and nature is corrupt, nature has fallen . . . we live in exile."[1] Neither Hinduism nor Buddhism have a concept of an original sin or primeval fall. Tantric and Taoist sexual union is viewed as a way to spiritual liberation, a consciousness of and identification with the Divine, and a way of becoming enlightened through one's embodiment and interaction with another. Can Western religious thought incorporate these sex-affirming Eastern views without scrapping much of our religious myths and beliefs? Can the spiritual and cosmic sense of sexuality be expressed in a Western world view without sanitizing or weakening sexual passion, or reducing its playful element?

"These ancient traditions celebrate the naturalness of sexual pleasure and the spiritual potential of sexual relations . . ."

Despite these questions and challenges, we need to remember that nuclear physicist Werner Heisenberg acknowledged that Indian philosophy helped him make sense of some of the seemingly "crazy" principles of quantum physics. And Western science and medicine increasingly acknowledges the value of ancient traditions, such as Ayurveda, the Hindu system of medicine, and techniques of acupuncture originating from China.

The life cycles of past civilizations clearly suggest that as they degenerate, their cultures tend to exaggerate the great primordial insights that led to their greatness. Western cultures have overvalued individualism at the expense of the environment, separated human nature from nurturing nature, and turned everything, including the human psyche, into objects to be manipulated, controlled, and exploited. The resultant technological superiority has given humankind dominance in our global village. It has given Western culture the leisure and affluence that has allowed women to regain some of the gender equality they experienced in the pre-Axial era. However, the violent, exploitive extremes of Western intellectual and moral assumptions contain the seeds of self-destruction. History suggests that Western culture may avoid self-destruction and achieve a transformation into a new global consciousness if it can integrate values that will bring forth a more balanced culture, respectful of the unit and harmony of all reality. Jaspers and others see in this renaissance the possible advent of a second Axial Period.[5,6,33]

Many critics have deplored the objectification of sex and the Western obsession with sexual performance. Christianity, for the most part, has not been able to integrate sexuality into a holistic philosophy or see sexual relations, pleasure, and passion as avenues for spiritual meaning and growth. There have been a few prophetic efforts in this direction, but many Christian churches are having difficulties dealing with sexual pleasure, apart from reproduction, and along with the spiritual dimension. For individuals or couples, the Eastern views may have rich meaning, but they will not help with the problem Western religions face in accepting and affirming alternates to heterosexual, exclusive monogamy in today's world.

Eastern sexual and spiritual traditions can help Westerners break out of the prevailing reduction of sexuality to genital activity. Taoist and Tantric sexual practices highlight all the senses and involve the whole energies of both partners in slow, sensual dances that are rich variations of what Western sexologists label the "outercourse" of the Sensate Focus Exercises. In addition, Eastern thought may help refocus our understanding and appreciation of male orgasm. The obsession in sexually explicit films and videos with ejaculation as the affirmation of masculinity leaves the male with an inevitable flaccid vulnerability that requires denial in a vicious cycle of repeated "conquests" followed by inevitable detumescence. Taoist practices can help a male achieve some parity with the multiorgasmic woman by controlling his ejaculation, much to the benefit of both sexes.

# Conclusion

Over the centuries, Tantriks and Taoists adopted philosophies and practices involving yoga from others and Yin and Yang from earlier Chinese, and borrowed aspects of the cultures of the pre-Aryans and (possibly) the paleolithic Europeans. Some Americans have already borrowed from the riches of Eastern sexual views. In the future this cross-fertilization may increase and become more sophisticated. The outcome could lead to new icons, archetypes, and meanings for sexual relations as expressions of love, passion, commitment, procreation, playful fun, and friendship as well as mystical transcendence and spiritual oneness.

The Western technological imperative needs a strong antidote to regain its health in the 21st century. Western culture may find a corrective to its highly successful but dangerously exaggerated technological imperative (Yang) in the ancient Eastern tradition of the nurturing potential of a panerotic sensuality (Yin). The health of Western culture can be improved by learning from key elements of the Taoist and Tantric traditions. At the same time, Eastern cultures are also caught up in the current revolution of human consciousness that some see as the advent of a second Axial Period, which is based on gender equality and a global and cosmic consciousness, sensitivity, and shared responsibility. This requires mutual collaboration and cross-fertilization on all sides.

# References

1.  Campbell, J. The power of myth. New York: Doubleday, 1988.
2.  Bullough, VL. Sexual variance in society and history. Chicago: University of Chicago Press, 1976.
3.  Gimbutas, M. The language of the Goddess. New York: Harper and Row, 1989.
4.  Rawson, P. Tantra: The Indian cult of ecstasy. New York: Avon Books, 1973.
5.  Jaspers, K. The Origin and goal of history. New Haven, CT: Yale University Press, 1953.
6.  Cousins, EH. Male-female aspects of the Trinity in Christian mysticism. In B Gupta, ed. Sexual archetypes: East & West. New York: Paragon House, 1986.
7.  Noss, DC. A History of the world's religions. New York: Macmillan, 8th edition, 1990.
8.  Sivaraman, K. The mysticism of male-female relationships: Some philosophical and lyrical motifs of Hinduism. In B Gupta, ed. Sexual archetypes: East & West. New York: Paragon House, 1986.
9.  Watts, A. Erotic spirituality: The vision of Konorak. New York: Collier Macmillan, 1971.
10. Deva, SK. Khajuraho. New Delhi: Brijbasi Printers, 1987.
11. Chia, M & Winn, M. Taoist secrets of love: Cultivating male sexual energy. Sante Fe: Aurora Press, 1984.
12. Ruan, FF. Sex in China: Studies in sexology in Chinese culture. New York: Plenum Press, 1991.
13. Chang, J. The Tao of love and sex: The ancient Chinese way to ecstasy. New York: Viking Penguin Arkana, 1977.
14. Van Gulik, RH. Sexual life in ancient China. Leiden, Netherlands: EJ. Brill, 1961.
15. Srinivasan, TM. Polar principles in yoga and Tantra. in B Gupta, ed. Sexual archetypes: East & West. New York: Paragon House, 1986.
16. Anand, M. The Art of sexual ecstasy: The path of sacred sexuality for Western lovers. Los Angeles: Jeremy Tarcher, 1989.
17. Douglas, N, & Slinger, P. Sexual secrets: The alchemy of ecstasy. New York: Destiny Books, 1979.

18. Needham, J. Science and civilization in China. Cambridge, England: University Press, 1956.
19. Rawson, P. The art of Tantra. Greenwich, CT: New York Graphic Society, 1973.
20. Chia, M & Chia, M. Healing love through the Tao: Cultivating female sexual energy. Huntington, NY: Healing Tao Books, 1986.
21. Turner, V. The ritual process: Structure and anti-structure. Ithaca, NY: Cornell University Press, 1969.
22. Blofeld, J. The Tantric mysticism of Tibet. Boston: Shambhala, 1970.
23. Sharma, PS, & Sharma, Yoga and sex. New York: Cornerstone Library, 1975.
24. Campbell, J. Transformations of myth through time. New York: Harper and Row, 1990.
25. Radha, S. Kundalini yoga for the West. Boston: Shambhala, 1985.
26. Hartman, W, & Fithian, M. Any man can. New York: St. Martin's Press, 1984.
27. Bentov, I. Stalking the wild pendulum. New York: E.P. Dutton, 1977.
28. Sannella, L. The Kundalini experience: Psychosis or transcendence. Lower Lake, CA: Integral Publishing, revised edition, 1987.
29. Herdt, G. Representations of homosexuality: An essay on cultural ontology and historical comparison, Part 1. *Journal of the History of Sexuality*, 1991, 1(3), 481–504.
30. Ogden, G., Women and sexual ecstasy: How can therapists help? *Women and Therapy*, 1988, 7(2,3), 43–56.
31. Lawrence, Jr, RJ. The poisoning of Eros: Sexual values in conflict. New York: Augustin Moore Press, 1989.
32. Rainke-Heinemann, U. Eunuchs for the kingdom of heaven: Women, sexuality, and the Catholic Church. New York: Doubleday, 1990.
33. Paglia, C. Sexual personae: Art and decadence from Nefertiti to Emily Dickinson. New York: Random House, 1990.

CPSIA information can be obtained at www.ICGtesting.com
Printed in the USA
LVOW09s2127140616

492615LV00001B/1/P

9 781465 208712